A Passenger Airplane

A knowledge of solid geometry assists in the designing and construction
of aircraft

SOLID GEOMETRY

By

A. M. WELCHONS

and

W. R. KRICKENBERGER

The Arsenal Technical High School
Indianapolis, Indiana

GINN AND COMPANY

BOSTON · NEW YORK · CHICAGO · LONDON · ATLANTA · DALLAS · COLUMBUS · SAN FRANCISCO

The Athenæum Press

GINN AND COMPANY · PRO-
PRIETORS · BOSTON · U.S.A.

FOREWORD

In presenting this text, the authors have in mind the need of a solid geometry which early in its development assists the student in acquiring spacial concepts, in applying the relations of figures in one plane to figures in more than one plane, in learning the proper method of attacking original theorems, in appreciating the geometric forms found in nature and architecture, and in applying the theorems and corollaries to the world about him.

SPECIAL FEATURES OF THE BOOK

1. *Conformity to Established Requirements.* The book follows the recommendations of the College Entrance Examination Board and of the National Committee on Mathematical Requirements.

The propositions on the required list of the College Entrance Board are marked (C) and those on the subsidiary list or those necessary for sequence are marked (c). Similarly, (N) and (n) are used for marking the propositions of the National Committee.

2. *Provision for Individual Differences.* The book has been arranged to meet the individual differences found in any one class as well as the differences in classes.

The exercises, in the main, have been arranged in two groups, Group A and Group B. Group A contains the exercises for all members of the class, and Group B contains exercises for the exceptional members of the class.

The miscellaneous exercises on pages 223–228 are grouped by chapters, and offer a supplementary review for Group B students after the completion of each chapter.

A minimum course includes all the proofs of the fundamental theorems and corollaries and of the subsidiary theorems listed by either the College Entrance Examination Board or the National Committee on Mathematical Requirements, an informal treatment of the subsidiary corollaries, and some of the exercises listed in Group A. In the minimum course §§ 284–294, 316, and Chapter VI may be omitted, if desired.

A medium course includes the proofs of all the theorems and corollaries on both the fundamental list and the subsidiary list of either the College Entrance Examination Board or the National Committee on Mathematical Requirements, and some of the exercises in Groups A and B.

A maximum course contains all the propositions and corollaries, and a majority of the exercises in both groups.

3. *Selection of Method.* Before the proof of a theorem is started, all possible methods of proving the theorem are cited, and from these methods the proper one is selected. The student, in recalling the various methods of proof, develops a habit of thought which is invaluable to him.

4. *Summary of Methods of Proof.* At the close of each chapter is a summary of methods of proof which are developed in the chapter. This summary is a valuable aid in proving the original theorems which follow.

5. *Word Lists.* Word lists containing the words which are most frequently misspelled are given at the end of each chapter.

6. *Tests.* At the end of each chapter is a set of carefully prepared tests covering the chapter. These may be used as tests of the student's mastery of the subject matter, as reviews, or as self-measuring tests for the individual student. The time limit given for each test is only suggestive, and may be varied to suit the needs of the class.

A. M. WELCHONS
W. R. KRICKENBERGER

CONTENTS

PAGE

LIST OF EXERCISES viii
SYMBOLS AND ABBREVIATIONS xii

INTRODUCTION 1
CHAPTER I. LINES AND PLANES IN SPACE 23
CHAPTER II. DIHEDRAL AND POLYHEDRAL ANGLES . . 55
CHAPTER III. PRISMS AND CYLINDERS 81
CHAPTER IV. PYRAMIDS AND CONES 119
CHAPTER V. SPHERES 151
CHAPTER VI. GENERAL POLYHEDRONS 205

MISCELLANEOUS EXERCISES 223
SUMMARY OF PRINCIPAL METHODS OF PROOF 229
SUPPLEMENTARY TOPICS
    BRIEF EXPLANATION OF LOGARITHMS 239
    APPLICATIONS OF TRIGONOMETRY 244
TABLES
    SQUARE ROOTS AND CUBE ROOTS 238
    MANTISSAS 242
    TRIGONOMETRIC RATIOS 249
    LOGARITHMS OF TRIGONOMETRIC RATIOS 250
    WEIGHTS AND MEASURES 253
    FORMULAS OF PLANE GEOMETRY 253
    FORMULAS OF SOLID GEOMETRY 254

INDEX 255

LIST OF EXERCISES REQUIRING IMPORTANT METHODS OF PROOF

EXERCISE	PAGE	EXERCISE	PAGE

Proving Lines Perpendicular

EXERCISE	PAGE	EXERCISE	PAGE
19A	32	9, 10	223
5B	66	6	224
5B	186		

Proving Lines Parallel

EXERCISE	PAGE	EXERCISE	PAGE
3, 5	41	2A	87
2B	59	4	223
10	74	14	224

Proving a Line Perpendicular to a Plane

EXERCISE	PAGE	EXERCISE	PAGE
5A	65	8A	193
9B	66	8	224
13	74		

Proving a Line Parallel to a Plane

EXERCISE	PAGE	EXERCISE	PAGE
6A	37	3A	59

Proving Two Planes Perpendicular

EXERCISE	PAGE	EXERCISE	PAGE
3, 5	57	1	224
4A, 1B	59	1	227
7	87		

Proving Two Planes Parallel

EXERCISE	PAGE	EXERCISE	PAGE
1	40	11A	154
6A	65		

Proving Two Line Segments Equal

EXERCISE	PAGE	EXERCISE	PAGE
17A	32	5A	91
1A, 2A	39	10A, 12A	154
3	40	4B	161
3B, 4B	46	5A	219
3	61	3, 5, 6	223
1A	65	7	224
3B	72	5	228
2A	87		

EXERCISE	PAGE	EXERCISE	PAGE

Proving Two Line Segments Unequal

EXERCISE	PAGE	EXERCISE	PAGE
18A	32	5	74
18	34	5A	85
7A	65	7B	154
6B, 7B	66		

Proving Two Plane Angles Equal

EXERCISE	PAGE	EXERCISE	PAGE
7	61	10B	66
1A, 4A	65	5, 10	224

Proving Dihedral Angles Equal

EXERCISE	PAGE	EXERCISE	PAGE
2	56	3	224
3B	59		

Proving Polyhedral Angles Equal or Symmetric

EXERCISE	PAGE	EXERCISE	PAGE
2A	71	1A	98
1B	72		

Sum of Face Angles of Polyhedral Angles

EXERCISE	PAGE	EXERCISE	PAGE
3A, 4A	71	7B	83
9	74	5B	90
24	75	Test 18: 2	222

Loci

EXERCISE	PAGE	EXERCISE	PAGE
7A–11A	37	3A, 4A	101
6	41	1A–4A	142
3A–5A	46	2A–4A	151
7A	59	6A, 7A, 5B	154
1, 3, 4	63	7–9	159
1A–7A	72	5A, 4B, 5B, 8B	163
1B–15B	73	1A	192
20	75	1	198
8A	83		

Lengths of Line Segments

EXERCISE	PAGE	EXERCISE	PAGE
15A, 16A	32	3A, 4A	93
1A, 2A	45	4B, 5B	96
1B	46	6A	98
7A, 4B	59	1B, 7B	99
6	61	9B, 11B	100
2	63	1B, 2B	107
2A, 3A	65	1, 5, 7–9	109
1B, 2B, 8B	66	13, 15, 18, 20, 22, 25	110
16–19	75	2B, 6B–8B	111
Test 6: 1–3, 5–7, 9	79	11	112
8A, 11A	85	8, 12, 13	117
6B	90	5, 8	120

EXERCISE	PAGE		EXERCISE	PAGE
4A	124		3A, 5A, 7A	191
7A, 8A, 5B, 7B, 8B	125		2B, 7B, 10B, 11B	192
9B, 11B–13B	126		3A, 6A, 7A	193
2B	127		1–4, 10	196
5A, 2B, 4B	129		9, 11, 18	204
5A, 2B	137		4A, 4B	213
2B	139		4A, 7A	219
2A	141		6B	220
5B	143		Test 18: 3	222
3, 5, 6, 10, 13	149		2–7, 9	225
2B	154		18, 20, 26, 28	226
7B, 9B, 10B	161		8, 10; 4, 7	227
8A, 9A	167		8; 3, 9	228
2B	171		2, 3, 7, 9, 10	247
2B, 4B	186			

Areas

EXERCISE	PAGE		EXERCISE	PAGE
6A	46		5A, 8A	142
Test 6: 8	79		7B, 11B	143
7A	85		3, 8, 9	149
6A	87		5A, 1B	154
1A–5A, 1B–3B	90		6B	163
1B	96		1A–7A	167
5A, 7A, 8A, 10A	98		1A–6A	168
2B	99		4A	183
10B	100		1A, 2A, 5A, 6A, 1B, 3B, 7B	186
2A–7A, 5B	107		5A, 6A, 10A, 11A	191
3, 5, 6	109		4B	192
17, 19, 23	110		10A, 11A, 2B, 3B	193
3B	111		6B	194
10	112		1, 5, 8, 12, 13, 15, 16	204
1, 2, 4, 5, 10, 16	117		1–3	205
6–8	120		1A, 3A	213
2A	121		6A, 3B	219
1A–3A, 5A	124		5B	220
6A, 9A, 1B–6B	125		Test 18: 4	222
10B	126		22; 4	226
1A	129		5, 9; 3, 5	227
1A–3A, 1B	137		9, 10; 1, 2, 7	228
3A	139		16, 17, 19, 20, 21	248
1A, 3A, 1B, 2B	141			

Volumes

EXERCISE	PAGE		EXERCISE	PAGE
3A	87		14, 16, 24	110
1A, 2A, 5A	93		1B, 4B, 5B	111
1A–7A	95		8	112
1B–3B	96		3, 6, 7, 9, 11, 14, 15	117
2A–4A, 8A, 9A	98		1A–4A, 1B, 5B	129
2B–6B, 8B	99		1A–5A	131
12B, 13B	100		4A	137
1A, 3A, 6A, 3B, 4B	107		1A–4A, 1B, 3B, 4B	139
2, 4–6, 10–12	109		1A, 4A, 1B–4B	141

EXERCISE	PAGE	EXERCISE	PAGE
6A, 7A, 1B–3B	142	2A, 3A, 5A, 6A, 1B–3B, 5B,	
4B, 6B, 9B, 10B	143	6B, 8B	213
1, 2, 7, 11, 12, 14	149	1B–4B	217
4A	154	1A–3A, 8A, 1B–4B	219
6B	163	8B	220
1A, 2A, 6A, 8A, 9A	191	Test 18: 5–7	222
1B, 5B, 8B, 9B, 13B, 2A	192	1, 10, 12, 16, 17	225
1B–5B	194	19, 21, 25; 1–3	226
5–7, 9, 11	196	6, 7; 6	227
17	198	2, 4, 6	228
2, 4, 6, 10, 17	204	4, 11, 12	247
		13–15, 18, 21, 23	248

Sections of Solids

EXERCISE	PAGE	EXERCISE	PAGE
3B, 4B	83	3A, 4A	104
6A	85	7B	213
4A, 8A	87	23	226
1A, 2A	91		

Spherical Distances

EXERCISE	PAGE	EXERCISE	PAGE
3B	154	1A, 9A	171
7B	163	14	204

Spherical Angles

EXERCISE	PAGE	EXERCISE	PAGE
1A, 4A	163	1A, 2A, 1B, 2B	175
2A, 6A	171	2	176
1A, 2A	173	8	196
1A, 2A	174	19	204

Spherical Polygons

EXERCISE	PAGE	EXERCISE	PAGE
1A, 6A, 3B, 7B	186	13, 15	204
10A, 12A	191	2	227
4A, 3B, 4B	193		

Lunes

EXERCISE	PAGE	EXERCISE	PAGE
2A–5A	183	6B	192
2A, 5A	186	11A	193
10A	191	8, 19	204

Zones

EXERCISE	PAGE	EXERCISE	PAGE
2A	183	12	204
4A, 1B	186	Chap. V, 9	228
11A	191		

SYMBOLS AND ABBREVIATIONS

The following symbols and abbreviations are used in this text. Each should be learned when it first occurs in the subject matter.

SYMBOLS

$\angle$	angle	$\perp$	(is) perpendicular to; perpendicular
$\rightarrow$	approaches as a limit; tends to	$\stackrel{\circ}{=}$	is equal in degrees to
$\frown$	arc	$\sim$	(is) similar to; similar
$\odot$	circle	$\square$	parallelogram
$=$	(is) equal to; equals; equal	§	article
$\neq$	is not equal to	$\therefore$	therefore
$>$	is greater than	$\triangle$	triangle
$<$	is less than	$x', x'', \cdots$	x-prime, x-second, $\cdots$
$\cong$	(is) congruent to; congruent	$x_1, x_2, \cdots$	x-sub-one, x-sub-two, $\cdots$
$\parallel$	(is) parallel to; parallel		

The plural of any symbol representing a noun is formed by adding the letter s. Thus ⊙s means *circles*.

ABBREVIATIONS

adj.	= adjacent	Iden.	= identity
alt.	= alternate	int.	= interior
Ax.	= axiom	isos.	= isosceles
comp.	= complementary	opp.	= opposite
Const.	= construction	Post.	= postulate
Cor.	= corollary	Prop.	= proposition
corr.	= corresponding	quad.	= quadrilateral
cos	= cosine	rect.	= rectangle
Def.	= definition	rt.	= right
Ex.	= exercise	sin	= sine
ext.	= exterior	st.	= straight
Fig.	= figure	supp.	= supplementary
Hyp.	= hypothesis	tan	= tangent

S.A.S. = If two triangles have two sides and the included angle of one equal respectively to two sides and the included angle of the other, the triangles are congruent.

A.S.A. = If two triangles have two angles and the included side of one equal respectively to two angles and the included side of the other, the triangles are congruent.

S.S.S. = If two triangles have the three sides of one equal respectively to the three sides of the other, the triangles are congruent.

SOLID GEOMETRY

INTRODUCTION

1. The Difference between Plane and Solid Geometry.
In plane geometry the figures consist of points and lines. They
are called *plane* figures since all the points and lines of each
figure lie in the same plane. In solid geometry the figures consist also of points and lines, but not all the points and lines of
each figure necessarily lie in the same plane. For example,
not all the points and lines of a cube lie in the same plane.

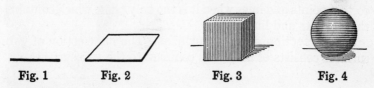

Fig. 1   Fig. 2   Fig. 3   Fig. 4

Figures in plane geometry have one or two dimensions. A
line has one dimension (length) and a parallelogram has two
dimensions (length and width). Figures in solid geometry have
one, two, or three dimensions. A cube has three dimensions
(length, width, and thickness).

2. Surfaces. A *plane* is a surface such that a straight line
joining any two points of the surface lies wholly in the surface.
Although a plane is indefinite in ex-
tent, it is pictured as a rectangle seen
obliquely. The parallelogram *ABCD*
represents a plane. This plane may
be referred to as plane *AC* or as
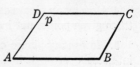
plane *p*. The lines *AB* and *BC* are drawn heavier than *AD*
and *DC* to make the plane appear horizontal.

1

A *curved surface* is a surface of which no part is plane, such as the surface *AD* shown in the figure at the right.

A surface may consist of two or more planes, or of two or more curved surfaces, or of a combination of planes and curved surfaces.

3. Geometric Solid. A *geometric solid* is a closed surface completely inclosing a portion of space.

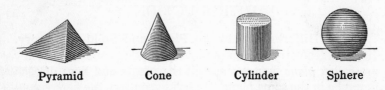

Pyramid   Cone   Cylinder   Sphere

The pyramid, cone, cylinder, and sphere are familiar examples of geometric solids.

4. Determination of a Plane. A plane is determined by certain points and lines when it is the only plane which contains these points and lines.

5. Intersection of Two Surfaces. The intersection of two surfaces consists of all points common to the two surfaces.

EXERCISES

1. What kind of line is formed when a piece of paper is folded in a sharp crease?

2. In your classroom find several cases of the intersection of two planes.

3. How many straight lines can be drawn through one point? through two points? through any three points?

4. How many planes can contain a given point? two given points? three given points not in a straight line?

5. How many planes can contain a given straight line? two given intersecting straight lines? two parallel lines?

6. How many planes can contain a given straight line and a given point without the line?

7. Two points, *A* and *B*, lie in plane *MN*. What can you say of line *AB*?

8. How many planes are determined by five points no four of which lie in the same plane?

9. Name five articles in the home which have curved surfaces.

10. Can you find two points on the curved surface of a cylinder such that the line segment joining them lies entirely in the surface of the cylinder? If so, why is this surface not a plane?

6. Collinear Points and Concurrent Lines.
Points lying in the same straight line are called *collinear points*. Lines passing through the same point are called *concurrent lines*.

7. Coplanar Points and Lines.
Points or lines lying in the same plane are called *coplanar points* or *lines*.

8. The Use of Plane Geometry in Solid Geometry.
All the definitions, axioms, postulates, and propositions of plane geometry are at the disposal of the student in the study of solid geometry, but much care must be used in applying the facts of plane geometry to figures in space.

All the axioms and most of the definitions of plane geometry apply without reference to any plane. The propositions of plane geometry that hold without reference to any plane are the congruence theorems, theorems on similarity, and theorems stating the relation of parts of two different figures. The proofs of these propositions do not depend on the fact that the figures lie in the same plane.

Some of the postulates and propositions of plane geometry are not written in full, the omitted part, "in a plane," being understood. Thus the postulate "*At any point in a straight line one, and only one, perpendicular can be drawn to that line*" really means "At any point in a straight line, one, and only one, perpendicular can be drawn in a plane containing the line." To avoid errors in reasoning, the student should be sure of the intended meaning of each postulate and proposition. The propositions and postulates of plane geometry that apply only to one plane cannot be used in solid geometry unless all the parts of the figure concerned lie in one plane.

EXERCISES

Referring to **postulates of plane geometry** on page 8, answer the following questions:

1. Do Postulates *a, b, c,* and *d* hold true if the points and lines are in space?

2. Does Postulate *e* hold true if the center is any point in space? If not, change it by inserting "in a plane."

3. May we consider Postulates *f, g, h,* and *i* true for solid geometry?

4. Are the wood spokes of an automobile wheel perpendicular to the axle? In space how many perpendiculars can be drawn to a line at a given point in the line? Will Postulate *j* hold true for space? If not, change it.

5. Will Postulate *l* hold true for solid geometry?

6. By using two pencils, illustrate two lines in space that are not parallel and do not intersect.

7. Will Postulate *r* hold true for space?

8. Study the remaining postulates of plane geometry and state which postulates will not hold true for space. Make any changes needed.

9. Fundamental Properties of Planes. The following properties of planes will be readily apparent.

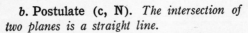

a. **Postulate.** *The intersection of a straight line and a plane is a point.*

(If there were two points in common, the line would lie in the plane.)

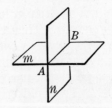

b. **Postulate (c, N).** *The intersection of two planes is a straight line.*

(The intersection of planes *m* and *n* is the straight line *AB.*)

c. **Postulate.** *A plane is determined by three noncollinear points.*

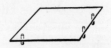

(The figure at the right shows the plane surface of a sheet of plate glass resting on three pegs.)

d. Corollary I. *A plane is determined by a line and a point without the line.*

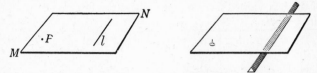

(The figure at the right above shows the plane surface of a sheet of glass resting on the point of a tack and one straight edge of a bar.)
Suggestion. Choose two points on line *l* and apply § 9 *c*.

e. Corollary II. *A plane is determined by two intersecting lines.*

f. Corollary III. *A plane is determined by two parallel lines.*

Suggestions. What are parallel lines? Can a plane contain both *l* and *l₁*? Show that no other plane can contain *l* and a point in *l₁*.

EXERCISES

1. Do any two straight lines necessarily lie in the same plane?

2. Do four points ever lie in the same plane? always?

3. What can you say of a straight line that has two points in common with a plane?

4. Why is it that a table with three legs will always stand firmly on a level floor and that a table with four legs will sometimes rock?

5. Why are tripods used for the support of a surveyor's transit and a camera?

6. *A*, *B*, *C*, and *D* are the lower ends of the legs of a table. By having taut threads from *A* to *C* and from *B* to *D*, how can you determine if the ends lie in the same plane?

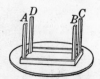

7. Place a small box, such as a chalk box, on a table and make a drawing of it as you see it directly from above. Make another drawing of the box viewed from a point where the top, one side, and one end are visible.

8. Draw two intersecting planes. Draw three planes intersecting in one line.

9. Draw three intersecting planes which do not have a common line of intersection.

10. Are all triangles plane figures? Why?

11. Is any figure having four sides necessarily a plane figure?

12. Can you determine whether or not a surface is a plane surface by one application of a straightedge?

13. To a line in space two perpendiculars are drawn. Are the perpendiculars parallel?

14. How many planes are determined by four points if no three of them are collinear? How many lines are determined by these points?

15. Show that five points no three of which are collinear determine ten lines.

16. Show that five points no four of which are coplanar determine ten planes.

17. How many planes are determined by three concurrent lines that are not coplanar? by four concurrent lines no three of which are coplanar?

18. How many planes are determined by three parallel lines that are not all in the same plane? by four parallel lines no three of which lie in the same plane?

19. What is the least number of planes that can inclose a space?

10. Definitions from Plane Geometry. The following terms from plane geometry, which will be used in solid geometry with the same meanings, are repeated here for convenient reference:

a. **Perpendicular Lines.** Two lines are *perpendicular* to each other if one of them forms two equal adjacent angles with the other.

b. **Right Angle.** The equal adjacent angles which are formed by a line and its perpendicular are called *right angles.*

c. **Polygon.** A *polygon* is a closed broken line in a plane.

d. **Congruent Figures.** Geometric figures are *congruent* if they can be made to coincide.

e. **Median.** A *median of a triangle* is a line segment joining any vertex to the midpoint of the opposite side.

f. **Altitude.** An *altitude of a triangle* is a perpendicular line segment from any vertex to the opposite side.

g. **Exterior Angle.** An *exterior angle of a triangle* is the angle formed by one side and another side produced.

h. **Parallel Lines.** Two lines are *parallel* if they lie in the same plane and do not intersect even if extended.

i. **Regular Polygon.** A *regular polygon* is a polygon which is both equilateral and equiangular.

j. **Quadrilateral.** A *quadrilateral* is a polygon having four sides.

k. **Parallelogram.** A *parallelogram* is a quadrilateral having two pairs of parallel sides.

l. **Rectangle.** A *rectangle* is a parallelogram having one right angle.

m. **Rhombus.** A *rhombus* is an equilateral parallelogram.

n. **Square.** A *square* is an equilateral rectangle.

o. **Trapezoid.** A *trapezoid* is a quadrilateral having one and only one pair of parallel sides.

p. **Isosceles Trapezoid.** An *isosceles trapezoid* is a trapezoid having the nonparallel sides equal.

q. **Circle.** A *circle* is a plane closed curve all points of which are equidistant from a point within called the center.

r. **Similar Polygons.** *Similar polygons* are polygons whose corresponding angles are equal and whose corresponding sides are proportional.

s. **Center of Regular Polygon.** The *center of a regular polygon* is the common center of the circumcircle and the incircle.

11. Axioms. The following axioms, already familiar from plane geometry, will be used in solid geometry as needed:

a. If equals are added to equals, the sums are equal.

b. If equals are subtracted from equals, the remainders are equal.

c. If equals are multiplied by equals, the products are equal.

d. If equals are divided by equals, the quotients are equal.

e. A quantity may be substituted for its equal.

f. Quantities which are equal to the same or equal quantities are equal to each other.

g. Like powers or like roots of equals are equal.

h. The whole is equal to the sum of its parts and is greater than any one of them.

i. Of two quantities of the same kind, the first is greater than, equal to, or less than the second.

j. If the first of three quantities is greater than the second, and the second is greater than the third, then the first is greater than the third.

k. If unequals are increased by, diminished by, multiplied by, or divided by positive equals, the results are unequal in the same order.

l. If unequals are subtracted from equals, the remainders are unequal in the reverse order.

m. If unequals are added to unequals in the same order, the sums are unequal in the same order.

n. Like positive powers and like positive roots of unequals are unequal in the same order.

12. Postulates of Plane Geometry. The following postulates of plane geometry are equally applicable to solid geometry with the exceptions that in Postulates *e*, *j*, *q*, and *t* the phrase "In a plane" should be prefixed:

a. One straight line, and only one, can be drawn through two points.

b. Two straight lines cannot intersect in more than one point.

c. A straight line segment can be extended indefinitely in two directions.

d. A straight line segment is the shortest line segment that can be drawn between two points.

e. One, and only one, circle can be drawn with any given point as a center and any given line segment as a radius.

f. Any geometric figure may be moved without changing its size or shape.

g. A straight line segment has one, and only one, midpoint.

h. An angle can be bisected by one, and only one, line.

i. All right angles are equal.

j. At any point in a straight line one, and only one, perpendicular can be drawn to the line.

k. The perpendicular is the shortest line segment that can be drawn from a given point to a given line.

l. The sum of all the angles about a point in a plane is two straight angles.

m. If two adjacent angles have their exterior sides in a straight line, they are supplementary; and conversely.

n. All radii of a circle or of equal circles are equal.

o. A straight line cannot intersect a circle in more than two points.

p. Corresponding parts of congruent polygons are equal; and polygons are congruent if their corresponding sides and angles are equal.

q. Two straight lines are either parallel lines or intersecting lines.

r. Through a given point there can be only one parallel to a given line.

s. Circles having equal radii are equal.

t. A point is within, on, or outside a circle if its distance from the center is less than, equal to, or greater than the radius.

u. Two minor arcs, or two major arcs, coincide if their end points and centers coincide; and conversely.

v. A central angle is equal in degrees to its intercepted arc.

w. The area of a rectangle is equal to the product of its base and its altitude.

x. If the number of sides of a regular inscribed (or circumscribed) polygon is indefinitely increased, the perimeter of the polygon approaches the circumference of the circle as a limit.

y. If the number of sides of a regular inscribed (or circumscribed) polygon is indefinitely increased, the area of the polygon approaches the area of the circle as a limit.

z. If the number of sides of a regular inscribed polygon is indefinitely increased, the apothem of the polygon approaches the radius of the circle as a limit.

SUMMARY OF PRINCIPAL METHODS OF PROOF
OF PLANE GEOMETRY

13. Triangles Congruent. The following theorems relate to conditions under which triangles are congruent:

a. If two triangles have two sides and the included angle of one equal respectively to two sides and the included angle of the other, the triangles are congruent (§ 48).*

b. If two right triangles have the two legs of one equal respectively to the two legs of the other, the triangles are congruent (§ 51).

---

* The references are to Welchons and Krickenberger's "Plane Geometry."

c. If two triangles have two angles and the included side of one equal respectively to two angles and the included side of the other, the triangles are congruent (§ 54).

d. If two triangles have the three sides of one equal respectively to the three sides of the other, the triangles are congruent (§ 61).

e. If two right triangles have the hypotenuse and an acute angle of one equal respectively to the hypotenuse and an acute angle of the other, the triangles are congruent (§ 90).

f. If two right triangles have the hypotenuse and a leg of one equal respectively to the hypotenuse and a leg of the other, the triangles are congruent (§ 97).

g. A diagonal divides a parallelogram into two congruent triangles (§ 128).

14. Line Segments Equal. The following statements relate to conditions under which line segments are equal :

a. All radii of a circle or of equal circles are equal (§ 27, Post. 15).

b. Corresponding sides of congruent polygons are equal (§ 56).

c. If two angles of a triangle are equal, the sides opposite these angles are equal (§ 92).

d. An equiangular triangle is equilateral (§ 93).

e. If one acute angle of a right triangle is 30°, the side opposite this angle is one half the hypotenuse (§ 95).

f. The opposite sides of a parallelogram are equal (§ 129).

g. Segments of parallels included between parallels are equal (§ 133).

h. The diagonals of a parallelogram bisect each other (§ 135).

i. If parallels intercept equal segments on one transversal, they intercept equal segments on any transversal (§ 140).

j. If a line bisects one side of a triangle and is parallel to a second side, it bisects the third side (§ 141).

k. The line segment joining the midpoints of two sides of a triangle is equal to one half the third side (§ 142).

l. The median of a trapezoid is equal to one half the sum of the bases (§ 144).

m. In a circle or in equal circles, equal arcs have equal chords (§ 170).

n. If a line through the center of a circle is perpendicular to a chord, it bisects the chord (§ 172).

o. In a circle or in equal circles, equal chords are equidistant from the center (§ 175).

p. In a circle or in equal circles, chords equidistant from the center are equal (§ 176).

q. The tangents to a circle from an external point are equal (§ 182).

r. The midpoint of the hypotenuse of a right triangle is equidistant from the vertices of the triangle (§ 198).

s. The locus of points within an angle equidistant from the sides is the bisector of the angle (§ 217).

t. The locus of points equidistant from two given points is the perpendicular bisector of the line segment joining the two points (§ 219).

15. Angles Equal. The following statements relate to conditions under which angles are equal :

a. All right angles are equal (§ 27, Post. 9).

b. Complements of the same or of equal angles are equal (§§ 38, 39).

c. Supplements of the same or of equal angles are equal (§§ 40, 41).

d. If two straight lines intersect, the vertical angles are equal (§ 42).

e. Corresponding angles of congruent polygons are equal (§ 56).

f. If two sides of a triangle are equal, the angles opposite these sides are equal (§ 59).

g. An equilateral triangle is equiangular (§ 60).

h. If two parallels are cut by a transversal, the alternate interior angles are equal (§ 78).

i. If two parallels are cut by a transversal, the corresponding angles are equal (§ 79).

j. If two angles have their sides parallel, right side to right side and left side to left side, the angles are equal (§ 84).

k. If two angles of one triangle are equal respectively to two angles of another triangle, the third angles are equal (§ 86).

l. If two angles have their sides perpendicular, right side to right side and left side to left side, the angles are equal (§ 91).

m. The opposite angles of a parallelogram are equal (§ 130).

n. In a circle or in equal circles, equal arcs have equal central angles (§ 167).

o. Inscribed angles which intercept the same arc are equal (§ 199).

p. Corresponding angles of similar polygons are equal (§ 275).

16. Angles Supplementary. The following statements relate to conditions under which angles are supplementary :

a. Two angles are supplementary when their sum is a straight angle (§ 17).

b. If two adjacent angles have their exterior sides in a straight line, they are supplementary (§ 27, Post. 13).

c. If two parallels are cut by a transversal, the two interior angles on the same side of the transversal are supplementary (§ 80).

d. Two consecutive angles of a parallelogram are supplementary (§ 131).

e. If a quadrilateral is inscribed in a circle, the opposite angles are supplementary (§ 200).

17. Angles Complementary.

The following statements relate to conditions under which angles are complementary:

a. Two angles are complementary when their sum is a right angle (§ 16).

b. The acute angles of a right triangle are complementary (§ 89).

18. Lines Perpendicular; Angle a Right Angle.

The following statements relate to conditions under which lines are perpendicular, or form a right angle:

a. Two lines are perpendicular if one of them forms two equal adjacent angles with the other; or if the lines form a right angle (§ 10).

b. The perpendicular is the shortest line segment that can be drawn from a given point to a given line (§ 27, Post. 11, and § 392).

c. There can be one, and only one, perpendicular to a line from an external point (§§ 67, 118).

d. If a line is perpendicular to one of two parallel lines, it is perpendicular to the other (§ 81).

e. A line passing through two points each equidistant from the end points of a line segment is the perpendicular bisector of the segment (§ 99).

f. All the angles of a rectangle are right angles (§ 132).

g. The diagonals of a rhombus are perpendicular (§ 136).

h. If a line through the center of a circle bisects a chord that is not a diameter, it is perpendicular to the chord (§ 173).

i. If a line is tangent to a circle, it is perpendicular to the radius drawn to the point of contact (§ 177).

j. If two circles intersect, the line of centers is the perpendicular bisector of the common chord (§ 183).

k. An angle inscribed in a semicircle is a right angle (§ 197).

l. The locus of points equidistant from two given points is the perpendicular bisector of the line segment joining the two points (§ 219).

19. Lines Parallel. The following statements relate to conditions under which lines are parallel:

a. Two lines are parallel if they lie in the same plane and do not intersect even if extended (§ 69).

b. Two straight lines (in the same plane) are either parallel lines or intersecting lines (§ 70).

c. If two lines form equal alternate interior angles with a transversal, the lines are parallel (§ 72).

d. If two lines form equal corresponding angles with a transversal, the lines are parallel (§ 73).

e. If two lines form supplementary interior angles on the same side of a transversal, the lines are parallel (§ 74).

f. Two lines (in the same plane) perpendicular to a third line are parallel (§ 75).

g. Two lines parallel to a third line are parallel to each other (§ 77).

h. A parallelogram is a quadrilateral having two pairs of parallel sides (§ 126).

i. The line segment joining the midpoints of two sides of a triangle is parallel to the third side (§ 142).

j. The median of a trapezoid is parallel to the bases (§ 144).

k. If a line divides two sides of a triangle proportionally, it is parallel to the third side (§ 267).

l. If a line divides two sides of a triangle so that either side is to one of its segments as the other side is to its corresponding segment, the line is parallel to the third side (§ 268).

20. When a Quadrilateral is a Parallelogram. The following statements relate to conditions under which a quadrilateral is a parallelogram:

a. A quadrilateral is a parallelogram if it has two pairs of parallel sides (§ 126).

b. If the opposite sides of a quadrilateral are equal, the figure is a parallelogram (§ 137).

c. If two sides of a quadrilateral are equal and parallel the figure is a parallelogram (§ 138).

d. If the diagonals of a quadrilateral bisect each other, the figure is a parallelogram (§ 139).

e. If both pairs of opposite angles of a quadrilateral are equal, the figure is a parallelogram.

21. Angles and Sums of Angles.

The following statements relate to angles and the sums of angles:

a. The sum of all the angles about a point in a plane is two straight angles (§ 27, Post. 12).

b. The sum of the angles of a triangle is a straight angle (§ 85).

c. An exterior angle of a triangle equals the sum of the two non-adjacent interior angles (§ 88).

d. The sum of the exterior angles of a convex polygon is two straight angles (§ 145).

e. The sum of the interior angles of a convex polygon having n sides is $(n - 2)$ straight angles (§ 147).

f. Each interior angle of a regular polygon of n sides is $\left(\dfrac{n-2}{n}\right)$ straight angles (§ 148).

g. The central angle of a regular polygon of n sides is $\dfrac{360°}{n}$ (§ 341).

22. Arcs Equal.

The following theorems relate to conditions under which arcs are equal:

a. In a circle or in equal circles, equal central angles have equal arcs (§ 165).

b. A diameter of a circle bisects the circle (§ 166).

c. In a circle or in equal circles, equal chords have equal arcs (§ 169).

d. If a line through the center of a circle is perpendicular to a chord, it bisects the arc of the chord (§ 172).

e. Parallel lines intercept equal arcs on a circle (§ 184).

23. Comparison of Angles and their Arcs.

The following statements relate to the measure of angles in the circle:

a. A central angle is equal in degrees to its intercepted arc (§ 194).

b. An inscribed angle is equal in degrees to one half its intercepted arc (§ 196).

c. An angle formed by a tangent and a chord drawn from the point of contact is equal in degrees to one half its intercepted arc (§ 201).

d. An angle formed by two chords intersecting within a circle is equal in degrees to one half the sum of the arcs intercepted by it and its vertical angle (§ 202).

e. An angle formed by two tangents, by a tangent and a secant, or by two secants intersecting outside a circle is equal in degrees to one half the difference of the intercepted arcs (§ 203).

24. Lines Passing through a Point. The following theorems relate to lines passing through a point:

a. Lines perpendicular to intersecting lines will intersect (§ 82).

b. The perpendicular bisector of a chord passes through the center of the circle (§ 174).

c. If a line is perpendicular to a tangent at the point of contact, it passes through the center of the circle (§ 178).

d. The perpendicular bisectors of the sides of a triangle are concurrent in a point equidistant from the vertices (§ 225).

e. The bisectors of the angles of a triangle are concurrent in a point equidistant from the sides (§ 227).

f. The altitudes of a triangle are concurrent (§ 229).

g. The medians of a triangle are concurrent in a point which is two thirds of the distance from each vertex to the midpoint of the opposite side (§ 231).

25. Line Segments in Proportion. The following statements relate to proportional line segments:

a. A line parallel to one side of a triangle divides the other two sides proportionally (§ 261).

b. A line parallel to one side of a triangle divides the other two sides so that either side is to one of its segments as the other side is to its corresponding segment (§ 262).

c. Parallel lines intercept proportional segments on two transversals (§ 263).

d. The bisector of an interior (or exterior) angle of a triangle divides the opposite side internally (or externally) into segments which are proportional to the adjacent sides (§§ 270, 271).

e. Any two corresponding sides of two similar polygons have the same ratio as two other corresponding sides (§ 275).

f. The corresponding altitudes of two similar triangles have the same ratio as any two corresponding sides (§ 278).

g. The altitude on the hypotenuse of a right triangle is the mean proportional between the segments of the hypotenuse (§ 284).

h. Either leg of a right triangle is the mean proportional between the hypotenuse and its projection on the hypotenuse (§ 286).

i. The perpendicular from any point on a circle to a diameter of the circle is the mean proportional between the segments of the diameter (§ 287).

j. If two chords intersect within a circle, the product of the segments of one is equal to the product of the segments of the other (§ 291).

k. If a tangent and a secant are drawn to a circle from the same point, the tangent is the mean proportional between the secant and its external segment (§ 293).

26. Proportions involving Polygons and Circles. The following theorems relate to proportions involving polygons and circles:

a. The perimeters of two similar polygons have the same ratio as any two corresponding sides (§ 294).

b. Two rectangles, parallelograms, or triangles having equal bases have the same ratio as their altitudes (§§ 308, 313, 315).

c. Two rectangles, parallelograms, or triangles having equal altitudes have the same ratio as their bases (§§ 309, 313, 316).

d. The areas of two triangles have the same ratio as the products of their bases and altitudes (§ 317).

e. The areas of two similar triangles have the same ratio as the squares of any two corresponding sides, or as the squares of any two corresponding altitudes (§§ 324, 325).

f. The areas of two similar polygons have the same ratio as the squares of any two corresponding sides (§ 326).

g. The areas of two regular polygons of the same number of sides have the same ratio as the squares of any two corresponding sides, or as the squares of their radii, or as the squares of their apothems (§§ 348, 350).

h. The circumferences of two circles have the same ratio as their radii, or as their diameters (§§ 357, 358).

i. The areas of two circles have the same ratio as the squares of their radii, or as the squares of their diameters (§ 366).

j. The area of a sector of a circle is to the area of the circle as the angle of the sector is to 360° (§ 367).

27. Polygons Similar. The following statements relate to conditions under which polygons are similar:

a. Similar polygons are polygons which have their corresponding angles equal and their corresponding sides proportional (§ 274).

b. If two triangles have two angles of one equal respectively to two angles of the other, the triangles are similar (§ 276).

c. If two right triangles have an acute angle of one equal to an acute angle of the other, the triangles are similar (§ 277).

d. If two triangles are similar to a third triangle, they are similar to each other (§ 279).

e. If two triangles have an angle of one equal to an angle of the other and the including sides proportional, the triangles are similar (§ 281).

f. If two triangles have their sides respectively proportional, they are similar (§ 282).

g. The altitude on the hypotenuse of a right triangle forms two triangles, which are similar to the given triangle and to each other (§ 283).

h. If two polygons are similar, they can be separated into triangles which are similar each to each (§ 295).

i. If two polygons are composed of the same number of triangles, similar each to each and similarly placed, the polygons are similar (§ 296).

j. Two regular polygons of the same number of sides are similar (§ 347).

28. Areas. The following statements relate to areas:

a. The area of a rectangle is equal to the product of its base and altitude (§ 307).

b. The area of a square is equal to the square of one of its sides (§ 310).

c. The area of a parallelogram is equal to the product of its base and altitude (§ 311).

d. The area of a triangle is equal to one half the product of its base and altitude (§ 314).

e. The area of a rhombus is equal to one half the product of its diagonals (§ 318).

f. The area of an equilateral triangle having a side s is expressed by the formula $A = \dfrac{s^2}{4}\sqrt{3}$ (§ 320).

g. The area of a triangle whose sides are a, b, and c is expressed by the formula $A = \sqrt{s(s-a)(s-b)(s-c)}$, where $s = \frac{1}{2}(a+b+c)$ (§ 321).

h. The area of a trapezoid is equal to one half the product of its altitude and the sum of its bases (§ 322).

i. The area of a regular polygon is equal to one half the product of its apothem and its perimeter (§ 346).

j. The area of a circle is equal to one half the product of its radius and its circumference (§ 364).

k. The area of a circle is expressed by the formula $A = \pi r^2$ (§ 365).

29. Figures Equal in Area.

The following theorems relate to figures equal in area:

a. Parallelograms having equal bases and equal altitudes are equivalent (§ 312).

b. If a triangle and a parallelogram have equal bases and equal altitudes, the area of the triangle is half the area of the parallelogram (§ 319).

c. The square on the hypotenuse of a right triangle is equal to the sum of the squares on the legs (§ 327).

30. Miscellaneous Numerical Relations.

The following statements cover miscellaneous numerical relations:

a. The square of the hypotenuse of a right triangle is equal to the sum of the squares of the legs (§ 289).

b. The diagonal of a square is equal to one side multiplied by $\sqrt{2}$ (§ 290).

c. The circumference of a circle is expressed by the formulas $c = \pi d$ and $c = 2 \pi r$ (§ 360).

d. $\pi = \dfrac{c}{d} = 3.1416$, approximately (§ 363).

e. In a proportion, the product of the means equals the product of the extremes (§ 250).

f. If the numerators of a proportion are equal, the denominators are equal; and conversely (§ 252).

g. In a series of equal ratios, the sum of the numerators is to the sum of the denominators as any numerator is to its denominator (§ 254).

31. Polygons Regular.

The following statements relate to conditions under which polygons are regular:

a. A regular polygon is a polygon which is both equilateral and equiangular (§ 125).

b. If a circle is divided into any number of equal arcs, the chords of these arcs form a regular inscribed polygon, and the tangents at the points of division form a regular circumscribed polygon (§§ 342, 345).

c. An equilateral polygon inscribed in a circle is a regular polygon (§ 343).

d. If the midpoints of the arcs of a regular inscribed polygon are joined to the extremities of the respective sides, a regular inscribed polygon of double the number of sides is formed (§ 344).

32. Inequalities. The following statements relate to inequalities:

a. The perpendicular is the shortest line segment that can be drawn from a given point to a given line (§ 27, Post. 11, and § 392).

b. An exterior angle of a triangle is greater than either nonadjacent interior angle (§ 66).

c. Each side of a triangle is less than the sum of the other two sides (§ 389).

d. If one side of a triangle is greater than a second side, the angle opposite the first side is greater than the angle opposite the second side (§ 390).

e. If one angle of a triangle is greater than a second angle, the side opposite the first angle is greater than the side opposite the second angle (§ 391).

f. The hypotenuse of a right triangle is greater than either leg (§ 393).

g. If two oblique line segments are drawn to a line from a point in a perpendicular to the line, the one having the greater projection on the line is the greater (§ 396) ; and conversely (§ 397).

h. If two triangles have two sides of one equal respectively to two sides of the other, and the included angle of the first is greater than the included angle of the second, the third side of the first is greater than the third side of the second (§ 394).

i. If two triangles have two sides of one equal respectively to two sides of the other, and the third side of the first is greater than the third side of the second, the angle opposite the third side of the first is greater than the angle opposite the third side of the second (§ 395).

j. In a circle or in equal circles, the greater of two unequal central angles has the greater arc (§ 398) ; and conversely (§ 399).

k. In a circle or in equal circles, the greater of two unequal chords has the greater arc (§ 400) ; and conversely (§ 401).

l. In a circle or in equal circles, the greater of two unequal chords is nearer the center (§ 402) ; and conversely (§ 403).

m. A diameter of a circle is greater than any other chord (§ 404).

33. Constructions. The following constructions, which are studied in plane geometry, are equally applicable to solid geometry provided that planes are determined before applying them:

a. To construct a triangle, given the three sides (§ 112).

b. To bisect a given angle (§ 113).

c. With a given vertex and a given side to construct an angle equal to a given angle (§ 114).

d. To construct a line segment equal to a given line segment (§ 22 *a*).

e. To construct a triangle, given two angles and the included side (§ 116); given two sides and the included angle (§ 115).

f. To construct a perpendicular to a given line from a given point without the line (§ 118).

g. To construct a perpendicular to a given line at a given point in the line (§ 119).

h. Through a given point to construct a line parallel to a given line (§ 120).

i. To bisect a given arc of a circle (§ 205).

j. To construct the tangent to a given circle at a given point on the circle (§ 206).

k. To construct a tangent to a given circle from a given external point (§ 207).

l. To inscribe a square in a given circle (§ 208).

m. To inscribe a regular hexagon in a given circle (§ 209).

n. To circumscribe a circle about a given triangle (§ 233).

o. To inscribe a circle in a given triangle (§ 238).

p. On a given line segment as a chord, to construct an arc of a circle in which a given angle can be inscribed (§ 241).

q. To construct the fourth proportional to three given line segments (§ 264).

r. To divide a given line segment into two parts which are proportional to two given line segments (§ 265).

s. To divide a given line segment into *n* parts which are proportional to *n* given line segments (§ 266).

t. To construct the mean proportional between two given line segments (§ 288).

WORD LIST

The following words in plane geometry are sometimes misspelled. Be sure you can spell and use each one correctly:

acute	equiangular	pentagon
adjacent	equidistant	perimeter
alternate	equilateral	perpendicular
altitude	equivalent	pi (π)
analysis	exterior	plane
angle	hexagon	proportional
apothem	horizontal	quadrilateral
arc	hypotenuse	radii
area	hypothesis	ratio
bisector	incircle	rectangle
center	isosceles	rhombus
chord	loci	secant
circumcenter	locus	sector
circumcircle	median	semicircle
circumference	midpoint	similar
complementary	oblique	supplementary
concurrent	obtuse	theorem
congruent	octagon	transversal
corollary	opposite	trapezoid
corresponding	orthocenter	trisect
definition	parallel	vertex
diagonal	parallelogram	vertical
diameter	pentadecagon	vertices

Mt. Wilson Solar Observatory, Pasadena, California

The observations of the heavenly bodies in space by astronomers have led to
problems that have enriched various fields of mathematics

CHAPTER I

LINES AND PLANES IN SPACE

34. Representation of Figures in Solid Geometry. At first some students have trouble in visualizing and drawing the figures of solid geometry, but after some practice these figures offer little more difficulty than those of plane geometry.

The figures of solid geometry have three dimensions, but must be represented on paper or blackboard, which has only two dimensions. To discover some means of making the figures of solids appear as solids and stand out, we may study three figures of the same cube. In each figure the square face

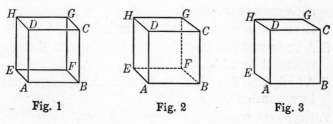

Fig. 1   Fig. 2   Fig. 3

ABCD represents a vertical square face of the cube, which seems to be parallel with the surface of the paper. All vertical lines of the figure represent vertical lines of the cube, and all slanting lines represent lines of the cube which recede from the face of the cube (or recede from the eye). The dotted lines in Fig. 2 represent lines of the cube which cannot be seen from the point of view from which the figures were drawn. Often the hidden lines are left out, as in Fig. 3. Notice that the lines representing the receding edges of the cube are shorter than those representing the other edges. Notice, too, that all angles of the figure are not right angles, as they are in the actual cube.

Figure 1 is the most difficult to visualize, since either the face *ABCD* or the face *EFGH* may appear to be nearer the eye. Figure 2 is drawn in perspective, that is, as it appears to the eye, the receding parallel lines of the cube not being represented by parallel lines, as in Fig. 1 and Fig. 3, but by lines which, if produced, would meet at a point. Although drawings made in perspective are more easily visualized, the drawings in geometry are often like those of Figs. 1 and 3.

In drawing geometric figures you will find the following directions useful:

1. Draw a solid with one face parallel to the top of the blackboard (or paper).
2. A plane that does not recede from the eye represent by a rectangle.
3. A plane that recedes from the eye represent by a parallelogram or trapezoid.
4. Represent a vertical line by a vertical line.
5. A horizontal line that does not recede from the eye represent by a horizontal line.
6. A horizontal line that recedes from the eye represent by a slanting line.
7. Represent parallel lines by parallel lines.
8. A circle that does not recede from the eye represent by a circle, and one that does, by an ellipse.

Thus, in the figure at the right, *MN* is a plane, represented by a parallelogram since it recedes from the eye; *AD* and *BC* are two parallel vertical lines meeting the plane at points *A* and *B* respectively; *AB* is a horizontal line that does not recede from the eye; and *EB* 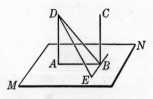 is a horizontal line that recedes from the eye. *CB*, *DB*, and *AB* are each perpendicular to *EB*. *AD* and *BC* are both perpendicular to *AB*.

If you are unable to visualize a figure found in the text, you will find it helpful to make a model of it. By using pasteboard or thin sheets of iron, glass, or wood to represent a plane, a thin stick or a wire to represent a line perpendicular to a plane, and a string to represent an oblique line, you can make a model of any figure with little or no expense. Models for some of the figures which are studied in solid geometry can be successfully carved from soap.

When beginning the study of a new figure, you would do well to study objects, in your home or in the schoolroom, which have the same shape as the figure you are studying. Thus, in studying a rectangular solid, you can use a chalk box or a candy box; in studying parallel planes, you can use the opposite faces of boxes, the opposite walls of a room, or the covers of a book; and the corners of a room you can use as good examples of three planes meeting at a point, of two lines perpendicular to a third line at a point, and of a line perpendicular to a plane.

35. Foot of a Line. The point of intersection of a straight line and a plane is called the *foot* of the line.

36. Line Perpendicular to a Plane. A line is *perpendicular to a plane* if it is perpendicular to every line in the plane passing through its foot. The plane is also said to be *perpendicular to the line*. If a line meets a plane and is not perpendicular to it, it is said to be *oblique* to the plane.

EXERCISES (GROUP A)

The following exercises refer to the figure on page 24:

1. If $AD \perp$ plane MN, is $AD \perp AB$?

2. If $AD \perp AB$, is $AD \perp$ plane MN?

3. If $CB \perp AB$ and EB, do you think $CB \perp$ plane MN?

4. If $AD \perp AB$ and $BC \perp AB$, is $AD \parallel BC$?

5. Which lines appear oblique to plane MN?

6. What is the foot of line AD? of ED? of BC?

7. Does line AB intersect plane MN?

Proposition I. Theorem (C, N)

37. *If a line is perpendicular to each of two intersecting lines at their point of intersection, it is perpendicular to the plane of the two lines.*

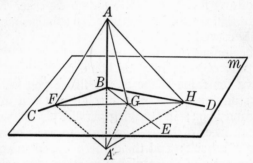

Given $AB \perp BC$ and BD, and m, the plane of the intersecting lines BC and BD.

To prove that $AB \perp$ plane m.

> *Selection of Method:* 1. Known methods of proving a line $\perp$ a
> plane: § 36.
> 2. Method to be used: § 36.

Proof:

STATEMENTS	REASONS
1. Through B draw any other line BE in plane m.	1. § 12 a.
2. Draw any line intersecting BC at F, BE at G, and BD at H.	2. § 12 a.
3. Extend AB to A' so that $BA' = BA$.	3. § 12 c.
4. Draw AF, AG, AH, $A'F$, $A'G$, and $A'H$.	4. § 12 a.
5. $\therefore AF = A'F$ and $AH = A'H$.	5. § 18 l.
6. $\therefore \triangle AFH \cong \triangle A'FH$.	6. § 13 d.
7. $\therefore \angle AFG = \angle A'FG$.	7. § 15 e.
8. $\therefore \triangle AFG \cong \triangle A'FG$.	8. § 13 a.
9. $\therefore AG = A'G$.	9. § 14 b.
10. $\therefore BG \perp AB$.	10. § 18 l.
11. $\therefore AB \perp m$.	11. § 36.

38. Corollary I (c, n). *Through a given point in a given line there can be one plane, and only one, perpendicular to the line.*

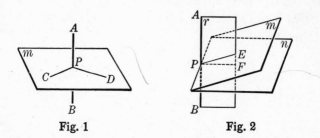

Fig. 1   Fig. 2

Using Fig. 1, let AB be the given line and P the given point in AB. Draw PC and PD each $\perp AB$ at P. Then PC and PD determine the plane m (§ 9 e). Then $m \perp AB$ at P (§ 37).

Using Fig. 2, suppose another plane $n \perp AB$ at P. Pass a plane r through AB and E, a point in m but not in n. Plane r intersects m in PE and n in PF (§ 9 b). In plane r, PE and PF are both $\perp AB$ at P. But this is impossible (§ 12 j). Therefore m is the only plane $\perp AB$ at P.

39. Corollary II (c, n). *Through a given external point there can be one plane, and only one, perpendicular to a given line.*

Let AB be the given line and P the given external point. Draw CP and $CD \perp AB$. CP and CD determine a plane $m \perp AB$ at C. Why?

Any plane $m \perp AB$ and passing through P contains a $\perp$ from P to AB (§ 36). Since there is only one $\perp$ from P to AB, all planes through $P \perp AB$ must intersect AB at C. Therefore m is the only plane $\perp AB$ through P (§ 38).

40. Corollary III (c, N). *All the perpendiculars to a line at a point in the line lie in a plane which is perpendicular to the line at that point.*

Proposition II. Theorem (c, n)

41. *Oblique lines drawn from a point to a plane meeting the plane at equal distances from the foot of the perpendicular are equal.*

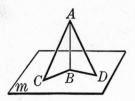

(The demonstration is left to the student.)

Proposition III. Theorem (c, n)

42. *Of two oblique lines from a point to a plane meeting the plane at unequal distances from the foot of the perpendicular, the more remote is the longer.*

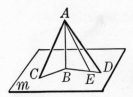

(The demonstration is left to the student.)

Suggestion. Construct $BE = BC$ and draw AE. $AD > AE$ (§32 g).

43. Corollary (c, n). *The perpendicular is the shortest line segment from a point to a plane.*

EXERCISES (GROUP A)

1. Find an example in your classroom in which each of three lines is perpendicular to each of the other two.

2. What theorem in plane geometry corresponds to Prop. II? to Prop. III? to the corollary in §43?

Proposition IV. Theorem (C, N)

44. *Through a given point in a plane there can be drawn one, and only one, perpendicular to the plane.*

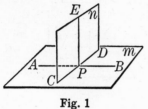

Fig. 1

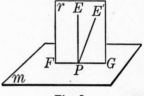

Fig. 2

Given the point P in plane m.

To prove that one $\perp$, and only one, can be drawn to m at P.

> *Selection of Method:* 1. Known methods of proving lines $\perp$ a plane: §§ 36, 37, 38, 39, 43.
> 2. Method to be used: § 37.

Proof:

STATEMENTS	REASONS
1. Using Fig. 1, in plane m draw any line AB through P.	1. § 12 a.
2. Pass plane $n \perp AB$ at P.	2. § 38.
3. n intersects m in CD.	3. Why?
4. In n draw $PE \perp CD$.	4. § 12 j.
5. Then $PB \perp PE$, or $PE \perp PB$.	5. § 36.
6. ∴ $PE \perp m$. Using Fig. 2, suppose PE' is also $\perp m$ at P.	6. § 37.
7. PE and PE' would determine a plane r.	7. Why?
8. r would intersect m in FG.	8. Why?
9. Then PE and PE', two lines in r, would both be $\perp FG$ at P.	9. Why?
10. Since this is impossible, PE is the only line $\perp m$ at P.	10. § 12 j.

Proposition V. Theorem (C, N)

45. *Through a given external point there can be drawn one, and only one, perpendicular to a plane.*

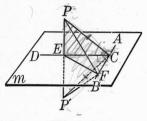

Fig. 1   Fig. 2

Given the plane m and external point P.

To prove that through P there can be drawn one, and only one, line $\perp m$.

[Selection of Method: 1. Known methods of proving lines $\perp$ a plane: §§ 36, 37, 38, 39, 43, 44.
                2. Method to be used : § 37.]

Proof: *STATEMENTS*   *REASONS*

	STATEMENTS	REASONS
1.	Using Fig. 1, in plane m draw any line AB.	1. § 12 a.
2.	In the plane determined by P and AB, draw $PC \perp AB$.	2. §§ 9 d, 18 c.
3.	In plane m draw $DC \perp AB$.	3. § 12 j.
4.	In the plane of P and CD draw $PE \perp CD$.	4. §§ 9 d, 18 c.
5.	Extend PE to P' so that $P'E = PE$.	5. Why possible?
6.	From E draw a line to F, any point in AB.	6. § 12 a.
7.	Draw PF, $P'C$, and $P'F$.	7. § 12 a.
8.	$AB \perp PC$ and EC.	8. Const.
9.	$\therefore AB \perp$ plane of PC and EC.	9. § 37.
10.	$\therefore AB \perp P'C$.	10. § 36.
11.	$\therefore PC = P'C$.	11. § 18 l.
12.	$\therefore FP = FP'$.	12. § 41.
13.	$\therefore FE \perp PP'$ or $PE \perp EF$.	13. § 18 l.

Proof: *STATEMENTS*   *REASONS*

14. But $PE \perp EC$.	14. Statement 4.
15. $\therefore PE \perp m$.	15. § 37.
Using Fig. 2, let us suppose PE' also $\perp m$ from P.	
16. PE and PE' would determine a plane n.	16. Why?
17. m would intersect n in line EE'.	17. Why?
18. In plane n, PE and PE' would both be $\perp EE'$.	18. Why?
19. Since this is impossible, PE is the only line $\perp m$ from P.	19. § 18 c.

EXERCISES (GROUP A). *LINES AND PLANES*

1. In a plane, how many lines may be drawn perpendicular to a given line at a point in the line?

2. In space, how many lines may be drawn perpendicular to a given line at a point in the line?

3. How many lines may be drawn perpendicular to a given plane at a given point in the plane?

4. If a line is perpendicular to a line in a plane, is it perpendicular to the plane?

5. If a line is perpendicular to a plane, is the plane perpendicular to the line?

6. If two lines are each perpendicular to a third line, are they parallel?

7. If a line is perpendicular to a plane, to what lines in the plane is it perpendicular?

8. If a line is oblique to a plane, to how many lines in the plane may it be perpendicular?

9. Find two lines in your classroom that are not parallel and do not meet.

10. Are all lines perpendicular to a vertical line horizontal?

11. Are all lines perpendicular to a horizontal line vertical?

12. In general, how many planes are determined by a straight line and two points?

13. Find an example in your classroom in which each of three lines is perpendicular to the plane of the other two.

14. A vertical flagpole PA is set on level ground. Guy wires from P are fastened to stakes at B, C, and D equidistant from A. Are the wires of equal length? Why?

15. In the figure of Ex. 14, let $PA = 90$ feet, $AB = 60$ feet, $AC = 65$ feet, and $AD = 62$ feet. Find the lengths of PB, PC, and PD.

16. Find the distance from an upper corner of your classroom to a lower opposite corner.

17. Prove that equal oblique line segments drawn from a point in a perpendicular to a plane meet the plane at equal distances from the foot of the perpendicular.

18. Prove that if two unequal oblique line segments are drawn from a point in a perpendicular to a plane, the greater line segment meets the plane at a greater distance from the foot of the perpendicular.

19. Prove that if from the foot of a perpendicular to a plane a line is drawn at right angles to any line in the plane, the line drawn from the point of their intersection to any point in the perpendicular is perpendicular to the line of the plane.

46. Distance of a Point from a Plane. The distance from a point to a plane is the length of the perpendicular from the point to the plane.

47. Locus of Points in Space. Locus has the same meaning in solid geometry as in plane geometry except that the locus is not confined to a plane. Thus in plane geometry the locus of points at a given distance from a given point is a circle, while in space the locus of points at a given distance from a given point is a sphere.

In the following exercises some of the fundamental loci of plane geometry will be considered when the locus is not confined to a plane.

EXERCISES (GROUP A).* *LOCI*

1. What is the locus of points in space equidistant from two given points?

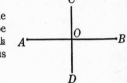

Suggestions. First recall the locus from plane geometry. In space, how many ⊥s may be drawn to AB at point O? Where do these ⊥s lie? (See § 40.) What do you think is the locus of points equidistant from A and B?

2. What is the locus of points in space equidistant from three noncollinear points?

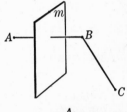

Suggestions. First represent the locus equidistant from two points such as A and B. Then represent the locus equidistant from B and C. Will the two planes intersect? Can you describe the locus?

3. What is the locus of points in space at a given distance from a given point?

4. What is the locus of points in space equidistant from all the points of a given circle?

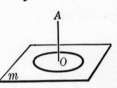

Suggestions. What is the locus of points equidistant from the points of the circle in plane m? If $AO \perp m$, can you prove that point A is equidistant from any three points on the circle?

5. What is the locus of points in space at a given distance from a given line?

Suggestions. If AB is the given line and d the given distance, will the two lines XY and ZW, each ∥ AB, represent the locus in a plane? How many planes can be passed through the line AB? Does each of these planes contain two lines at the given distance d from AB? Can you tell what kind of surface all these lines at the distance d from AB will form?

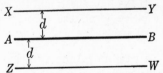

6. If a line passing through two given points, A and B, is oblique to a plane m, draw a figure to show the locus of points in m equidistant from A and B.

* No attempt should be made to prove the locus theorems in these exercises, as the student has not had all the requisite theorems. All these exercises will appear later in the text, at which time they should be proved.

7. What is the locus of points in space at a given distance from a given plane?

8. In a plane, what is the locus of the centers of all circles tangent to a given line at a given point? What would be the locus in space?

9. What is the locus of points in space equidistant from two given parallel lines?

10. Where are all the points equidistant from the floor and ceiling of your classroom?

11. If a point P is 12 inches from plane m, what is the locus of points in m 13 inches from P? What is the locus of points in m 12 inches from P?

As in plane geometry, a locus in space is established by proving

(a) that every point on the assumed locus satisfies the given condition;

and

(b) either that every point which satisfies the given condition is on the assumed locus or that every point outside the assumed locus does not satisfy the given condition.

To establish a locus, it is necessary to prove a theorem and either its converse or its opposite.

If the hypothesis and the conclusion of a theorem are interchanged, the theorem thus obtained is called the *converse* theorem.

If the hypothesis and the conclusion of a theorem are changed to negative form, the theorem thus obtained is called the *opposite* theorem.

In plane geometry a locus satisfying one condition is usually a line or a group of lines, and a locus satisfying two conditions is usually a point or a group of points. In solid geometry a locus satisfying one condition is usually a surface or a group of surfaces, a locus satisfying two conditions is a line or a group of lines, and a locus satisfying three conditions is a point or a group of points.

Proposition VI.   Theorem (c, n)

48. *The locus of points equidistant from two given points is the plane perpendicular to the line joining them, at its midpoint.*

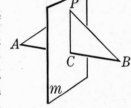

Suggestions. 1. Prove that any point P in plane m is equidistant from the given points A and B.
2. Prove that any point P which is equidistant from A and B lies in the $\perp$ bisector of AB, the line connecting the given points (§ 18 l), and that this $\perp$ bisector lies in m (§ 40). Or prove that any point P which is not in m is not equidistant from A and B. To prove this, draw PA and PB. Let PA intersect m in D. Draw DB and use § 32 c.

Proposition VII.   Theorem (c, n)

49. *The locus of points equidistant from the vertices of a triangle is the line through the center of the circumcircle, perpendicular to the plane of the triangle.*

Suggestions. 1. Using Fig. 1, prove that any point P in the $\perp$ is equidistant from A, B, and C (§ 41).
2. Using Fig. 2, prove that any point P which is not in the $\perp$ is not equi-

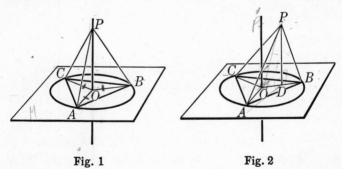

Fig. 1   Fig. 2

distant from A, B, and C. To prove this, draw the line $PD \perp$ plane ABC. The point D does not coincide with O. Why? Then D is not equidistant from A, B, and C. Why? Then P is not equidistant from A, B, and C (§ 42).

Proposition VIII. Theorem (C, N)

50. *Two lines perpendicular to the same plane are parallel.*

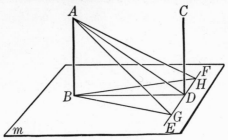

Given *AB* and *CD* each ⊥ plane *m*.

To prove that *AB* ∥ *CD*.

⌈*Selection of Method:* 1. Known methods of proving lines ∥ : § 19.⌉
⌊   2. Method to be used : § 19 *f*.⌋

Proof: STATEMENTS   REASONS

STATEMENTS	REASONS
1. Draw *BD* and *AD*.	1. § 12 *a*.
2. In plane *m* draw *EF* ⊥ *BD*.	2. § 33 *g*.
3. On *EF* construct *HD* = *DG*.	3. § 33 *d*.
4. Draw *AH*, *AG*, *BH*, and *BG*.	4. § 12 *a*.
5. *BH* = *BG*.	5. § 18 *l*.
6. ∴ *AH* = *AG*.	6. § 41.
7. ∴ *AD* ⊥ *HG*.	7. § 18 *l*.
8. *CD* ⊥ *EF*.	8. § 36.
9. ∴ *BD*, *AD*, and *CD* lie in the same plane.	9. § 40.
10. Also, *AB* lies in this plane.	10. § 2.
11. *AB* ⊥ *BD* and *CD* ⊥ *BD*.	11. § 36.
12. ∴ *AB* ∥ *CD*.	12. § 19 *f*.

51. Corollary I (c). *If one of two parallel lines is perpendicular to a plane, the other is also perpendicular to the plane.*

Suggestions. Draw *C'D* ⊥ plane *m* at *D*. Then it follows that *C'D* ∥ *AB* and therefore coincides with *CD* (§ 12 *r*).

52. Corollary II (c, n). *If two lines are parallel to a third line, they are parallel to each other.*

Given AB ‖ EF and CD ‖ EF.

To prove that AB ‖ CD.

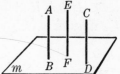

Suggestion. Draw plane *m* ⊥ *EF* and use §§ 51 and 50.

53. Parallel Planes and Lines. A *line* and a *plane* are *parallel* if they do not meet even if extended. Two *planes* are *parallel* if they do not meet even if extended.

54. Skew Lines. Two lines in space that are neither parallel nor intersecting are called *skew lines*. Skew lines cannot lie in the same plane. Why?

EXERCISES (GROUP A)

1. Are two plumb lines parallel?

2. Can two skew lines intersect? be perpendicular to each other?

3. Can two skew lines both be vertical? horizontal?

4. A *skew quadrilateral* is a quadrilateral whose vertices do not all lie in the same plane. Do the diagonals of a skew quadrilateral intersect?

5. The lines joining the midpoints of the sides of a skew quadrilateral taken in order form a parallelogram.

6. If a line is parallel to the intersection of two planes, it is parallel to each of the planes.

7. What is the locus of points equidistant from a circle?

8. Find the locus of points in a given plane which are equidistant from two given points not in the plane.

9. If two planes are parallel, is every line in one of the planes parallel to the other plane?

10. What is the locus of all straight lines which make right angles with a given line at a given point in the line?

11. What is the locus of points in a plane at a given distance from a given point without the plane?

Proposition IX. Theorem (c, N)

55. *If two lines are parallel, every plane containing one of the lines, and only one, is parallel to the other.*

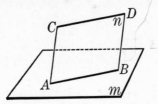

Given *AB* ‖ *CD* and plane *m* containing *AB* but not *CD*.

To prove that *CD* ‖ *m*.

⎡ *Selection of Method:* 1. Known methods of proving a line ‖ a plane: § 53.
        2. Method to be used: § 53. ⎤

Proof:

STATEMENTS	REASONS
1. *CD* and *AB* determine a plane *n*.	1. Why?
2. Since *CD* lies in *n*, if it would meet *m* it would meet *AB*, the intersection of *m* and *n*.	2. § 5.
3. But *CD* cannot meet *AB*.	3. § 10 *h*.
4. ∴ *CD* ‖ *m*.	4. § 53.

56. Corollary I (c, n). *If a line is parallel to a plane, it is parallel to the intersection of that plane with any plane through the line.*

57. Corollary II (c). *If a line and a plane are parallel, a parallel to the line through any point in the plane lies in the plane.*

58. Corollary III (c). *Through either of two skew lines there can be one plane, and only one, parallel to the other line.*

Let *AB* and *CD* be the two skew lines. Through a point *O* in *CD* draw *EF* ‖ *AB*. Draw the plane *m* determined by *CD* and *EF*. Why possible? Then *AB* ‖ *m*. Why?

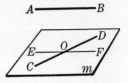

Suppose another plane m' could be passed through $OD \parallel AB$. The plane n determined by AB and OF would intersect m' in a line OF'. Why? OF and OF' do not coincide, since m and m' intersect in OD. Why? Then AB would be $\parallel OF'$. Why? But $AB \parallel OF$. Then through O in n there would be two lines $\parallel AB$. Since this is impossible (§ 12 r), there can be only one plane through $OD \parallel AB$.

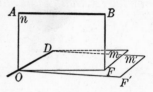

59. Corollary IV (c). *Through a given point in space there can be one plane, and only one, parallel to two skew lines, or else parallel to one line and containing the other.*

Let AB and CD be the two skew lines and P a point in space. Through P draw $EF \parallel AB$ and $GH \parallel CD$. GH and EF determine a plane m. Why? $AB \parallel m$ or else lies in m. Also $CD \parallel m$ or else lies in m. Both AB and CD cannot lie in m. Why? Therefore both CD and AB are $\parallel m$ or else one lies in m and the other is $\parallel m$. If there could be another plane through $P \parallel AB$ and CD, it would contain EF and GH (§ 57), but this is impossible (§ 9 e).

EXERCISES (GROUP A)

1. Parallel lines drawn to a plane from points in a line parallel to the plane are equal.

2. If a line and a plane are parallel, the distance from any point in the line to the plane is constant.

EXERCISES (GROUP B)

1. Can two skew lines both be parallel to a plane? Can two parallel lines both be parallel to a plane? Can two perpendicular lines both be parallel to a plane?

2. If two lines are parallel and lie in different planes, are the planes parallel to each other?

Proposition X.　Theorem (c, N)

60. *If two parallel planes are cut by a third plane, the lines of intersection are parallel.*

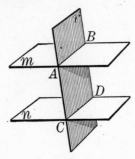

Given the ∥ planes *m* and *n* intersected by plane *r* in *AB* and *CD* respectively.

To prove that *AB* ∥ *CD*.

⎡*Selection of Method:* 1. Known methods of proving lines ∥: §§ 19,
　　　　　　　　　　　　　　　50, 52, 56.
　　　　　　　　　　　　2. Method to be used: § 19 *a*.⎤

Proof:　　　　　*STATEMENTS*　　　　　　　　　　*REASONS*

1. *AB* and *CD* lie in the same plane *r*.	1. Given.
2. *AB* in *m* cannot meet *CD* in *n*.	2. § 53.
3. ∴ *AB* ∥ *CD*.	3. § 19 *a*.

EXERCISES.　*PARALLELS AND PERPENDICULARS*

1. If two planes are parallel to a third plane, they are parallel to each other.

2. Name some applications of Prop. X in your classroom.

3. Parallel lines included between parallel planes are equal.

4. With a 10-foot pole how would you determine a point in the floor directly under a point in the ceiling which is 9 feet high?

5. Using two carpenter's squares, how could you determine a line perpendicular to a plane?

Proposition XI.   Theorem (c, N)

61. *Two planes perpendicular to the same line are parallel.*

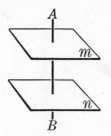

Given the planes *m* and *n* each ⊥ *AB*.

To prove that *m* ∥ *n*.

⎡ *Selection of Method:* 1. Known methods of proving planes ∥ : § 53. ⎤
⎣   2. Method to be used : § 53. ⎦

Proof: *STATEMENTS*   *REASONS*

STATEMENTS	REASONS
1. If *m* and *n* were not ∥, they would meet.	1. § 53.
2. But that is impossible, for then *m* and *n* would be two planes through the same point ⊥ the same straight line.	2. § 39.
3. ∴ *m* ∥ *n*.	3. § 53.

EXERCISES

1. What theorem in plane geometry corresponds to Prop. XI?

2. With a pair of compasses opened 5 inches show how a circle of 4-inch radius can be drawn.

3. Prove that the four lines in which two parallel planes intersect two other parallel planes are parallel.

4. If three planes are each parallel to the same line, are they parallel to each other?

5. If one plane intersects each of two intersecting planes, the three lines of intersection are either parallel or concurrent.

6. *AC* and *BD* are each perpendicular to *AB*. What is the locus of *AC* and *BD* as they revolve about *AB* as an axis? What relation do the two loci bear to each other?

Proposition XII. Theorem (c, n)

62. *A line perpendicular to one of two parallel planes is perpendicular to the other.*

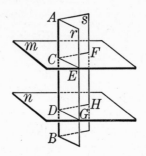

Given the ∥ planes *m* and *n* and *AB* ⊥ *m*.

To prove that *AB* ⊥ *n*.

⎡*Selection of Method:* 1. Known methods of proving a line ⊥ a⎤
                         plane: §§ 36, 37, 38, 39, 43, 48, 49, 51.
⎣   2. Method to be used: § 37.   ⎦

Proof:

STATEMENTS	REASONS
1. Through *AB* pass plane *r* intersecting *m* and *n* in *CE* and *DG* respectively; also through *AB* pass plane *s* intersecting *m* and *n* in *CF* and *DH* respectively.	1. §§ 9 *d*, 9 *b*.
2. *CE* ∥ *DG* and *CF* ∥ *DH*.	2. § 60.
3. *AB* ⊥ *CE* and *CF*.	3. § 36.
4. ∴ *AB* ⊥ *DG* and *DH*.	4. § 18 *d*.
5. ∴ *AB* ⊥ *n*.	5. § 37.

63. Corollary I (c, n). *Through a point outside a plane there can be one plane, and only one, parallel to a given plane.*

Suggestions. Let *P* be the given point and *m* the given plane. Draw *PA* ⊥ *m*. Draw plane *n* ⊥ *PA* at *P*.

64. Corollary II (c, n). *Two parallel planes are everywhere equidistant.*

Proposition XIII.   Theorem (c, n)

65. *If two intersecting lines are each parallel to a plane, the plane of these lines is parallel to that plane.*

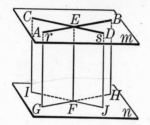

Given *AB* and *CD* two intersecting lines in plane *m*, each ‖ plane *n*.

To prove that *m* ‖ *n*.

⎡ *Selection of Method:* 1. Known methods of proving planes ‖ :
⎢   §§ 53, 61.
⎢   2. Method to be used : § 61.
⎣

Proof: STATEMENTS   REASONS

1. Draw *EF* ⊥ *n*.	1. § 45.
2. *AB* and *EF* determine a plane *r* intersecting *n* in *GH*; also *CD* and *EF* determine a plane *s* intersecting *n* in *IJ*.	2. §§ 9 *e*, 9 *b*.
3. *AB* ‖ *GH* and *CD* ‖ *IJ*.	3. § 56.
4. *EF* ⊥ *GH* and *IJ*.	4. § 36.
5. *EF* ⊥ *AB* and *CD*.	5. § 18 *d*.
6. *EF* ⊥ *m*.	6. § 37.
7. ∴ *m* ‖ *n*.	7. § 61.

EXERCISES (GROUP A)

1. If a line intersects one of two parallel planes, will it intersect the other?

2. If three line segments not in the same plane are equal and parallel, prove that the triangles formed by joining their extremities are congruent.

Proposition XIV. Theorem (C, N)

66. *If two angles not in the same plane have their sides parallel and extending in the same direction, they are equal and their planes are parallel.*

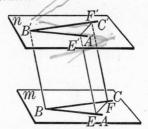

Given the $\measuredangle ABC$ and $A'B'C'$ in planes m and n respectively, with $AB \parallel A'B'$ and $BC \parallel B'C'$.

To prove that $\angle ABC = \angle A'B'C'$ and that $m \parallel n$.

$\Big[$ *Selection of Method:* 1. Known methods of proving (*a*) $\measuredangle =$: § 15;
(*b*) planes $\parallel$: §§ 53, 61, 65.
2. Methods to be used: (*a*) § 15 *e*; (*b*) § 65. $\Big]$

Proof:

STATEMENTS	REASONS
1. Construct $BE = B'E'$ and $BF = B'F'$.	1. § 33 *d*.
2. Draw EF, $E'F'$, BB', EE', and FF'.	2. § 12 *a*.
3. $BF = B'F'$ and $BF \parallel B'F'$.	3. Why?
4. $\therefore BFF'B'$ is a $\square$.	4. Why?
5. $\therefore FF' = BB'$ and $FF' \parallel BB'$.	5. Why?
6. In like manner, $EE' = BB'$ and $EE' \parallel BB'$.	6. Statements 3–5.
7. $\therefore EE' = FF'$ and $EE' \parallel FF'$.	7. Why?
8. $\therefore EE'F'F$ is a $\square$.	8. Why?
9. $\therefore EF = E'F'$.	9. Why?
10. $\therefore \triangle EBF \cong \triangle E'B'F'$.	10. Why?
11. $\therefore \angle ABC = \angle A'B'C'$.	11. Why?
12. $BA \parallel B'A'$ and $BC \parallel B'C'$.	12. Why?
13. $BA \parallel n$ and $BC \parallel n$.	13. § 55.
14. $\therefore m \parallel n$.	14. § 65.

Proposition XV.   Theorem (c, n)

67. *If two lines are cut by three parallel planes, their corresponding segments are proportional.*

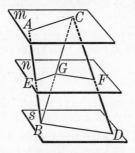

Given AB and CD cut by the $\parallel$ planes m, n, and s at A, E, B and C, F, D respectively.

To prove that $\dfrac{AE}{EB} = \dfrac{CF}{FD}$.

$\Big[$ *Selection of Method:* 1. Known methods of proving line segments proportional: § 25.
2. Method to be used: § 25 a. $\Big]$

Proof: *STATEMENTS*   *REASONS*

1. Draw BC, intersecting n in G.	1. § 12 *a.*
2. The plane of BA and BC intersects n in EG and m in AC. Also the plane of BC and DC intersects s in BD and n in GF.	2. Why?
3. $EG \parallel AC$ and $GF \parallel BD$.	3. § 60.
4. $\therefore \dfrac{AE}{EB} = \dfrac{CG}{GB}$ and $\dfrac{CG}{GB} = \dfrac{CF}{FD}$.	4. § 25 *a.*
5. $\therefore \dfrac{AE}{EB} = \dfrac{CF}{FD}$.	5. § 11 *f.*

EXERCISES (GROUP A)

1. In the figure above, if $AE = 24$, $EB = 15$, and $CF = 36$, find FD.

2. In the figure above, if $AE = 12$, $EB = 18$, and $CD = 40$, find CF.

MISCELLANEOUS EXERCISES (GROUP A)

1. Do two lines each parallel to a plane determine a plane parallel to the given plane?

2. What is the locus of points equidistant from two given parallel planes?

3. Where are all the points that are equidistant from two parallel planes and also equidistant from two given points in space?

4. What is the locus of points at a given distance from a given plane?

5. Where are all the points equidistant from two parallel planes and at a given distance from a third plane?

6. From a point P, 4 inches from a plane m, an oblique line PB is drawn to the plane and made to turn around the perpendicular PA dropped from P to the plane. Find the area of the circle described by the point B.

EXERCISES (GROUP B)

1. In the plane m is drawn a circle with its center at B and with a radius of 6 inches. A perpendicular AB, 8 inches long, is drawn to the plane; a tangent DC, 24 inches long, is drawn to the circle at C. Find the distance from A to D.

2. Find a point in a plane such that the sum of its distances from two given points on the same side of the plane shall be a minimum.

3. If a plane contains one of the diagonals of a parallelogram, the perpendiculars to the plane from the extremities of the other diagonal are equal.

4. If perpendiculars are drawn to a plane from the vertices of an external parallelogram, their sum is equal to four times the perpendicular to the plane from the intersection of the diagonals.

REVIEW QUESTIONS

1. What are the methods you have had in this chapter of proving

a. Lines parallel?

b. Lines perpendicular?

c. Planes parallel?

d. Lines equal?

e. A line and a plane parallel?

f. A line and a plane perpendicular?

g. Angles equal?

h. Loci?

2. If a line intersects two parallel lines, do all three lines lie in the same plane?

3. If a line intersects two skew lines, do all three lines lie in the same plane?

4. What is the name of the intersection of a line and a plane? of two planes?

5. How many intersecting lines may be parallel to a line? to a plane?

6. How many intersecting planes may be parallel to a line? to a plane?

7. At a given point in a plane, how many lines may be drawn perpendicular to the plane?

8. At a given point in a line, how many lines may be drawn perpendicular to the line?

9. Through an external point, how many lines may be drawn perpendicular to a given plane?

10. Through an external point, how many planes may be drawn parallel to a given plane?

11. What is the name of the intersection of a line and a plane perpendicular to the line?

12. What is the shortest distance from a point to a line? to a plane? to a line in the plane?

13. Through a given point in a line, how many planes perpendicular to the line can be drawn?

14. Can a line be parallel to a plane and perpendicular to a line in the plane?

15. Can a line be perpendicular to two lines in a plane?

16. If two lines are parallel to the same line, are they parallel?

17. If two lines are perpendicular to the same line, are they parallel?

18. If a line is perpendicular to two lines of a plane, does it lie in the plane?

19. Can a line be parallel to a plane and oblique to a line in the plane?

20. Can a line be perpendicular to a plane and parallel to a line in the plane?

21. Can two lines be parallel to the same plane? perpendicular to the same plane?

22. Can a line be drawn that will intersect two given skew lines and be parallel to another given line?

23. If two lines are perpendicular to the same plane, are they parallel?

24. When can a plane be perpendicular both to a given plane and to a given line?

25. Complete: If two parallel planes are cut by a third plane, ‑ ‑ ‑ ‑ ‑ ‑ ‑ ‑ ‑ .

26. If AB cannot meet CD, is $AB \parallel CD$?

27. What is the locus of points equidistant from two given points? equidistant from the sides of an angle? equidistant from a circle?

28. AB and CD are two skew lines. Can a plane contain both of them? Can a plane contain one of them and be parallel to the other? Can a plane be perpendicular to both of them? Can a plane be perpendicular to one of them and parallel to the other?

29. If a line is parallel to the intersection of two planes, is it parallel to both of the planes?

SUMMARY OF PRINCIPAL METHODS OF PROOF

68. *A Line Perpendicular to a Plane*

   a. A line is perpendicular to a plane if it is perpendicular to every line in the plane passing through its foot.

   b. If a line is perpendicular to each of two intersecting lines at their point of intersection, it is perpendicular to the plane of the two lines.

   c. Through a given point in (or without) a given line there can be one plane, and only one, perpendicular to the line.

   d. The perpendicular is the shortest line segment from a point to a plane.

   e. Through a given point there can be drawn one, and only one, perpendicular to a plane.

   f. If one of two parallel lines is perpendicular to a plane, the other is also perpendicular to the plane.

   g. A line perpendicular to one of two parallel planes is perpendicular to the other.

69. *A Line Parallel to a Plane*

a. A line and a plane are parallel if they cannot meet even if extended.

b. If two lines are parallel, every plane containing one of the lines, and only one, is parallel to the other.

c. Through either of two skew lines there can be one, and only one, plane parallel to the other line.

d. Through a given point in space there can be one plane, and only one, parallel to two skew lines, or else parallel to one line and containing the other.

70. *Two Planes Parallel*

a. Two planes are parallel if they cannot meet even if extended.

b. Two planes perpendicular to the same line are parallel.

c. Through a point outside a plane there can be one, and only one, plane parallel to a given plane.

d. If two intersecting lines are each parallel to a plane, the plane of these lines is parallel to that plane.

e. If two angles not in the same plane have their sides parallel and extending in the same direction, their planes are parallel.

71. *Two Lines Parallel*

a. Two lines perpendicular to the same plane are parallel.

b. If two lines are parallel to a third line, they are parallel to each other.

c. If a line is parallel to a plane, it is parallel to the intersection of that plane with any plane through the line.

d. If two parallel planes are cut by a third plane, the lines of intersection are parallel.

72. *Two Line Segments Equal*

a. Oblique lines drawn from a point to a plane meeting the plane at equal distances from the foot of the perpendicular are equal.

b. Two parallel planes are everywhere equidistant.

73. *Loci*

   a. The locus of points equidistant from two given points is the plane perpendicular to the line joining them, at its midpoint.

   b. The locus of points equidistant from the vertices of a triangle is the line through the center of the circumcircle, perpendicular to the plane of the triangle.

WORD LIST

At this time you should be able to spell and know the meaning of each of the following words:

collinear	intersection	plane
coplanar	oblique	skew
equidistant	parallel	surface
horizontal	perpendicular	vertical

TEST 1

True-False Statements *(Fifteen Minutes)*

Copy the numbers of these statements on your paper. Then if a statement is *always* true, write T after its number. If a statement is *not always* true, write F after its number. Do not guess.

1. If a line is perpendicular to a line in a plane, it is perpendicular to the plane.

2. A plane is determined by three points which are not in the same straight line.

3. If two lines are perpendicular to each other, either may contain a plane perpendicular to the other.

4. Any two lines determine a plane.

5. Two skew lines do not lie in the same plane.

6. If a line is parallel to a plane, it may be parallel to two lines in the plane.

7. If a line and a plane never meet, they are parallel.

8. It is possible for a line to be perpendicular to two intersecting lines.

9. A line which is perpendicular to a horizontal line is vertical.

10. If a line is parallel to two planes, the planes are parallel.

11. If two or more parallel lines meet a given straight line, they lie in the same plane.

12. Two planes perpendicular to a third plane are parallel.

13. The locus of points equidistant from two given points is the plane which is the perpendicular bisector of the line segment joining the points.

14. If two planes are parallel to the same plane, they are parallel.

15. If two lines are not skew lines, they are parallel.

16. A line oblique to a plane is not parallel to the plane.

17. It is not possible for a line to be perpendicular to two intersecting planes.

18. The diagonals of a skew quadrilateral bisect each other.

19. A plane can contain one of two skew lines and be parallel to the other.

20. There is a point in space through which it is possible to pass a plane parallel to two skew lines.

21. If a line is perpendicular to two planes, the planes are parallel.

22. Two lines perpendicular to another line are parallel.

23. Two transversals of two parallel lines determine a plane.

24. The locus of points in space at a given distance from a given plane is a plane parallel to the given plane and at the given distance from it.

25. A line can be drawn perpendicular to two skew lines.

26. Three parallel lines determine either one plane or three planes.

27. Through a point in a plane there can be drawn in the plane a line parallel to a given line.

28. If two lines in a plane are parallel respectively to two lines in another plane, the planes are parallel.

29. If a line and a plane are both perpendicular to the same line, they are parallel.

TEST 2

Completing Statements (*Eighteen Minutes*)

On your paper write one word, and only one, for each blank to make the following statements true:

1. A plane is determined by _____ points.

2. A plane is determined by _____ line and one _____ _____ the line.

3. The point of intersection of a straight line and a plane is called the _____ of the line.

4. At a given point in a given line there can be only one _____ perpendicular to the given line.

5. Three lines lie in the same plane if they are perpendicular to the same _____ at a given _____ on that _____.

6. If a _____ is perpendicular to one of two intersecting lines, it is not perpendicular to the other.

7. From a given external point there can be one, and only one, _____ perpendicular to a given plane.

8. All lines which are perpendicular to a horizontal plane are _____.

9. If one of two parallel lines is perpendicular to a given plane, the other line is _____ to the plane.

10. The locus of points, in space, equidistant from three given points not in a straight line, is a _____ perpendicular to the _____ of the three points and passing through the _____ of the _____ through the points.

11. Two lines _____ to the same plane are _____.

12. Two lines _____ to the same line are _____.

13. Two lines which do not lie in the same plane are called _____ lines.

14. The locus of points equidistant from two given parallel planes is a _____ halfway between them.

15. Segments of parallel lines included between parallel planes are _____.

16. Two parallel planes are everywhere _____.

17. Two points determine a _____ and three noncollinear points determine a _____.

18. Two _____ are equal if they do not lie in the same _____ and if their sides are respectively _____ and extend in the same _____.

19. Through a given point not in a given plane there can be drawn _____ _____ _____ lines parallel to the plane.

20. If a line is _____ to two _____ lines at their point of _____, it is _____ to the _____ of these lines.

21. Three parallel planes m, n, and p are intersected by one line in points A, E, and B respectively; they are intersected by another line in points C, F, and D respectively. If $AE = 8$, $BE = 18$, and $DF = 12$, then $CF = $ _____.

22. A _____ is the shortest line segment between two skew lines.

TEST 3

Supplying Reasons (*Fifteen Minutes*)

Supply the correct reasons in the following demonstration:

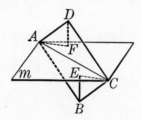

Given $\square$ *ABCD* with plane m passing through diagonal AC, $BE \perp m$, and $DF \perp m$.

To prove that $DF = BE$.

Proof:

STATEMENTS	REASONS
1. Draw AF and CE.	1. Why possible?
2. $BE \perp m$ and $DF \perp m$.	2. Why?
3. $DF \perp AF$ and $BE \perp EC$.	3. Why?
4. $AD = BC$ and $AD \parallel BC$.	4. Why?
5. $BE \parallel DF$.	5. Why?
6. $\angle ADF = \angle EBC$.	6. Why?
7. $\therefore$ rt. $\triangle ADF \cong$ rt. $\triangle BCE$.	7. Why?
8. $\therefore DF = BE$.	8. Why?

Supply the correct reasons in the following demonstration:

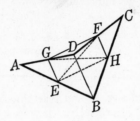

Given $ABCD$ a skew quadrilateral with E the midpoint of AB, F the midpoint of DC, G the midpoint of AD, and H the midpoint of BC.

To prove that EF bisects GH and GH bisects EF.

Proof: *STATEMENTS*   *REASONS*

STATEMENTS	REASONS
1. Draw GE, FH, EH, GF, and BD.	1. Why possible?
2. $FH \parallel BD$ and $EG \parallel BD$.	2. Why?
3. $\therefore FH \parallel EG$.	3. Why?
4. FH and EG determine a plane.	4. Why?
5. $FH = \frac{1}{2} BD$ and $EG = \frac{1}{2} BD$.	5. Why?
6. $\therefore FH = EG$.	6. Why?
7. $\therefore EHFG$ is a $\square$.	7. Why?
8. $\therefore EF$ bisects GH and GH bisects EF.	8. Why?

CHAPTER II

DIHEDRAL AND POLYHEDRAL ANGLES

74. Dihedral Angles. A *dihedral* (dī hē′drăl) *angle* is an angle formed by two planes that meet. The two planes are called the *faces*, and their line of meeting the *edge*, of the dihedral angle. A dihedral angle may be read by naming a point in one face, the edge, and a point in the other face, as dihedral $\angle A\text{-}BC\text{-}D$. When there is no doubt as to the meaning, a dihedral angle may be read by naming its edge, as dihedral $\angle BC$.

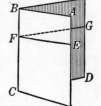

75. Plane Angle of a Dihedral Angle. The *plane angle of a dihedral angle* is formed by two lines, one in each face, drawn perpendicular to the edge of the dihedral angle at the same point. Thus $\angle EFG$ is the plane angle of the dihedral $\angle A\text{-}BC\text{-}D$. All plane angles of any given dihedral angle are equal, since their sides are parallel and extend in the same direction (§ 66).

76. Names of Dihedral Angles. A dihedral angle is *acute*, *right*, or *obtuse* if its plane angle is acute, right, or obtuse respectively.

77. Pairs of Dihedral Angles. Dihedral angles are *adjacent*, *vertical*, *complementary*, or *supplementary* if their plane angles are adjacent, vertical, complementary, or supplementary; and conversely. These angles may be defined by substituting a plane for a line and a line for a point in the corresponding definitions of plane geometry.

78. Perpendicular Planes. *Two planes are perpendicular if the plane angle of their dihedral angle is a right angle.*

79. Equal Dihedral Angles. Two dihedral angles are equal (or congruent) if they can be made to coincide.

80. Theorem (c, n). *Two dihedral angles are equal if their plane angles are equal; and conversely.*

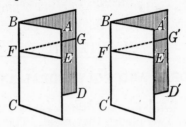

Given the ∡ *EFG* and *E'F'G'*, the plane ∡ of dihedral ∡ *A-BC-D* and *A'-B'C'-D'* respectively, and ∠ *EFG* = ∠ *E'F'G'*.

To prove that ∠ *A-BC-D* = ∠ *A'-B'C'-D'*.

⌈ *Selection of Method:* 1. Known methods of proving dihedral ∡ = : ⌉
⌊ § 79. ⌋
2. Method to be used : § 79.

Proof:

STATEMENTS	REASONS
1. Place ∠ *A-BC-D* on ∠ *A'-B'C'-D'* so that ∠ *EFG* coincides with ∠ *E'F'G'*.	1. §§ 12 *f*, 10 *d*.
2. *BC* ⊥ plane *EFG* or plane *E'F'G'* ; *B'C'* ⊥ plane *E'F'G'*.	2. §§ 9 *e*, 37.
3. ∴ *BC* coincides with *B'C'*.	3. § 44.
4. Plane *AC* coincides with plane *A'C'* and plane *BD* with plane *B'D'*.	4. § 9 *e*.
5. ∴ ∠ *A-BC-D* = ∠ *A'-B'C'-D'*.	5. § 10 *d*.

(The demonstration of the converse is left to the student. Use §§ 79 and 75.)

EXERCISES. *DIHEDRAL ANGLES*

1. Name five examples of dihedral angles.

2. Prove that vertical dihedral angles are equal.

3. Prove that if the sum of two adjacent dihedral angles is a straight angle, their exterior faces lie in the same plane.

4. State and prove the converse of Ex. 3.

Proposition I. Theorem (C, N)

81. *If a line is perpendicular to a given plane, every plane which contains this line is perpendicular to the given plane.*

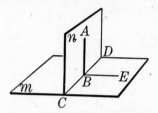

Given $AB \perp$ plane m, and n any plane containing AB and intersecting m in CD.

To prove that $n \perp m$.

⌈ *Selection of Method:* 1. Known method of proving planes $\perp$: § 78. ⌉
└　　　　　　　　　2. Method to be used : § 78.　　　　　　　┘

Proof:　　　*STATEMENTS*　　　　　　　　　　*REASONS*

1. In m draw $BE \perp CD$ at B.	1. Why possible?
2. $AB \perp CD$.	2. Why?
3. $\therefore \angle ABE$ is the plane $\angle$ of $\angle A\text{-}CD\text{-}E$.	3. § 75.
4. But $AB \perp BE$, or $\angle ABE$ is a rt. $\angle$.	4. Why?
5. $\therefore n \perp m$.	5. § 78.

EXERCISES. *REVIEW*

1. Does the size of a dihedral angle depend on the extent of its faces?

2. Name the six dihedral angles of this pyramid.

3. A plane perpendicular to the edge of a dihedral angle is perpendicular to its faces.

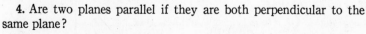

4. Are two planes parallel if they are both perpendicular to the same plane?

5. The planes which bisect a pair of supplementary adjacent dihedral angles are perpendicular.

Proposition II. Theorem (C, N)

82. *If two planes are perpendicular to each other, a line drawn in one of them perpendicular to their intersection is perpendicular to the other.*

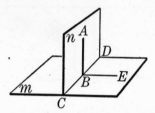

Given the plane $m \perp$ plane n, CD their line of intersection, and AB in $n \perp CD$.

To prove that $AB \perp m$.

⎡ *Selection of Method:* 1. Known methods of proving a line $\perp$ a plane: ⎤
⎢ 　　　　　§§ 36, 37, 38, 39, 40, 43, 48, 49, 51, 62. ⎥
⎣ 　　　　　2. Method to be used : § 37. ⎦

Proof:　　　　*STATEMENTS*　　　　　　　　*REASONS*

1. Draw BE in $m \perp CD$ at B.	1. Why possible?
2. Then $\angle ABE$ is the plane $\angle$ of $\angle A\text{-}CD\text{-}E$.	2. Why?
3. But $n \perp m$.	3. Why?
4. $\therefore \angle ABE$ is a rt. $\angle$.	4. § 78.
5. $\therefore AB \perp BE$.	5. Why?
6. $AB \perp CD$.	6. Why?
7. $\therefore AB \perp m$.	7. Why?

83. Corollary I (c). *If two planes are perpendicular to each other, a line perpendicular to one of them at any point of their intersection will lie in the other.*

Suggestions. Let AB be $\perp m$ at B and n be $\perp m$. In n assume $A'B \perp CD$ at B. Then $A'B \perp m$ at B. Why? Then AB coincides with $A'B$ (§ 44). Then AB lies in n. Why?

84. Corollary II (c). *If two planes are perpendicular to each other, a line drawn perpendicular to one of them through any point of the other will lie in this other plane.* (The proof is similar to that of Cor. I.)

EXERCISES (GROUP A)

1. Explain why the door of your classroom is perpendicular to the floor.

2. How can you determine if the floor of your classroom is level by using a plumb line and a carpenter's square? by using a carpenter's level?

3. Prove that a line and a plane are parallel if they are both perpendicular to the same line.

4. If a line in one plane is perpendicular to another plane, the planes are perpendicular.

5. How can you determine if two opposite walls of your classroom are parallel by the use of a string?

6. If a line is drawn in one face of a dihedral angle perpendicular to its edge, is it perpendicular to the other face?

7. Draw the locus of points 6 inches from point A and 8 inches from point B when A is 10 inches from B. Find the length of the locus.

EXERCISES (GROUP B)

1. Through any point within a dihedral angle a plane may be passed perpendicular to each face.

2. If a plane parallel to the edge of a dihedral angle intersects the faces of the angle, its intersections with the faces are parallel lines.

3. Two dihedral angles whose faces are parallel, each to each, are either equal or supplementary.

4. A circle whose radius is 8 inches is divided into six equal parts by diameters. A plane containing one of these diameters makes an angle of 30° with the plane of the circle. What is the distance of each division point of the circle from the plane?

5. If a plane is perpendicular to one of two parallel planes, is it perpendicular to the other?

Proposition III. Theorem (C, N)

85. *If two intersecting planes are perpendicular to a third plane, their intersection is also perpendicular to that plane.*

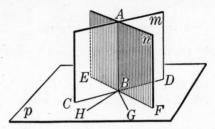

Given the planes *m* and *n* each ⊥ plane *p* and *AB* their line of intersection.

To prove that *AB* ⊥ *p*.

[*Selection of Method:* 1. Methods of proving a line ⊥ a plane:
  §§ 36, 37, 38, 39, 40, 43, 48, 49, 51, 62, 82.
  2. Method to be used : § 37.]

Proof: *STATEMENTS*   *REASONS*

1. In *p* draw *BG* ⊥ *CD* and *BH* ⊥ *EF*.	1. § 12 *j*.
2. Then *BG* ⊥ *m* and *BH* ⊥ *n*.	2. § 82.
3. ∴ *BG* ⊥ *AB* and *BH* ⊥ *AB*.	3. § 36.
4. ∴ *AB* ⊥ *p*.	4. § 37.

Note. This theorem was proved by Archytas about 400 B.C. He was the first to apply mathematics in any noteworthy way to mechanics, music, and metaphysics.

86. Corollary (c, n). *Through a line not perpendicular to a plane there can be drawn one plane, and only one, perpendicular to the given plane.*

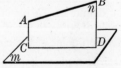

Suggestions. From *A* draw *AC* ⊥ *m*. *AC* and *AB* determine a plane *n* ⊥ *m*. Why? If another plane *n′* could be drawn through *AB* ⊥ *m*, then *AB* would be ⊥ *m* (§ 85). But *AB* is not ⊥ *m*. Why?

87. Projection on a Plane. *The projection of a point* on a plane is the foot of the perpendicular drawn from the point

to the plane. *The projection of a line* on a plane is the locus of the projections of all the points of the line on the plane. Thus, in the figure, $A'B'$ is the projection of AB on m.

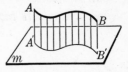

88. Corollary. *The projection on a plane of a straight line not perpendicular to the plane is a straight line.*

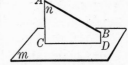

Suggestions. Through AB draw a plane $n \perp m$ (§ 86). All the ⊥s from AB to m lie in n (§ 84). Hence the feet of these ⊥s lie in CD, the intersection of m and n. Why?

The *angle* which an oblique line makes with a plane is the acute angle which it makes with its projection on the plane.

EXERCISES. *PROJECTION*

1. What is the projection of a point on a plane?

2. What is the projection of a line segment perpendicular to a plane?

3. If a line segment is parallel to a plane, prove that it equals its projection on the plane.

4. Can the projection of a curve be a straight line?

5. Can the projection of a triangle on a plane be a triangle? a line? a point?

6. Find the length of the projection on a plane of a 6-inch line segment that makes an angle of 60° with its projection.

7. If two equal line segments are drawn to a plane from a point outside the plane, they make equal angles with their projections on the plane.

8. The angle which a straight line makes with its projection on a plane is the least angle which it makes with any line of the plane.

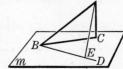

Suggestions. Let ABC be the acute ∠ that AB makes with its projection BC and let BD be any other line in plane m. Construct $BE = BC$ and use § 32 i.

Proposition IV. Theorem (c, n)

89. *The locus of points equidistant from the faces of a dihedral angle is the plane bisecting the dihedral angle.*

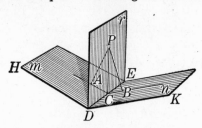

Given the plane r bisecting the dihedral $\angle$ *H-DE-K*.

To prove that r is the locus of points equidistant from m and n; that is, (Part I) any point P in r is equidistant from m and n, and (Part II) any point P equidistant from m and n is in r.

PART I

⌈*Selection of Method:* 1. Known methods of proving line segments⌉
$=$: §§ 14, 41, 48, 49.
⌊2. Method to be used : § 14 *b*.⌋

Proof: *STATEMENTS*   *REASONS*

STATEMENTS	REASONS
1. Through any point P in r draw $PA \perp m$ and $PB \perp n$.	1. Why possible ?
2. PA and PB determine a plane $\perp m$ and n, intersecting m in AC, r in PC, and n in BC.	2. §§ 81, 9 *b*.
3. $\therefore DC \perp$ plane APB.	3. § 85.
4. Then $DC \perp AC$, PC, and BC.	4. Why?
5. $\therefore \angle PCA$ and $\angle PCB$ are the plane angles of the dihedral $\angle$ *H-DE-P* and *K-DE-P*.	5. § 75.
6. $\angle PCA = \angle PCB$.	6. § 80, converse.
7. $PA \perp AC$ and $PB \perp BC$.	7. Why?
8. $\therefore$ rt. $\triangle PAC \cong$ rt. $\triangle PBC$.	8. Give proof.
9. $\therefore PA = PB$.	9. § 14 *b*.

PART II

> *Selection of Method:* 1. Known methods of proving dihedral ⊿
> =: § 80.
> 2. Method to be used: § 80.

Proof: *STATEMENTS*   *REASONS*

1. Through P, any point equidistant from m and n, draw $PA \perp m$ and $PB \perp n$.	1. Why possible?
2. PA and PB determine a plane $\perp m$ and n intersecting m in AC and n in BC.	2. §§ 81, 9 b.
3. Draw PC.	3. Why possible?
4. PC and DE determine a plane r.	4. Why?
5. $DC \perp$ plane PAB.	5. § 85.
6. $DC \perp AC$, PC, and BC.	6. § 36.
7. ∴ $\angle PCA$ and $\angle PCB$ are the plane ⊿ of the dihedral ⊿ H-DE-P and K-DE-P.	7. Why?
8. Rt. $\triangle PAC \cong$ rt. $\triangle PBC$.	8. Give proof.
9. ∴ $\angle PCA = \angle PCB$.	9. Why?
10. ∴ $\angle H$-DE-$P = \angle K$-DE-P.	10. § 80.
11. ∴ plane r bisects $\angle H$-DE-K.	11. Why?
12. ∴ plane r is the locus of points equidistant from m and n.	12. Why?

EXERCISES. *LOCI*

1. What is the locus of points equidistant from two given intersecting planes?

2. A point in the bisector of a right dihedral angle is 30 inches from the edge of the angle. Find the distance to each face of the angle.

3. What is the locus of points that bisect all line segments drawn between two parallel planes?

4. What is the locus of points which are equidistant from two given intersecting planes and lie in a third given plane?

5. The dihedral angle formed by two planes is 78° 46′. Find the size of the angle formed by the perpendiculars to the planes from any point in the bisector of the dihedral angle.

Proposition V. Theorem (c, n)

90. *Between any two skew lines there is one, and only one, common perpendicular.*

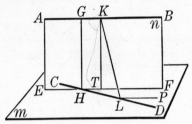

Given AB and CD any two skew lines.

To prove that between AB and CD there can be one, and only one, common ⊥.

```
⎡ Selection of Method: 1. Known methods of proving lines ⊥ : ⎤
⎢                         §§ 18, 36.                           ⎥
⎢                       2. Method to be used : § 18 d.         ⎥
⎣                                                             ⎦
```

Proof: *STATEMENTS*   *REASONS*

STATEMENTS	REASONS
1. Through CD pass plane m ∥ AB.	1. § 58.
2. Through AB pass plane n ⊥ m, intersecting m in EF.	2. §§ 86, 9 b.
3. Then EF ∥ AB.	3. § 56.
4. If CD ∥ EF, then CD ∥ AB.	4. § 52.
5. But CD is not ∥ AB.	5. Given.
6. ∴ EF and CD intersect at some point H.	6. § 12 q.
7. In n draw GH ⊥ EF.	7. Why possible?
8. GH ⊥ m and ∴ ⊥ CD.	8. §§ 82, 36.
9. ∴ GH ⊥ AB and GH is the common ⊥.	9. § 18 d.
Suppose another line KL ⊥ both AB and CD.	
10. In m draw LP ∥ EF.	10. Why possible?
11. Then LP would be ∥ AB.	11. § 52.

Proof: *STATEMENTS*   *REASONS*

12. Then KL would be $\perp$ LP.	12. § 18 *d*.
13. And KL would be $\perp$ *m*.	13. § 37.
14. In *n* draw $KT \perp EF$.	14. Why possible?
15. Then $KT \perp m$.	15. § 82.
16. Then KL and KT would be $\perp$ *m*.	16. Statements 13, 15.
17. Since this is impossible, only one common $\perp$ can be drawn between AB and CD.	17. § 45.

EXERCISES (GROUP A)

1. *Given* plane *ABCDE* ∥ plane *A′B′C′D′E′* and *AA′* ∥ *BB′* ∥ *CC′* ∥ *DD′* ∥ *EE′*.

   a. Prove that *ABB′A′, BCC′B′,* ⋯ are planes.

   b. Prove that *AB = A′B′, BC = B′C′,* ⋯.

   c. Prove that *AA′ = BB′ = CC′,* ⋯.

   d. Prove that ∠ *ABC* = ∠ *A′B′C′*.

   e. What can you prove concerning the figures *ABCDE* and *A′B′C′D′E′*?

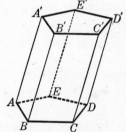

2. A line segment 12 inches long makes an angle of 30° with a plane *m*. What is the length of its projection on *m*?

3. A line segment 18 inches long makes an angle of 45° with a plane. What is the length of its projection on the plane?

4. If two equal line segments are drawn from a point to a plane, they make equal angles with the plane.

5. If three lines are perpendicular to one another at a common point, each line is perpendicular to the plane determined by the other two.

6. If two planes are each perpendicular to both of two intersecting planes, they are parallel.

7. *OAE* is the path of a ray of light from an object *O*, when reflected by a mirror *m* at the point *A*. The path of the reflected light, *AE*, is found by drawing *OP* $\perp$ *m*, producing *OP* to *O′*, making *PO′=PO*, and drawing *O′E* intersecting *m* at *A*. Prove that *OA + AE* is less than any other path, such as *OB + BE*.

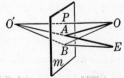

EXERCISES (GROUP B)

1. A line segment 8 inches in length makes an angle of 30° with plane *m*. Find the length of its projection on *m*.

2. A line segment $10\sqrt{2}$ inches long makes an angle of 60° with a plane. What is the length of its projection on the plane?

3. If three equal line segments connect three points of a plane to a point outside the plane, and a perpendicular is drawn from the point to the plane, the foot of this perpendicular is the center of a circle which can be passed through the three points of the plane.

4. If two unequal line segments are drawn from a point to a plane, the longer segment makes the smaller angle with the plane.

5. *Given AB* ⊥ plane *m* and *AC* ⊥ plane *n*. *Prove* that *BC* ⊥ *DE*.

Suggestions. Prove plane of *ABC* ⊥ both *m* and *n* and use § 85.

6. State and prove the converse of Ex. 4.

7. The shortest line segment between two skew lines is their common perpendicular.

Suggestion. Using the figure for Prop. V, show that $GH = KT < KL$.

8. From a point *P*, 48 inches from a plane *m*, a perpendicular *PA* is drawn to *m*. With *A* as a center, a circle with a diameter of 72 inches is drawn in plane *m*. From a point *B* on this circle a tangent *BC*, 144 inches long, is drawn. Find the distance from *P* to *C*. (If desired, the square root may be found by logarithms. See page 242.)

9. *Given AC* ⊥ *DC*, *BC* ⊥ *DC*, and ∠ *A-BD-C* a rt. ∠.
Prove that *AB* ⊥ plane *DBC* (*m*).

Suggestions. *DC* ⊥ plane *ABC*. Why? Prove plane *ABC* ⊥ *m* (§ 81). Then use § 85.

10. The equal sides of an isosceles triangle make equal angles with any plane that contains the base.

11. The projection of a parallelogram on a plane is either a parallelogram or a straight line.

12. The projections of two parallel line segments on a plane have the same ratio as the line segments.

91. Polyhedral Angle. *A polyhedral angle* is an angle formed by three or more planes that meet in a point. The portions of the planes which form the polyhedral angle are called its *faces*, and the common point of meeting of the planes is called the *vertex* of the polyhedral angle. The dihedral angles formed by the faces are called the *dihedral angles of the polyhedral angle*. The edges of the dihedral angles are the *edges* of the polyhedral angle. The plane angles of the faces are called the *face angles* of the polyhedral angle. Thus, ∠ *APB* is a face angle of the polyhedral angle.

A polyhedral angle may be read by naming the vertex or by naming the vertex and a point on each edge. Thus the polyhedral angle in the figure may be read "polyhedral ∠ *P*" or "polyhedral ∠ *P-ABCDE*."

92. Names of Polyhedral Angles. A polyhedral angle having three faces is called a *trihedral angle*. Polyhedral angles of four, five, six, eight faces are called respectively *tetrahedral, pentahedral, hexahedral, octahedral angles*.

A polyhedral angle is convex if a plane section of the faces is a convex polygon.

93. Equal or Congruent Polyhedral Angles. Two polyhedral angles are equal or congruent if they can be made to coincide. *Two polyhedral angles are congruent if the face angles and dihedral angles of one are equal, each to each, to the face angles and dihedral angles of the other and are arranged in the same order,* for they can be made to coincide.

94. Symmetric Polyhedral Angles. *Two polyhedral angles are* 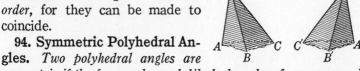 *symmetric if the face angles and dihedral angles of one are equal, each to each, to the face angles and dihedral angles of the other and are arranged in opposite order.* In the figure, ∠ *P-ABC* is symmetric to ∠ *P'-A'B'C'*. Make a model to show that they will not coincide.

Proposition VI. Theorem (c, n)

95. *The sum of any two face angles of a trihedral angle is greater than the third face angle.*

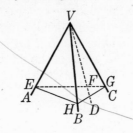

Given the trihedral $\angle V\text{-}ABC$ with $\angle AVC$ the largest face $\angle$.

To prove that $\angle AVB + \angle BVC > \angle AVC$.

⌈ *Selection of Method:* 1. Known methods of proving inequalities:
§§ 11 *j-n*, 32.
2. Method to be used: § 32 *i*. ⌋

Proof: STATEMENTS REASONS

1. In face AVC make $\angle AVD = \angle AVB$.	1. Why possible?
2. Draw any line intersecting VA in E, VD in F, and VC in G.	2. Why possible?
3. On VB mark off $VH = VF$.	3. Why possible?
4. Draw EH and HG.	4. Why possible?
5. $\triangle EVH \cong \triangle EVF$.	5. Give proof.
6. $\therefore EH = EF$.	6. Why?
7. $EH + HG > EF + FG$.	7. Why?
8. $\therefore HG > FG$.	8. § 11 *k*.
9. In $\triangle$ HVG and FVG, $VH = VF$ and $VG = VG$.	9. Why?
10. From (8) and (9), $\angle HVG > \angle FVG$.	10. § 32 *i*.
11. But $\angle EVH = \angle EVF$.	11. Const.
12. $\therefore \angle EVH + \angle HVG > \angle EVF + \angle FVG$,	12. § 11 *k*.
13. or $\angle AVB + \angle BVC > \angle AVC$.	13. Why?

Proposition VII. Theorem (c, n)

96. *The sum of the face angles of any convex polyhedral angle is less than 360°.*

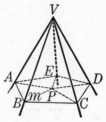

Given the polyhedral ∠ *V*.

To prove that the sum of the face ∡ at *V* < 360°.

> *Selection of Method:* 1. Known methods of proving inequalities:
> §§ 11 *j-n*, 32, 95.
> 2. Method to be used: § 95.

Proof:

STATEMENTS	REASONS
1. Pass a plane cutting all the edges of *V* in points *A*, *B*, *C*, *D*, *E*, and the faces in *AB*, *BC*, *CD*, *DE*, and *EA*.	1. §§ 9 *a*, 9 *b*.
2. From any point *P* in *ABCDE* draw *PA*, *PB*, *PC*, *PD*, and *PE*.	2. Why possible?
3. The sum of the ∡ of the *n* ∆ whose vertices are at *V* = the sum of the ∡ of the *n* ∆ whose vertices are at *P*.	3. Each sum = *n* st. ∡.
4. But ∠*VBA* + ∠*VBC* > ∠*PBA* + ∠*PBC*, ∠*VCB* + ∠*VCD* > ∠*PCB* + ∠*PCD*, ∠*VDC* + ∠*VDE* > ∠*PDC* + ∠*PDE*, etc.	4. § 95.
5. Adding, the sum of the base ∡ of the *n* ∆ whose vertices are at *V* > the sum of the base ∡ of the *n* ∆ whose vertices are at *P*.	5. § 11 *m*.
6. From (3) and (5), the sum of the vertex ∡ at *V* < the sum of the vertex ∡ at *P*.	6. § 11 *l*.
7. But the sum of the ∡ at *P* = 360°.	7. § 12 *l*.
8. ∴ the sum of the face ∡ at *V* < 360°.	8. Why?

Proposition VIII. Theorem (c, n)

97. *Two trihedral angles are either equal or symmetric if the three face angles of one are equal respectively to the three face angles of the other.*

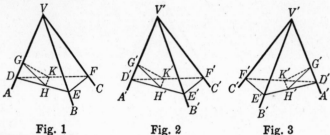

Fig. 1   Fig. 2   Fig. 3

Given the trihedral ∡ *V* and *V'* with ∠ *AVB* = ∠ *A'V'B'*, ∠ *BVC* = ∠ *B'V'C'*, and ∠ *AVC* = ∠ *A'V'C'*.

To prove that *V* is either = or symmetric to *V'*.

> *Selection of Method:* 1. Known methods of proving trihedral ∡ = or symmetric : §§ 93, 94.
> 2. Method to be used : §§ 93, 94.

Proof:

STATEMENTS	REASONS
1. On the edges of the trihedral angles construct $VD = VE = VF = V'D' = V'E' = V'F'$, and draw *DE*, *EF*, *DF*, *D'E'*, *E'F'*, and *D'F'*.	1. Why possible?
2. △ *VDE* ≅ △ *V'D'E'*, △ *VEF* ≅ △ *V'E'F'*, and △ *VFD* ≅ *V'F'D'*.	2. Give proof.
3. ∴ *DE* = *D'E'*, *EF* = *E'F'*, and *DF* = *D'F'*.	3. Why?
4. ∴ △ *DEF* ≅ △ *D'E'F'*.	4. Why?
5. From some point *G* in *VD* draw *GH* in plane *AVB* ⊥ *AV* and *GK* in plane *AVC* ⊥ *AV*, forming the plane ∠ *HGK* of the dihedral ∠ *B-AV-C*. (These ⊥s meet *DE* and *DF*, for ∡ *VDE* and *VDF* are acute.)	5. §§ 12*j*, 75.

Proof: *STATEMENTS*   *REASONS*

6. On $A'V'$ construct $D'G' = DG$, and construct $\angle H'G'K'$ the plane $\angle$ of dihedral $\angle B'\text{-}A'V'\text{-}C'$.	6. Why possible?
7. Draw HK and $H'K'$.	7. Why possible?
8. $\angle VDE = \angle V'D'E'$ and $\angle VDF = \angle V'D'F'$.	8. § 15 *e*.
9. $DG = D'G'$.	9. Const.
10. Rt. $\triangle DGH \cong$ rt. $\triangle D'G'H'$, and rt. $\triangle DGK \cong$ rt. $\triangle D'G'K'$.	10. Why?
11. $\therefore DH = D'H'$ and $DK = D'K'$.	11. Why?
12. From (4), $\angle HDK = \angle H'D'K'$.	12. Why?
13. $\therefore \triangle DHK \cong \triangle D'H'K'$.	13. Why?
14. $\therefore HK = H'K'$.	14. Why?
15. $\triangle GHK \cong \triangle G'H'K'$.	15. Give proof.
16. $\therefore \angle HGK = \angle H'G'K'$.	16. Why?
17. $\therefore \angle B\text{-}AV\text{-}C = \angle B'\text{-}A'V'\text{-}C'$.	17. § 80.
18. In like manner it may be proved that $\angle A\text{-}BV\text{-}C = \angle A'\text{-}B'V'\text{-}C'$ and $\angle B\text{-}CV\text{-}A = \angle B'\text{-}C'V'\text{-}A'$.	18. Statements 1–17.
19. $\therefore$ trihedral $\angle V =$ trihedral $\angle V'$ (Fig. 2).	19. § 93.
20. $\therefore$ trihedral $\angle V$ is symmetric to trihedral $\angle V'$ (Fig. 3).	20. § 94.

EXERCISES (GROUP A). *POLYHEDRAL ANGLES*

1. Name two facts you have proved concerning a trihedral angle; one fact you have proved concerning any polyhedral angle.

2. Two trihedral angles are equal if the three dihedral angles of each are right dihedral angles.

3. Is it possible to have a trihedral angle whose face angles are
   a. 45°, 45°, 90°?   *c.* 140°, 70°, 171°?
   b. 60°, 60°, 60°?   *d.* 105°, 118°, 130°?

4. Is it possible to have a polyhedral angle whose face angles are
   a. 18°, 36°, 74°, 90°?   *c.* 128°, 114°, 135°, 111°?
   b. 10°, 13°, 35°, 60°?   *d.* All right angles?

5. Is a dihedral angle a polyhedral angle?

EXERCISES (GROUP B). *POLYHEDRAL ANGLES*

1. If two trihedral angles are symmetric, and if two dihedral angles of one trihedral angle are equal, are the two trihedral angles equal?

2. Planes determined by the edges and the bisectors of the opposite face angles of a trihedral angle meet in a line.

3. In a trihedral angle, the three planes bisecting the three face angles at right angles to their respective planes intersect in a line, every point of which is equidistant from the three edges of the trihedral angle.

EXERCISES (GROUP A). *LOCI*

1. What is the locus of points in space equidistant from two parallel lines?

2. What is the locus of points in space equidistant from two parallel planes?

3. In a given plane, what is the locus of points at a given distance from a point not in the plane?

4. Determine the locus of points in space equidistant from the sides of a given triangle.

5. Determine the locus of points equidistant from two intersecting lines.

6. In a given plane, what is the locus of points 4 inches from a second given plane?

7. Where are the points 13 inches from the vertices of a right triangle whose sides are 6 inches, 8 inches, and 10 inches respectively?

EXERCISES (GROUP B). *COMPOUND LOCI*

Sometimes points are required to satisfy two separate conditions. In such cases the points will be the intersection of the separate loci determined by each condition. A *compound locus* is determined by the intersection of two or more loci.

In solving a locus problem place the given parts in the most general positions in order to determine the most general locus, and then in a discussion state the locus for all special conditions.

Many problems concerning loci cannot be studied in this course, as they lead to forms not considered in elementary geometry. For example, the locus of points equidistant from two different elements, such as a point and a line or a line and a plane, is a surface that is not studied in elementary geometry.

1. What is the locus of points equidistant from two given intersecting planes and also equidistant from two given parallel planes?

2. What is the locus of points equidistant from two given points and also equidistant from two given parallel planes?

3. Determine the locus of points equidistant from two given intersecting planes and also at a given distance from a given plane.

4. Find a point equidistant from four noncoplanar points.

5. Find the locus of points equidistant from two given points and also equidistant from two given parallel lines.

6. Determine the locus of points equidistant from three noncoplanar parallel lines.

7. Find the locus of points equidistant from the faces of a given dihedral angle and also equidistant from three given noncollinear points.

8. Prove that the locus of points equidistant from the three faces of a trihedral angle is the common intersection of the planes bisecting the dihedral angles of the trihedral angle.

9. Find a point which is equidistant from the vertices of a given triangle and also equidistant from two given parallel planes.

10. Determine the locus of points equidistant from two given intersecting planes and also equidistant from two given points.

11. Find the locus of all points equidistant from the edges of a trihedral angle.

12. What is the locus of a line making equal angles with two given intersecting lines?

13. Determine the locus of points equidistant from each pair of opposite vertices of a parallelogram.

14. Is there a locus of points equidistant from the vertices of a square?

15. A point P is 12 inches from a plane m. Find the locus of points in m 13 inches from P.

REVIEW EXERCISES

1. Through a line perpendicular to a plane, how many planes perpendicular to the given plane may be drawn? Through a line oblique to the plane, how many planes perpendicular to the given plane may be drawn? Through a line parallel to a given plane, how many planes perpendicular to the given plane may be drawn?

2. If a line is parallel to a given plane, is a plane that is parallel to the line parallel to the given plane also?

3. If two planes are parallel to the same plane, are they parallel to each other?

4. Are two planes parallel if they are perpendicular to the same line?

5. Prove that the shortest line segment between two parallel planes is the common perpendicular to them.

6. Can two lines perpendicular to each other have a common perpendicular? Can any two parallel lines have a common perpendicular? Can any two skew lines have a common perpendicular?

7. A line is perpendicular to two lines in a plane. Where is the first line if the second and third lines are parallel? if the second and third lines intersect?

8. If a plane contains one of two parallel lines, is it parallel to the other?

9. Can you have a trihedral angle whose face angles are (*a*) 60°, 80°, 40°? (*b*) 180°, 100°, 90°? (*c*) 40°, 30°, 80°?

10. Prove that the projections on a plane of two equal parallel oblique line segments are parallel. (Use §§ 88, 66, 60.)

11. Prove that the common perpendicular between two skew lines is the shortest line segment between them.

12. Prove that any face angle of a polyhedral angle is less than the sum of the remaining face angles.

13. If the edges of one trihedral angle are perpendicular to the faces of another, the edges of the second are perpendicular to the faces of the first.

14. Define: two parallel lines; two parallel planes; a line perpendicular to a plane; skew lines.

15. Point out the following in your schoolroom: two parallel straight lines; two perpendicular planes; a line perpendicular to a plane; the intersection of two planes which are perpendicular to a third plane; two skew lines; a dihedral angle; a trihedral angle.

16. The inside dimensions of a chalk box are 6 inches, 4 inches, and $3\frac{1}{2}$ inches. What is the length of an inside diagonal of the box?

17. Line AB intersects the parallel planes m, n, and p in points A, B, and C respectively. Another line DF intersects m, n, and p in points D, E, and F respectively. If AB is 15 inches, BC is 21 inches, and EF is 28 inches, find the length of DE.

18. The projection of a line segment on a plane is 8 inches long. Find the length of the segment if its inclination on the plane is 45°.

19. A point moves so as to be equidistant from the faces of a dihedral angle of 60°. When the point is 16 inches from one face of the angle, how far is it from the edge of the angle?

20. A square 4 inches on a side revolves about one of its diagonals. What is the length of the locus of each of its vertices? What is the locus of the other diagonal? What is the locus of its sides?

21. How can you tell whether a flagpole is vertical by using a carpenter's square?

22. Tell how you would level a plot of ground for a tennis court.

23. What theorem states that the spokes of a wheel which are perpendicular to the axle lie in one plane?

24. How many kinds of polyhedral angles can be formed whose face angles are each 60°? How many whose face angles are each 108°? How many whose face angles are each 120°?

25. If a line is parallel to a plane, is a plane containing the line parallel to the given plane?

26. How can a plane be passed through the vertex of a trihedral angle so that the edges shall be equally inclined to the plane?

27. What is the locus of points equidistant from two given points?

28. Complete the following theorems:

a. Two trihedral angles are equal $\cdots$.

b. The sum of any two face angles $\cdots$.

c. The sum of the face angles of any convex $\cdots$.

d. Between any two skew lines there $\cdots$.

e. The locus of points equidistant from the faces $\cdots$.

SUMMARY OF PRINCIPAL METHODS OF PROOF

98.   *A Line Perpendicular to a Plane*

a. If two planes are perpendicular to each other, a line drawn in one of them perpendicular to their intersection is perpendicular to the other.

b. If two intersecting planes are perpendicular to a third plane, their intersection is also perpendicular to that plane.

99.   *Planes Perpendicular*

a. Two planes are perpendicular if the plane angle of their dihedral angle is a right angle.

b. If a line is perpendicular to a given plane, every plane which contains this line is perpendicular to the given plane.

c. Through a line not perpendicular to a plane there can be one plane, and only one, perpendicular to the given plane.

100.   *Loci*

The locus of points equidistant from the faces of a dihedral angle is the plane bisecting the dihedral angle.

101.   *Dihedral Angles Equal*

a. Two dihedral angles are equal (or congruent) if they coincide.

b. Two dihedral angles are equal if their plane angles are equal.

102.   *Trihedral Angles Equal or Symmetric*

Two trihedral angles are either equal or symmetric if the three face angles of one are equal respectively to the three face angles of the other.

103.   *Sum of Face Angles of Polyhedral Angles*

a. The sum of any two face angles of a trihedral angle is greater than the third face angle.

b. The sum of the face angles of any convex polyhedral angle is less than 360°.

WORD LIST

converse	face	pyramid
convex	polyhedral	symmetric
dihedral	projection	trihedral

TEST 4

True-False Statements (*Twenty Minutes*)

Copy the numbers of these statements on your paper. Then if a statement is *always* true, write T after its number. If a statement is *not always* true, write F after its number. Do not guess.

1. Two dihedral angles are equal if their plane angles are equal.

2. A dihedral angle is a polyhedral angle.

3. A dihedral angle has two edges.

4. A plane perpendicular to the edge of a dihedral angle is perpendicular to the faces of the angle.

5. The size of a dihedral angle depends on the extent of its faces.

6. Two points are necessary to determine a plane that is perpendicular to a given line.

7. If a line is perpendicular to one of two parallel lines, it is perpendicular to the plane through these lines.

8. A line and a plane are parallel if they are both perpendicular to the same line.

9. If three planes intersect, they form a trihedral angle.

10. If line AB is parallel to plane m, only one plane can contain AB and be perpendicular to m.

11. If line AB is oblique to plane m, no plane can contain AB and be perpendicular to m.

12. The obtuse angle which a line makes with its projection produced is the largest angle which it makes with any line of the plane through its foot.

13. If two trihedral angles have the three face angles of one equal respectively to the three face angles of the other, the corresponding dihedral angles are equal.

14. If three lines meet at a point, it is always possible to draw a line making equal angles with the three lines.

15. A trihedral angle could have face angles of 87°, 120°, and 23°.

16. It is possible to have a polyhedral angle whose face angles are 119°, 80°, 76°, and 85°.

17. The plane which bisects a dihedral angle bisects any line segment whose end points are in the faces of the angle.

18. Two trihedral angles are congruent if the three face angles of one are equal respectively to the three face angles of the other.

19. The sum of the face angles of the trihedral angle formed by the ceiling, front wall, and right side wall of a room is 270°.

20. Any line segment is greater than its projection on a plane.

21. A line segment and its projection on a plane determine another plane.

22. If a given plane is perpendicular to one of two intersecting planes, its intersection with the second plane is perpendicular to the first plane.

23. A trihedral angle has two acute face angles.

TEST 5

Completing Statements (*Ten Minutes*)

On your paper write one word, and only one, for each blank to make the following statements true:

1. A _____ angle is the opening between two planes that meet.

2. A right _____ angle is one whose _____ angle is a right angle.

3. If a _____ is perpendicular to each of two intersecting _____, it is perpendicular to their intersection.

4. If a line not in a plane is either _____ or _____ to a given plane, there can be one plane, and only one, which contains it and is perpendicular to the given plane.

5. A line segment has the greatest projection on a plane when it is _____ to the plane, and the least projection when it is _____ to the plane.

6. The locus of points equidistant from the faces of a dihedral angle is the _____ which is the _____ of the dihedral angle.

7. The locus of points in a room equidistant from two opposite walls is a _____ which is _____ between them and _____ to them.

8. There can be only one common perpendicular between two _____ _____.

9. The locus of points in a room equidistant from two adjacent walls and the ceiling is a _____.

10. The sum of the face angles of any convex polyhedral angle is less than _____ right angles.

11. A polyhedral angle has _____ vertex (or vertices) and _____ or more edges.

TEST 6

Applications (*Forty Minutes*)

1. Find the length of the projection of a line segment 10 inches long on a plane if the line is parallel to the plane.

2. A line segment 15 inches long makes an angle of 45° with a plane. Find the length of its projection on the plane.

3. A point in the bisector of a right dihedral angle is 24 inches from the edge of the angle. Find the distance to each face of the angle.

4. A dihedral angle contains 84° 30′. Find the size of the angle formed by the perpendiculars drawn to the faces from any point in the plane bisecting the dihedral angle.

5. A line 14 inches long makes an angle of 30° with a plane. What is the length of its projection on the plane?

6. The projections of two parallel line segments, *AB* and *CD*, on a plane have the ratio 2 : 5. If *AB* is 10 inches long, what is the length of *CD*?

7. From a point *A*, 3 inches from a plane *m*, a line segment *AC*, 5 inches long, is drawn to the plane. Find the length of the locus of *C* in the plane *m* as *AC* is made to turn around the perpendicular *AB* to *m*.

8. What is the area of the projection on a plane of a square 8 inches on a side if one side of the square is parallel to the plane and another side forms an angle of 45° with the plane?

9. An equilateral △ *ABC*, whose sides are each 6 inches long, has side *AB* parallel to plane *m*, and plane *ABC* forms an angle of 30° with plane *m*. What is the perimeter of the projection of △ *ABC* on plane *m*?

An Artistic Example of Classical Architecture

CHAPTER III

PRISMS AND CYLINDERS

104. Polyhedron. A *polyhedron* is a solid formed by portions of plane surfaces. The portions of planes are called the *faces* of the polyhedron.

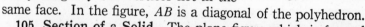

The lines of intersection of the faces are the *edges* of the polyhedron, and the intersections of the edges are the *vertices* of the polyhedron.

A *diagonal* of a polyhedron is a straight line joining any two vertices not in the same face. In the figure, AB is a diagonal of the polyhedron.

105. Section of a Solid. The plane figure which is formed by the intersection of a plane and a solid is called a *section* of the solid. The section of a polyhedron is a polygon. Why?

106. Convex Polyhedron. A polyhedron is *convex* if every section of it is a convex polygon.

Only convex polyhedrons are considered in this text.

107. Closed Prismatic Surface. A moving straight line which always intersects and completely traverses a fixed polygon, always remaining parallel to a fixed straight line not in the plane of the polygon, generates a *closed prismatic surface*. The moving line is called the *generatrix* (jĕn ĕr ā'trĭks), and the polygon is called the *directrix* (dĭ rĕk'trĭks). The generatrix in any one of its positions is called an *element* of the surface. In the figure, the generatrix AF is parallel to HK and intersects the polygon $ABCDE$, generating a closed prismatic surface. The line l is one of the elements of the surface.

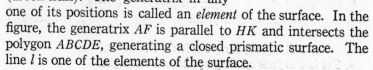

81

108. Prism. A *prism* is a polyhedron formed by a closed prismatic surface and two parallel planes cutting all the elements. The sections made by the two parallel planes are the *bases* of the prism. In prism *AD'*, the polygons *ABCDE* and *A'B'C'D'E'* are the bases of the prism. The remaining faces of the prism are called *lateral faces*, and the intersections of the lateral faces are called *lateral edges*.

The *lateral area* of the prism is the sum of the areas of the lateral faces. The *total area* is the sum of the lateral area and the areas of the two bases. The *altitude* of a prism is the common perpendicular between the bases. Why are all altitudes of a prism equal?

109. Right Section of a Prism. A *right section* of a prism is a section made by a plane perpendicular to one of the lateral edges. An *oblique section* is made by a plane oblique to one of the lateral edges.

110. Right Prism. A *right prism* is a prism whose bases are right sections. Prisms *A* and *B* are right prisms. An

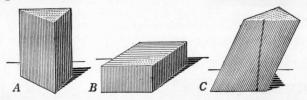

oblique prism is a prism whose bases are not right sections. Prism *C* is an oblique prism.

111. Regular Prism. A *regular prism* is a right prism whose bases are regular polygons.

112. Theorems (c, n). Properties of prisms.

a. The lateral faces of a prism are parallelograms (use §§ 108 and 60).

b. The lateral edges of a prism are parallel and equal.

c. The lateral edges of a prism are perpendicular to the plane of a right section.

d. The lateral edges of a right prism are altitudes.

e. The lateral faces of a right prism are rectangles.

113. Prisms Classified as to their Bases. Prisms are triangular, quadrangular, pentagonal, etc., according as their bases are triangles, quadrilaterals, pentagons, etc.

EXERCISES (GROUP A). *PRISMS*

1. Draw a right triangular prism; an oblique quadrangular prism; a regular hexagonal prism.

2. Using two pencils and a polygon, show how a prismatic surface is generated.

3. What is the least number of faces that a polyhedron can have? the greatest?

4. What is the least number of faces a prism can have? the greatest?

5. If an oblique prism has a square base, is a right section of it a square?

6. How many faces has a triangular prism? a quadrangular prism? a pentagonal prism?

7. How many edges has a hexagonal prism? a pentagonal prism?

8. What is the locus of points equidistant from the planes of the bases of a prism?

9. If a lateral edge of a prism is an altitude, what kind of a prism is it?

EXERCISES (GROUP B). *PRISMS*

1. Are the corresponding sides of the bases of a prism parallel?

2. If two adjacent lateral faces of a prism are rectangles, the prism is a right prism.

3. Prove that the section of a prism made by a plane parallel to a lateral face is a parallelogram.

4. If the bases of a quadrangular prism are trapezoids, any section made by a plane cutting all the lateral edges is a trapezoid.

5. How many degrees are in a dihedral angle formed by two adjacent lateral faces of a regular pentagonal prism?

6. Prove that the midpoints of the edges of a prism are coplanar.

7. Find the sum of the face angles of a hexagonal prism.

Proposition I. Theorem (C, N)

114. *The sections of a prism made by parallel planes intersecting the lateral edges are congruent polygons.*

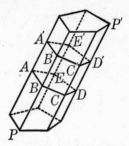

Given the sections *ABCDE* and *A'B'C'D'E'* made by parallel planes intersecting the lateral edges of prism *PP'*.

To prove that polygon *ABCDE* ≅ polygon *A'B'C'D'E'*.

> *Selection of Method:* 1. Known methods of proving polygons ≅ :
> § 12 *p*.
> 2. Method to be used : § 12 *p*.

Proof: STATEMENTS   REASONS

1. *AB* ∥ *A'B'*, *BC* ∥ *B'C'*, *CD* ∥ *C'D'*, etc.	1. § 60.
2. ∠ *ABC* = ∠ *A'B'C'*, ∠ *BCD* = ∠ *B'C'D'*, etc.	2. § 66.
3. *AA'* ∥ *BB'* ∥ *CC'*, etc.	3. § 112 *b*.
4. ∴ *AB* = *A'B'*, *BC* = *B'C'*, *CD* = *C'D'*, etc.	4. § 14 *g*.
5. ∴ *ABCDE* ≅ *A'B'C'D'E'*.	5. § 12 *p*.

115. Corollary I (c, n). *The bases of a prism are congruent polygons.*

116. Corollary II. *Every section of a prism made by a plane parallel to the base is congruent to the base.*

117. Truncated Prism. A *truncated prism* is the polyhedron formed by a closed prismatic surface and two nonparallel planes cutting all the elements. The figure *T* is a truncated prism.

EXERCISES (GROUP A). *PRISMS*

1. How can you make a hexagonal prism out of a hexagonal pencil?

2. Is a chalk box a prism? a right prism? a truncated prism?

3. Do the bases of a prism lie in parallel planes?

4. Do §§ 112, 114, 115, and 116 apply to truncated prisms?

5. Prove that the altitude of an oblique prism is less than a lateral edge.

6. Prove that a section of a prism made by a plane parallel to a lateral edge is a parallelogram.

7. The base of a right prism is a square 4 feet on a side, and the altitude of the prism is 6 feet. Find the lateral area of the prism; the total area of the prism.

8. Find the length of the diagonal of a right prism 30 feet high whose base is a rectangle 20 feet by 24 feet.

9. If one lateral face of a quadrangular prism is a rectangle, are any of the remaining lateral faces rectangles?

10. Is it possible for all faces of a prism to be parallelograms? rectangles? squares?

11. One edge of an oblique prism forms an angle of 30° with its projection on the plane of one base. If the lateral edge is 10 inches long, find the length of the altitude of the prism.

118. Volume of a Solid. The volume of a solid is the number of cubic units of measure inclosed by the solid. A cubic unit of measure is a cube whose edge is one linear unit.

119. Congruent Solids. Two solids are *congruent* if they coincide.

120. Equal (Equivalent) Solids. Two solids are *equal*, or *equivalent*, if they have equal volumes. Congruent solids are equal. Why?

Two prisms may be equal in volume and not be congruent. Thus a sphere and a prism may have equal volumes, but they are not congruent. Two solids have the same volume if they can be separated into solids which are respectively congruent. If the congruent parts are arranged in the same order, the solids are equal in volume and congruent; if the congruent parts are not arranged in the same order, the solids are equal in volume but not congruent.

Proposition II. Theorem (c)

121. *Two prisms are congruent if the three faces which include a trihedral angle of one are congruent respectively to the three faces which include a trihedral angle of the other, and are similarly placed.*

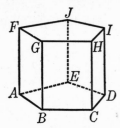 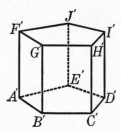

Given the prisms AI and $A'I'$ with face $AD \cong$ face $A'D'$, face $AG \cong$ face $A'G'$, and face $BH \cong$ face $B'H'$.

To prove that prism $AI \cong$ prism $A'I'$.

⎡*Selection of Method:* 1. Known methods of proving solids $\cong$: § 119.⎤
⎣   2. Method to be used : § 119.   ⎦

Proof:

STATEMENTS	REASONS
1. $\angle ABG = \angle A'B'G'$, $\angle ABC = \angle A'B'C'$, and $\angle GBC = \angle G'B'C'$.	1. § 12 p.
2. ∴ trihedral $\angle B =$ trihedral $\angle B'$.	2. § 97.
3. Place prism AI upon prism $A'I'$ so that trihedral $\angle B$ coincides with trihedral $\angle B'$.	3. §§ 12 f, 10 d.
4. Then faces BF, BD, and BH coincide with faces $B'F'$, $B'D'$, and $B'H'$ respectively.	4. § 10 d.
5. ∴ points F, G, and H coincide with points F', G', and H', respectively, and points D and E coincide with points D' and E' respectively.	5. Reason 4.
6. ∴ plane FGH coincides with plane $F'G'H'$.	6. § 9 c.

Proof:

STATEMENTS	REASONS
7. But face $GI \cong$ face BD and face $G'I' \cong$ face $B'D'$.	7. § 115.
8. Face $BD \cong$ face $B'D'$.	8. Statement 4.
9. ∴ face $GI \cong$ face $G'I'$.	9. Why?
10. Hence face GI will coincide with face $G'I'$.	10. § 10 d.
11. ∴ DI and EJ coincide with $D'I'$ and $E'J'$ respectively.	11. Why?
12. ∴ prism $AI \cong$ prism $A'I'$.	12. § 119.

122. Corollary (c, n). *Two right prisms are congruent if they have congruent bases and equal altitudes.*

123. Theorem (c, n). *Two truncated prisms are congruent if the three faces which include a trihedral angle of one are congruent respectively to the three faces which include a trihedral angle of the other, and are similarly placed.*

(Proof similar to that of Prop. II.)

EXERCISES (GROUP A). *PROPERTIES OF PRISMS*

1. Are all prisms polyhedrons? Are all polyhedrons prisms?

2. Prove that the corresponding diagonals of the bases of a prism are parallel and equal.

3. Two triangular prisms are congruent if the lateral faces of one are congruent respectively to the lateral faces of the other, and are similarly placed.

4. A section of a regular quadrangular prism made by a plane intersecting all the lateral edges is a parallelogram.

5. If two prisms have equal altitudes and congruent bases, are the lateral edges necessarily equal?

6. Find the lateral area of a regular quadrangular prism if its altitude is 10 inches and one side of the base is 4 inches. Find the total area of the prism.

7. Prove that if a right section of a prism is a rectangle, the adjacent lateral faces of the prism are perpendicular to each other.

8. Can a section of a prism be a trapezoid?

Proposition III. Theorem (C, N)

124. *An oblique prism is equal to a right prism whose base is a right section of the oblique prism, and whose altitude is equal to a lateral edge of the oblique prism.*

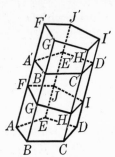

Given the oblique prism AD' and the rt. prism FI' whose base FI is a rt. section of AD' and whose altitude or lateral edge HH' = lateral edge CC' of AD'.

To prove that prism AD' = prism FI'.

⌈*Selection of Method:* 1. Known methods of proving solids =: ⌉
⌊ §§ 120, 121, 122, 123. ⌋
  2. Method to be used : § 120.

Proof: *STATEMENTS*   *REASONS*

1. Edge AA' = edge FF'.	1. Why?
2. ∴ $AF = A'F'$. Likewise, $BG = B'G'$.	2. § 11 b.
3. $AB = A'B'$ and $FG = F'G'$.	3. §§ 112 a, 14 f.
4. $\angle ABG = \angle A'B'G'$, $\angle BGF = \angle B'G'F'$, $\angle GFA = \angle G'F'A'$, $\angle FAB = \angle F'A'B'$.	4. Why?
5. ∴ polygon $ABGF \cong$ polygon $A'B'G'F'$.	5. Why?
6. Polygon $BCHG \cong$ polygon $B'C'H'G'$.	6. Statements 1–5.
7. Polygon $ABCDE \cong$ polygon $A'B'C'D'E'$.	7. § 115.
8. ∴ $AI \cong A'I'$.	8. § 123.
9. $AI + FD' = A'I' + FD'$.	9. § 11 a.
10. ∴ prism AD' = prism FI'.	10. §120.

Proposition IV. Theorem (C, N)

125. *The lateral area of a prism is equal to the product of a lateral edge and the perimeter of a right section ($S = ep$).*

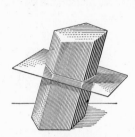
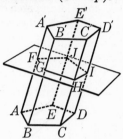

Given the prism AD' with rt. section GI. Denote the lateral area by S, the perimeter of the rt. section by p, and the length of a lateral edge by e.

To prove that $S = ep$.

⎡*Selection of Method:* 1. Known methods of finding areas of prisms:
§ 108.
2. Method to be used: § 108.⎤

Proof:

STATEMENTS	REASONS
1. $AA' = BB' = CC' = DD' = EE' = e$.	1. § 112 b.
2. Each lateral face of the prism, such as $ABB'A'$, is a $\square$.	2. § 112 a.
3. Plane $GI \perp AA'$.	3. § 109.
4. $\therefore FG \perp AA'$.	4. § 36.
5. $\therefore$ area $\square ABB'A' = AA' \times FG = e \times FG$.	5. § 28 c.
6. Likewise, $\square BCC'B' = e \times GH$, etc.	6. Reasons 1–5.
7. $\therefore S = e \times FG + e \times GH + e \times HI + e \times IJ + e \times JF$.	7. §§ 11 a, 108.
8. $\therefore S = e(FG + GH + HI + IJ + JF)$.	8. § 11 e.
9. $\therefore S = ep$.	9. § 11 e.

126. Corollary. *The lateral area of a right prism is equal to the product of its altitude and the perimeter of its base.*

EXERCISES (GROUP A). *AREA OF PRISMS*

1. The lateral edge of a prism is 14 inches and the perimeter of a right section is 24 inches. Find the lateral area.

2. Find the lateral area of a right prism whose altitude is 20 inches and whose base is a square 7 inches on a side.

3. Find the lateral area of a right prism whose altitude is 16 inches and whose base is an equilateral triangle with a side 9 inches long. Find the total area of the prism.

4. Find the lateral area of a right triangular prism whose altitude is 14 inches and whose base is a right triangle with a hypotenuse of 26 inches and one leg of 10 inches.

5. Find the lateral area of a right prism whose altitude is 15 inches and whose base is a rhombus with diagonals 6 inches and 8 inches. Find the total area of the prism.

6. Two prisms have equal bases and equal altitudes. Do the prisms have the same lateral area?

EXERCISES (GROUP B). *PRACTICAL MEASUREMENTS*

1. Find the lateral area of a regular hexagonal prism each side of whose base is 1 foot and whose altitude is 3 feet. Find the total area of the prism.

2. Find the cost, at $1.15 a square yard, of glazing the lateral faces of a column in the form of a regular octagonal prism, if the height of the column is 36 feet and a side of the base is 18 inches.

3. A truncated right prism has a square base with 6-inch edges. Two adjacent lateral edges are 10 inches long and the two other lateral edges are 7 inches long. Find the lateral area and the total area.

4. Find the number of degrees in the sum of the dihedral angles whose edges are the lateral edges of a triangular prism.

5. Find the sum of the face angles of a quadrangular prism.

6. What is the shortest distance that can be measured on the walls and floor of a room from an upper corner to the lower diagonally opposite corner, if the room is 12 feet wide, 18 feet long, and 9 feet high?

PARALLELEPIPEDS

127. Parallelepiped. A *parallelepiped* (păr ă lĕl ē pi'pĕd) is a prism whose bases are parallelograms.

128. Right Parallelepiped. A *right parallelepiped* is a parallelepiped that is a right prism. By § 112 *d*, all the lateral edges of a right parallelepiped are perpendicular to the planes of the bases.

129. Oblique Parallelepiped. An *oblique parallelepiped* is a parallelepiped that is an oblique prism. The lateral edges of an oblique parallelepiped are oblique to the planes of the bases.

130. Rectangular Parallelepiped. A *rectangular parallelepiped* is a right parallelepiped whose bases are rectangles. It is often called a *rectangular solid*.

131. Cube. A *cube* is a rectangular parallelepiped whose edges are all equal.

132. Theorems. Properties of parallelepipeds.

a. All the faces of a parallelepiped are parallelograms.

b. All the faces of a rectangular solid are rectangles.

c. (c, n) *The opposite faces of a parallelepiped are parallel* (§§ 132 *a*, 66).

d. (c, N) *The opposite faces of a parallelepiped are congruent.*

e. All the faces of a cube are congruent squares.

EXERCISES (GROUP A). *PARALLELEPIPEDS*

1. The section of a parallelepiped made by a plane passed through two diagonally opposite edges is a parallelogram.

2. The section of a cube made by a plane passed through two diagonally opposite edges is a rectangle.

3. The square of a diagonal of a rectangular parallelepiped is equal to the sum of the squares of three concurrent edges.

4. If a parallelepiped has a rectangular base, is it necessarily a right parallelepiped?

5. Prove that the diagonals of a rectangular parallelepiped are equal.

Proposition V. Theorem (C, N)

133. *The plane passed through two diagonally opposite edges of a parallelepiped divides it into two equal triangular prisms.*

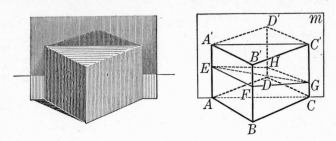

Given the parallelepiped *AC'* with a plane *m* passed through the edges *AA'* and *CC'*.

To prove that prism *ABC-A'B'C'* = prism *ACD-A'C'D'*.

⌈ *Selection of Method:* 1. Known methods of proving prisms =: ⌉
§§ 120, 121, 122, 123, 124.
2. Method to be used : § 122.
⌊ ⌋

Proof: STATEMENTS   REASONS

STATEMENTS	REASONS
1. Draw the rt. section *EFGH* through *E* in *AA'*.	1. § 38.
2. Plane *m* intersects plane *EFGH* in *EG*.	2. Why ?
3. *EH* ∥ *FG* and *EF* ∥ *HG*.	3. §§ 132 *c*, 60.
4. ∴ *EFGH* is a ▱.	4. 10 *k*.
5. ∴ △ *EFG* ≅ △ *EGH*.	5. § 13 *g*.
6. Prism *ABC-A'B'C'* = a rt. prism having *EFG* as a base and *AA'* as an altitude.	6. § 124.
7. Prism *ACD-A'C'D'* = a rt. prism having *EGH* as a base and *AA'* as an altitude.	7. § 124.
8. These rt. prisms are ≅.	8. § 122.
9. ∴ prism *ABC-A'B'C'* = prism *ACD-A'C'D'*.	9. § 11 *f*.

134. Unit of Volume. In § 118 the volume of a solid was defined as the number of cubic units of measure contained in the solid. The unit for measuring the volume of a solid is a cube whose edges are equal to some unit for measuring length. This cube is called a *unit of volume.*

135. Volume of a Rectangular Solid. The rectangular solid shown here is 5 units long, 4 units wide, and 3 units high. The solid consists of three layers, each layer containing 5 × 4, or 20, cubic units.

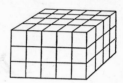

The three layers contain 3 × 20, or 60, cubic units. The volume of the solid equals 4 × 5 × 3, or 60, cubic units. If the dimensions of a rectangular solid are incommensurable (do not have a common unit of measure), it can be proved that the volume of this solid also is equal to the product of its three dimensions. Thus a rectangular solid whose dimensions are 6, $\sqrt{15}$, and 18 has a volume of $6 \times 18 \times \sqrt{15} = 108 \sqrt{15}$. From this discussion we shall assume the following postulate:

136. Postulate. *The volume of a rectangular solid is the product of its three dimensions.* ($V = abc$, where a, b, and c are the dimensions.)

137. Corollary I (c, n). *The volume of a rectangular solid is the product of its base and altitude.*

138. Corollary II. *The volume of a cube is equal to the cube of an edge.*

EXERCISES (GROUP A). *VOLUMES*

1. Find the volume of a cube 12 inches on an edge.

2. Find the volume of a cube whose area is 294 square feet.

3. The volume of a rectangular solid is 5376 cubic inches. If the base is 24 inches by 16 inches, find the altitude of the solid.

4. A wooden beam of lumber 16 feet long contains 16 cubic feet. If its cross section is a square, find the perimeter of the section.

5. A schoolroom is 24 feet wide, 36 feet long, and 12 feet high. What is its volume in cubic yards?

Proposition VI. Theorem (c, N)

139. *The volume of any parallelepiped is equal to the product of its base and altitude.*

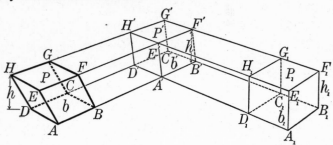

Given the parallelepiped P having base b, altitude h, and volume V.

To prove that $V = bh$.

> *Selection of Method:* 1. Known methods of finding volumes of solids: §§ 136, 137, 138.
> 2. Method to be used: § 137.

Proof:

STATEMENTS	REASONS
1. Extend AB, DC, EF, and HG; on AB extended construct $A'B' = AB$.	1. Why possible?
2. Through A' and B' draw planes $\perp A'B'$.	2. Why possible?
3. These planes are each $\perp D'C'$, $E'F'$, and $H'G'$.	3. Why?
4. $\therefore P'$ is a rt. prism having $A'D'H'E'$ as a base and $A'B'$ as an altitude.	4. § 110.
5. $\therefore P' = P$.	5. § 124.
6. In the same manner, by extending $D'A'$, $H'E'$, $G'F'$, $C'B'$, and by constructing $C_1B_1 = C'B'$, a rectangular solid P_1 can be formed having $A_1B_1F_1E_1$ as a base and B_1C_1 as an altitude.	6. Reasons 1–4.
7. Then $P_1 = P'$.	7. Reason 5.
8. $\therefore P = P_1$.	8. Why?

Proof: *STATEMENTS* *REASONS*

Denote $A'B'C'D'$ by b', $A_1B_1C_1D_1$ by b_1, the altitude of P' by h', and the altitude of P_1 by h_1.

9. $b = b' = b_1$.	9. § 29 *a*.
10. $h = h' = h_1$.	10. § 64.
11. Volume of $P_1 = b_1h_1$.	11. § 137.
12. ∴ $V = bh$.	12. Why?

140. Corollary I. *Two parallelepipeds having equal bases have the same ratio as their altitudes.*

141. Corollary II. *Two parallelepipeds having equal altitudes have the same ratio as their bases.*

142. Corollary III. *Two parallelepipeds have the same ratio as the products of their three dimensions.*

143. Corollary IV. *Two parallelepipeds having equal bases and equal altitudes are equal.*

EXERCISES (GROUP A). *COMPUTATIONS*

1. Find the volume of a parallelepiped having an altitude of 16 inches and a rectangular base 10 inches long and 5 inches wide.

2. Find the ratio of two rectangular parallelepipeds both of whose altitudes are 10 inches, and whose bases are 5 inches by 6 inches and 9 inches by 10 inches respectively.

3. How many bricks 8 inches by 4 inches by 2 inches are necessary to build a wall 40 feet long, 12 feet high, and 12 inches thick, if 10 per cent of the wall is mortar?

4. Each of the inside dimensions of a cubical box is 5 feet. How many bushels of grain will the box hold? (1 bushel = 2150.42 cubic inches.)

5. The total surface of a cube is 486 square inches. Find its volume.

6. The volume of one rectangular solid is twice that of another. If they have equal bases, what is the ratio of their altitudes?

7. Find the weight of a wooden beam 6 inches by 10 inches by 20 feet weighing 48 pounds per cubic foot.

1. The diagonal of a cube is $8\sqrt{3}$. Find the area and volume of the cube.

2. Find the ratio of the volumes of two rectangular solids which have the dimensions a, b, c and $3\,a$, $4\,b$, $5\,c$ respectively.

3. How many cubic yards are there in a rectangular solid x feet long, y feet deep, and z feet wide?

4. The volume of a rectangular parallelepiped is 192 cubic feet. Each side of its square base is $\frac{1}{3}$ of its altitude. Find the side of the base.

5. The edge of a cube is a. Find the edge of a cube twice as large.

144. Duplication of the Cube. The problem of *duplicating the cube* (constructing a cube twice as large as a given cube) in ancient times was known as the Delian problem. It received this name from the following legend:

In 430 B.C. the Athenians, who were suffering from a plague, consulted the oracle at Delos, the birthplace of Apollo and Diana, as to how the plague could be ended. Apollo answered that they must double the size of his altar, which had the shape of a cube. Then the Athenians constructed a new altar each of whose edges were double those of the old one. Since the new altar was eight times as large as the old one, Apollo became indignant and the plague became worse than before. The Athenians then consulted Plato, who referred them to the geometricians.

The duplication of the cube, in Greek geometry one of the three famous problems of antiquity, was not solved immediately. Like the trisection of the angle, the problem could not be solved by the instruments of plane geometry. Many solutions using curves other than the circle have since been used to solve the problem. About 340 B.C. Menæchmus gave the following solution, using parabolas:

Construct the parabolas whose equations are $y^2 = 2\,ax$ and $x^2 = ay$. These parabolas intersect at a point whose abscissa is given by $x^3 = 2\,a^3$. Thus if a is a side of a given cube, x is a side of another cube twice as large.

Proposition VII. Theorem (C, N)

145. *The volume of a triangular prism is equal to the product of its base and altitude.*

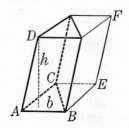

Given the triangular prism *ABC-D*, with base *b*, altitude *h*, and volume *V*.

To prove that $V = bh$.

> *Selection of Method:* 1. Known methods of finding volumes of solids: §§ 136, 137, 138, 139.
> 2. Method to be used: § 139.

Proof:

STATEMENTS	REASONS
1. In plane *ABC*, draw *CE* ∥ *AB* and *BE* ∥ *AC*, intersecting at *E*.	1. Why possible?
2. Then *ABEC* is a ▱.	2. Why?
3. Draw parallelepiped *AF* having *ABEC* as a base and *AD* as an edge.	3. § 127.
4. *ABEC-D* = *ABEC* · *h*.	4. § 139.
5. But *ABEC-D* = 2 *ABC-D*, or 2 *V*.	5. §§ 133, 11 *e*.
6. ▱ *ABEC* = 2 △ *ABC*, or 2 *b*.	6. §§ 13 *g*, 11 *e*.
7. ∴ 2 *V* = 2 *bh*.	7. § 11 *e*.
8. ∴ *V* = *bh*.	8. § 11 *d*.

EXERCISE

The base of a prism is a right triangle with legs 10 inches and 24 inches respectively. Find the volume of the prism if its altitude is 35 inches.

146. Corollary (c, N). *The volume of any prism is equal to the product of its base and altitude.*

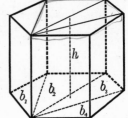

Suggestions. Divide the prism into triangular prisms by drawing planes through one edge and the nonadjacent edges. Let b_1, b_2, b_3, etc. denote the bases of these prisms, and v_1, v_2, v_3, etc. their respective volumes. Then $v_1 = b_1 h$, $v_2 = b_2 h$, etc.

Then $v_1 + v_2 + v_3 + $ etc. $= (b_1 + b_2 + b_3 + $ etc.$)h$.

$$v = ?$$

EXERCISES (GROUP A). *PRISMS*

1. Are the opposite trihedral angles of a parallelepiped equal? Are they symmetric?

2. Two prisms have equal altitudes and congruent bases. Do they have equal lateral areas? equal volumes? If their lateral areas are equal, are their total areas equal?

3. Find the cost of excavating a cellar 6 feet deep, 50 feet long, and 28 feet wide at $1.25 a cubic yard.

4. A cistern in the form of a rectangular solid is 4 feet wide, 6 feet long, and 8 feet deep. How many gallons of water will it hold? * How many barrels will it hold?

5. If the length of a rectangular solid is 12 inches, its width 8 inches, and its height 6 inches, find the area of its surface.

6. The perimeter of the base of a right prism is 14.6, and its lateral area is 621.4. Find its height.

7. Find the area of the base of a prism whose volume is 516.6 cubic feet and whose height is 16.4 inches.

8. Find the volume and total area of a rectangular solid whose dimensions are m, n, and r.

9. Find the weight of a rectangular block of granite 10 feet long, $1\frac{1}{2}$ feet wide, and 1 foot thick, if a cubic foot of the stone weighs 162.5 pounds.

10. A garage is 20 feet long, 18 feet wide, 10 feet high at the eaves, and 16 feet high at the ridgepole. In painting the garage, how many square feet of surface are to be covered?

*See Tables for Reference, page 245.

EXERCISES (GROUP B). *COMPUTATIONS*

Example 1. The length of a rectangular parallelepiped is three times the height, and the width is twice the height. If a diagonal is 28, find the volume.

Solution. Let $\quad x =$ the height.
Then $\qquad 2\,x =$ the width,
and $\qquad 3\,x =$ the length.
$$4\,x^2 + 9\,x^2 = m^2.$$
$$m^2 + x^2 = \overline{28}^2.$$
$$4\,x^2 + 9\,x^2 + x^2 = \overline{28}^2.$$
$$14\,x^2 = 784.$$
$$x = \sqrt{56} \text{ or } 2\sqrt{14}.$$
The volume $= 3\,x \cdot 2\,x \cdot x = 48\sqrt{(14)^3} = 672\sqrt{14}.$

Example 2. The dimensions of a rectangular parallelepiped are as $2:3:5$ and its volume is 82,320. Find the dimensions.

Solution. Let $\qquad 2\,x =$ one dimension,
$\qquad 3\,x =$ a second dimension,
and $\qquad 5\,x =$ the third dimension.
Then $\qquad 30\,x^3 = 82,320.$
$$x^3 = 2744.$$
$$\log 2744 = 3.4384.*$$
$$\tfrac{1}{3}\log 2744 = 1.1461.$$
$$x = \text{antilog } 1.1461 = 14.$$
$$2\,x = 28, \quad 3\,x = 42, \quad \text{and} \quad 5\,x = 70.$$

1. Find the edge of a cube whose volume is 1000 cubic feet.

2. Find the volume and area of a cube if one of the diagonals of its faces is $7\sqrt{2}$ inches.

3. The diagonal of a cube is d. Find its volume V in terms of d.

4. The area of the surface of a cube is A. Find its volume V in terms of A.

5. The diagonal of a cube is $144\sqrt{3}$ inches. Find its volume.

6. A steel bar is 10 feet long, 3 inches wide, and $1\frac{3}{8}$ inches thick. What is its weight, if one cubic foot of steel weighs 490 pounds?

7. Find the height of a prism whose volume is 420 cubic inches and whose base is a triangle with sides of 5, 12, and 13 inches.

8. Each lateral edge of a triangular prism is 18 inches in length and makes an angle of 45° with the plane of the base. Find the volume of the prism, if the sides of the base are 8, 10, and 12 inches respectively.

* For an explanation of the use of logarithms, see pages 239–241.

9. The volume of a rectangular solid is V, and the dimensions are as $a : b : c$. Find the dimensions.

10. Find the total area of a right prism having a square base, if each side of the base is 4.2 inches and the volume is 369.892 cubic inches.

11. The ceiling and walls of a room have an area of 816 square feet. Find the height of the room, if the floor is 12 feet by 20 feet.

12. Find the weight of 1000 feet of iron bar whose cross section is a regular hexagon $\frac{1}{2}$ inch on a side. (1 cubic foot of iron weighs 450 pounds.)

13. If V denotes the volume of a cube and T its surface, show that $V = \dfrac{T}{36} \sqrt{6\,T}$.

CYLINDERS

147. Cylindrical Surface. A moving straight line which always intersects a plane curve, and remains parallel to a fixed straight line not in the plane of the curve, generates a *cylindrical surface*.

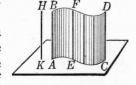

This moving line, as in the case of a closed prismatic surface, is called the *generatrix*, and the curve is called the *directrix*. The generatrix in any one of its positions is called an *element* of the surface. In the figure, the generatrix AB is parallel to a fixed straight line KH and intersects the directrix AC, generating the cylindrical surface $ACDB$. The line EF, one of the positions of AB, is one of the elements of the surface.

148. Cylinder. A cylinder is a solid formed by a closed cylindrical surface and two parallel planes cutting all the elements. The parallel plane sections are the *bases* of the cylinder, and the *lateral surface* is the cylindrical surface. The *altitude* of a cylinder is the common perpendicular between the planes of the bases.

149. Right Section of a Cylinder. A *right section* of a cylinder is a section made by a plane perpendicular to one of the elements. It follows that the plane is perpendicular to all the elements. Why?

150. Right Cylinder. A *right cylinder* is a cylinder in which the planes of the bases are perpendicular to one of the elements. These planes are perpendicular to all the elements. Why?

151. Oblique Cylinder. An *oblique cylinder* is one in which the planes of the bases are oblique to one and hence to all the elements.

152. Circular Cylinder. A *circular cylinder* is one whose bases are circles. The line segment joining the centers of the bases is called the *axis* of the cylinder. A *right circular cylinder* is sometimes called a *cylinder of revolution*, since it may be generated by revolving a rectangle about one of its sides as an axis. If the rectangle *ABCD* is revolved about *AD* as an axis, *BC* generates a cylindrical surface, and *AB* and *DC* generate the planes of the bases.

Since the circle is the only plane curve studied in plane geometry, the theorems and exercises which follow will refer only to circular cylinders.

153. Theorem. *The elements of a cylinder are parallel and equal.*

EXERCISES (GROUP A). *CYLINDERS*

1. Draw a right circular cylinder; an oblique circular cylinder.

2. Are all circular cylinders necessarily cylinders of revolution? Are all cylinders of revolution necessarily circular cylinders? right cylinders?

3. What is the locus of a line which is parallel to and has a given distance from a given line?

4. What is the locus of points having a distance *d* from a line *l*?

5. What is the difference between the directrix of a closed prismatic surface and the directrix of a closed cylindrical surface? What is the difference between a plane surface and a cylindrical surface?

6. Is it possible for all points of a straight line to lie in a cylindrical surface?

Proposition VIII. Theorem (c, n)

154. *The bases of a cylinder are congruent.*

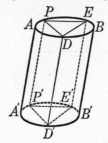

Given the cylinder AB' having bases AB and $A'B'$.

To prove that base $AB \cong$ base $A'B'$.

⎡ *Selection of Method:* 1. Known methods of proving closed curves ⎤
　　　　　　　　　　　　 $\cong$: §§ 10 *d*, 12 *s*.
　　　　　　　　　　　　2. Method to be used : § 10 *d*.

Proof: 　　　STATEMENTS 　　　　　　　　REASONS

1. Draw DD' and EE' any two elements of the cylinder and let P be any other point, besides D and E, in the base AB.	1. § 12 *r*.
2. Draw the element PP'.	2. § 12 *r*.
3. Draw DE, EP, PD, $D'E'$, $E'P'$, and $P'D'$.	3. § 12 *a*.
4. $DD' = EE'$ and $DD' \parallel EE'$.	4. Why?
5. $\therefore DEE'D'$ is a $\square$.	5. Why?
6. Likewise $EPP'E'$ and $DPP'D'$ are $\boxed{s}$.	6. Why?
7. $\therefore DE = D'E'$, $PE = P'E'$, and $PD = P'D'$.	7. Why?
8. $\therefore \triangle PDE \cong \triangle P'D'E'$.	8. Why?
9. Place base AB upon base $A'B'$ so that DE coincides with its equal $D'E'$. Then, since $\triangle PDE \cong \triangle P'D'E'$, P will coincide with P'.	9. § 10 *d*.
10. Since P is any point in base AB, all points of base AB will coincide with corresponding points in base $A'B'$, and conversely.	10. Reasons 1–9.
11. $\therefore$ base $AB \cong$ base $A'B'$.	11. § 10 *d*.

155. Corollary I. *Sections of a cylinder made by parallel planes cutting all the elements, are congruent.*

156. Corollary II. *A section of a circular cylinder made by a plane parallel to the plane of the base is a circle.*

MEASUREMENT OF CYLINDERS

157. Plane Tangent to a Cylinder. A plane is tangent to a cylinder if it contains an element and no other point of the cylinder. In the figure, plane *m* is tangent to cylinder *C*.

158. Inscribed Prism. A prism is *inscribed* in a cylinder when its lateral edges are elements of the cylinder, and its bases lie in the planes of the bases of the cylinder. When a prism is inscribed in a cylinder, the cylinder is *circumscribed* about the prism.

159. Circumscribed Prism. A prism is *circumscribed* about a cylinder when the lateral faces of the prism are tangent

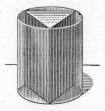
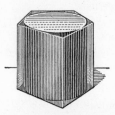

to the cylinder, and the bases of the prism lie in the planes of the bases of the cylinder. When a prism is circumscribed about a cylinder, the cylinder is *inscribed* in the prism. At this time the student should review the subject of limits from plane geometry. (See § 12 *x*, *y*, and *z*.)

160. Theorems on Limits. By reviewing the theorems on the mensuration of the circle, you will find that their proofs depend on two basic theorems. In solid geometry the proofs of the theorems on the mensuration of the cylinder, cone, and sphere also depend on these two theorems. These two theorems will be assumed without proofs, which may be found in college algebra.

a. **Theorem (c, n).** *If a variable x approaches a limit k, and if c is a constant, then cx approaches ck as a limit.* (If $x \rightarrow k$, then $cx \rightarrow ck$.)

b. **Theorem (c, n).** *If two equal variables continue to be equal while approaching their respective limits, their limits are equal.* (If $x = y$, as $x \rightarrow m$ and $y \rightarrow n$, then $m = n$.)

161. Limits Relating to the Cylinder. If a prism whose bases are regular polygons is inscribed in, or circumscribed about, a circular cylinder, its lateral area may be found by § 125, and its volume by § 146.

Now if the number of lateral faces of either prism is doubled a great number of times, the lateral area of either prism will almost equal the lateral area of the cylinder, and the volume of either prism will almost equal the volume of the cylinder. Hence we shall assume the following postulate:

162. Postulate on Cylinders. *If a prism whose bases are regular polygons is inscribed in, or circumscribed about, a circular cylinder, and if the number of lateral faces of the prism is indefinitely increased,*

a. *The lateral area of the prism approaches the lateral area of the cylinder as a limit;*

b. *The volume of the prism approaches the volume of the cylinder as a limit;*

c. *The perimeter of a right section of the prism approaches the perimeter of a right section of the cylinder as a limit.*

EXERCISES (GROUP A)

1. If a plane is tangent to a circular cylinder, its intersection with the plane of the base is tangent to the base.

2. A plane passing through a tangent to the base of a circular cylinder and the element drawn through the point of tangency is tangent to the cylinder.

3. Prove that every section of a cylinder made by a plane passing through an element is a parallelogram.

4. What kind of cylinder may have a rectangle as a section?

Proposition IX.   Theorem (c, N)

163. *The lateral area of a circular cylinder is equal to the product of an element and the perimeter of a right section.*

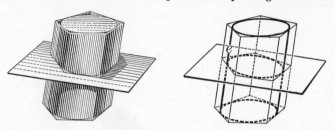

Given a circular cylinder with lateral area S, perimeter of a rt. section p, and element e.

To prove that $S = ep$.

> *Selection of Method:* 1. Known methods of finding areas of solids: §§ 108, 125, 126.
> 2. Method to be used: § 125.

Proof: STATEMENTS   REASONS

1. About the cylinder circumscribe a prism whose bases are regular polygons. Denote its area by S' and the perimeter of a rt. section by p'.	1. § 159.
2. Then $S' = ep'$.	2. § 125.
3. If the number of faces of the prism is increased indefinitely, $$S' \rightarrow S$$ and $p' \rightarrow p$.	3. §§ 162 a, 162 c.
4. $ep' \rightarrow ep$.	4. § 160 a.
5. But S' is always equal to ep'.	5. Statement 2.
6. $\therefore S = ep$.	6. § 160 b.

164. Corollary (c, n). *If S denotes the lateral area, T the total area, h the altitude, and r the radius of the base of a right circular cylinder, then $S = 2\pi rh$, and $T = 2\pi r(r + h)$.*

Proposition X. Theorem (c, N)

165. *The volume of a circular cylinder is equal to the product of its base and altitude.*

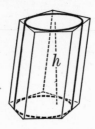

Given a circular cylinder with volume V, area of the base b, and altitude h.

To prove that $V = bh$.

⎡*Selection of Method:* 1. Known methods of finding volumes of⎤
⎢   solids: §§ 136, 137, 138, 139, 145, 146.⎥
⎣   2. Method to be used: § 146.⎦

Proof: *STATEMENTS*   *REASONS*

1. About the cylinder circumscribe a prism whose bases are regular polygons. Denote its volume by V' and the area of its base by b'.	1. § 159.
2. Then $V' = b'h$.	2. § 146.
3. If the number of faces of the prism is increased indefinitely, $\qquad\qquad V' \rightarrowtail V$ and $\qquad\qquad b' \rightarrowtail b$.	3. §§ 162 *b*, 12 *y*.
4. $\qquad\qquad b'h \rightarrowtail bh$.	4. § 160 *a*.
5. But V' is always equal to $b'h$.	5. Statement 2.
6. ∴ $V = bh$.	6. § 160 *b*.

166. Corollary (c, n). *The volume of a right circular cylinder is expressed by $V = \pi r^2 h$, where r is the radius of the base and h is the altitude.*

EXERCISES (GROUP A). *CYLINDERS*

1. A cylindrical pail is 12 inches deep, and the radius of its base is 5 inches. How many cubic inches does it contain?

2. Find the lateral surface of the pail in Ex. 1.

3. Find the area and volume of a cylindrical oil tank which is 30 feet long and has a diameter of 8 feet.

4. Find the lateral area of a circular cylinder if the perimeter of a right section is 42 and the length of an element is 8.

5. Find the surface of a right circular cylinder having an altitude of 7 inches and a base whose radius is 5 inches.

6. Find the surface and volume of a cylinder of revolution whose altitude is 18 feet and whose base has a radius of 12 feet.

7. A concrete roller is 8 feet long and 26 inches in diameter. What area does it cover in 500 revolutions?

EXERCISES (GROUP B). *CYLINDERS*

1. A right circular cylinder whose base has a radius of 5 feet is equivalent to a cube having an edge of 15 feet. What is the altitude of the cylinder?

2. A 75-gallon gasoline tank is 30 inches in diameter. What is its height?

3. What is the ratio of the volume of a regular triangular prism to the volume of the circumscribed cylinder?

4. What is the ratio of the volume of a cylinder to the volume of the regular quadrangular prism circumscribed about it?

5. How many square feet of tin are required to make a cylindrical bucket having a diameter of 8 inches and a height of 12 inches, allowing 10 per cent for waste?

6. Neglecting friction, find how many 2-inch water pipes can be supplied by a 36-inch water main.

167. Similar Cylinders of Revolution. Similar cylinders of revolution are cylinders generated by the revolution of similar rectangles about corresponding sides.

Proposition XI. Theorem (c, N)

168. *The lateral areas or the total areas of two similar cylinders of revolution have the same ratio as the squares of their altitudes or as the squares of the radii of their bases; and their volumes have the same ratio as the cubes of their altitudes or as the cubes of the radii of their bases.*

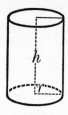

Given two $\sim$ cylinders of revolution with the lateral areas S and S', the total areas T and T', the volumes V and V', the radii r and r', and the altitudes h and h', respectively.

To prove that $\dfrac{S}{S'} = \dfrac{T}{T'} = \dfrac{h^2}{h'^2} = \dfrac{r^2}{r'^2}$, and $\dfrac{V}{V'} = \dfrac{h^3}{h'^3} = \dfrac{r^3}{r'^3}$.

Proof:

STATEMENTS	REASONS
1. $\dfrac{r}{r'} = \dfrac{h}{h'}$ and $\dfrac{r+h}{r'+h'} = \dfrac{h}{h'} = \dfrac{r}{r'}$.	1. §§ 10 r, 30 g.
2. $S = 2\pi rh$ and $S' = 2\pi r'h'$.	2. § 164.
3. $\therefore \dfrac{S}{S'} = \dfrac{2\pi rh}{2\pi r'h'} = \dfrac{r}{r'} \cdot \dfrac{h}{h'} = \dfrac{r^2}{r'^2} = \dfrac{h^2}{h'^2}$.	3. § 11 d, e.
4. $T = 2\pi r(r+h)$ and $T' = 2\pi r'(r'+h')$.	4. § 164.
5. $\therefore \dfrac{T}{T'} = \dfrac{2\pi r(r+h)}{2\pi r'(r'+h')} = \dfrac{r}{r'} \cdot \dfrac{r+h}{r'+h'}$ $= \dfrac{r^2}{r'^2} = \dfrac{h^2}{h'^2}$.	5. Give reasons.
6. $V = \pi r^2 h$ and $V' = \pi r'^2 h'$.	6. § 166.
7. $\therefore \dfrac{V}{V'} = \dfrac{\pi r^2 h}{\pi r'^2 h'} = \dfrac{r^2}{r'^2} \cdot \dfrac{h}{h'} = \dfrac{r^2}{r'^2} \cdot \dfrac{r}{r'} = \dfrac{r^3}{r'^3} = \dfrac{h^3}{h'^3}$.	7. Give reasons.

MISCELLANEOUS EXERCISES

1. If a ton of coal occupies 36 cubic feet, what must be the length of a coal bin 6 feet high and 8 feet wide to hold 14 tons?

2. A granary 4 feet wide and 8 feet long, inside dimensions, contains wheat to a depth of $7\frac{1}{2}$ feet. What is the value of the wheat at \$1.21 a bushel?

3. How many square inches of leather are required to cover the curved surface of a pulley 18 inches wide and 36 inches in diameter?

4. The water in a well 5 feet in diameter is 18 feet deep. How long will it take to draw out the water if the water runs in at the rate of 2 gallons a minute and is drawn out at the rate of 10 gallons a minute?

5. Find the volume, area, and length of a diagonal of a rectangular solid whose dimensions are 6 feet, 8 feet, and 12 feet.

6. The dimensions of one cylinder of revolution are 4 times those of a similar cylinder. What is the ratio of their lateral areas? of their total areas? of their volumes?

Suggestion. Let r and $4\,r$ be the radii of their bases, and h and $4\,h$ their altitudes.

7. The volume of a regular quadrangular prism is 6647 cubic inches, and its altitude is 23 inches. Find the dimensions of its base.

8. Find the dimensions of a cube whose area is numerically equal to its volume.

9. A bar of copper 3 feet long, 6 inches wide, and 1 inch thick is rolled into a plate 8 feet by 4 feet. What is the thickness of the plate?

10. When a casting is submerged in a right circular cylindrical vessel resting on a base, the water is raised $4\frac{1}{4}$ inches. If the diameter of the vessel is 16 inches, what is the volume of the casting?

11. A cylindrical vessel $18\frac{1}{2}$ inches in diameter and 8 inches deep contains 1 bushel. Find the number of cubic inches in a bushel.

12. What is the weight of a block of ice 18 inches by 20 inches by 12 inches if the specific gravity of ice is .92 and if one cubic foot of water weighs 62.4 pounds.

Note. Specific gravity of .92 means ".92 times as heavy as the same volume of water."

13. Solve $V = \pi r^2 h$ for r.

14. A cylindrical gasoline tank is lying on its side in a horizontal position. If the tank is 3.5 feet long and 16 inches in diameter, how many gallons does it contain when the depth of the gasoline is 4 inches?

15. The diagonal of the face of a cube is 312. Find the diagonal of the cube.

16. Find the volume of a cylinder inscribed in a cube having an edge of 6 inches.

17. Draw a figure representing a cube of edge 8 inches. Let O be the center of one face of the cube and let AB be one edge of the opposite face. Find the area of the triangle OAB, leaving your answer in radical form.

18. Find the height of a right circular cylinder of radius r whose volume is equal to a rectangular solid whose dimensions are a, b, and c.

19. A lead cylinder 56 inches in diameter and 7 inches high is melted and recast in the form of a regular quadrangular prism having the same altitude. Find the area of the prism.

20. The inside dimensions of a box are 2, 3, and 5. What are the dimensions of a similar box which holds 8 times as much?

21. The base of a right triangular prism is an isosceles triangle ABC with AB and AC each equal to 10 inches and BC equal to 12 inches. A plane is passed through BC meeting the lateral edge through A at A' so that AA' equals 8 inches. Show that the dihedral angle A-BC-A' is 45°.

22. A right triangular prism with bases ABC and $A'B'C'$ has its faces which meet at A mutually perpendicular. AA' is 10 inches long, AB is 12 inches long, and AC is 9 inches long. A plane is passed through the edge AC cutting the opposite edge, BB', in a point E 3 inches from B. Find the distance from B to this plane.

23. The edge of a cube is e. Find the area of a section made by a plane through two diagonally opposite edges.

24. A regular hexagonal prism is inscribed in a right circular cylinder whose base has a radius of 8 inches. Compare their volumes.

25. The number of cubic inches in the volume of a right circular cylinder is equal to the number of square inches in its lateral surface. Find the radius of its base.

EXERCISES (GROUP B)

1. How many cubic yards of material are removed in excavating a tunnel 1000 yards long if a cross section of the tunnel is a semicircle with a radius of 18 feet?

2. Find the height of a cylindrical quart can if its inside diameter is 5 inches.

3. Find the pressure necessary to punch a $\frac{1}{4}$-inch circular hole through a boiler plate if 80,000 pounds pressure is required for each square inch of surface cut.

4. Find the volume of a wash boiler 20 inches deep if its bottom is in the form of a rectangle with a semicircle at each end, and the rectangle is 12 inches wide and 18 inches long.

5. Find the per cent of increase in the volume of a cylinder if the altitude is increased 10 per cent and the radius of the base is increased 25 per cent.

6. Solve the formula $T = 2\,\pi r^2 + 2\,\pi r h$ for h, and state the resulting formula in words.

7. Solve $T = 2\pi r^2 + 2\,\pi r h$ for r, and tell how to find the radius of the base of a cylinder of revolution when the height and total area are known.

8. Find the length of a bar that can be made from a cubic foot of iron if the bar has a rectangular cross section 1 inch by $1\frac{1}{4}$ inches.

REVIEW QUESTIONS

1. What is a polyhedron? a prismatic surface? a cylindrical surface? a prism? a cylinder?

2. What is the name of the polyhedron whose bases are parallel, and whose lateral faces are parallelograms? of the polyhedron whose six faces are parallelograms? of the polyhedron whose six faces are congruent?

3. What is the name of the prism whose lateral faces are rectangles?

4. If the dimensions of one prism are three times those of a similar prism, what is the ratio of two corresponding diagonals? What is the ratio of their areas? of their volumes?

5. If two parallelepipeds have equal areas, do they have equal volumes?

6. State in words the following formulas:

a. $S = ep$. *d.* $V = abc$. *g.* $S = 2 \pi r h$.

b. $A = \pi r^2$. *e.* $V = e^3$. *h.* $V = \pi r^2 h$.

c. $A = \dfrac{s^2}{4} \sqrt{3}$. *f.* $V = bh$. *i.* $T = 2 \pi r h + 2 \pi r^2$.

7. Are two cylinders congruent and equal

a. If they have congruent bases and equal altitudes?

b. If they are right cylinders and have congruent bases and equal altitudes?

8. If a prism is inscribed in a cylinder, is its lateral area greater or less than the lateral area of the cylinder? How do the two volumes compare?

9. If a prism is inscribed in a circular cylinder, where do the vertices of the prism lie?

10. What is the lateral area of a cylinder whose element is 8 inches and whose right section has a perimeter of 24 inches?

11. The inside diameter of a garden hose is $\frac{3}{4}$ inch. What length of hose can be filled with a gallon of water?

SUMMARY OF PRINCIPAL METHODS OF PROOF

169.   *Congruent Polygons of Prisms*

a. The sections of a prism made by parallel planes intersecting all the lateral edges are congruent polygons.

b. The bases of a prism are congruent polygons.

c. Every section of a prism made by a plane parallel to the base is congruent to the base.

d. The opposite faces of a parallelepiped are congruent.

170.   *Congruent Prisms*

a. Two prisms are congruent if they coincide.

b. Two prisms are congruent if the three faces which include a trihedral angle of one are congruent respectively to the three faces which include a trihedral angle of the other, and are similarly placed.

c. Two right prisms are congruent if they have congruent bases and equal altitudes.

d. Two truncated prisms are congruent if the three faces which include a trihedral angle of one are congruent respectively to the three faces which include a trihedral angle of the other, and are similarly placed.

171. *Prisms Equal in Volume*

a. Two prisms are equal if they have equal volumes.

b. An oblique prism is equal to a right prism whose base is a right section of the oblique prism and whose altitude is equal to a lateral edge of the oblique prism.

c. The plane passed through two diagonally opposite edges of a parallelepiped divides it into equal triangular prisms.

d. Two parallelepipeds having equal bases and equal altitudes are equal.

172. *Areas of Prisms*

a. The lateral area of a prism is the sum of the areas of the lateral faces.

b. The lateral area of a prism is equal to the product of a lateral edge and the perimeter of a right section. ($S = ep$.)

c. The lateral area of a right prism is equal to the product of its altitude and the perimeter of its base.

173. *Volumes of Prisms*

a. The volume of any prism is equal to the product of its base and altitude.

b. The volume of a cube is equal to the cube of an edge.

c. Two parallelepipeds having equal bases have the same ratio as their altitudes.

d. Two parallelepipeds having equal altitudes have the same ratio as their bases.

e. Two parallelepipeds have the same ratio as the products of their three dimensions.

174. *Areas of Cylinders*

a. The lateral area of a circular cylinder is equal to the product of an element and the perimeter of a right section.

b. The lateral area S and the total area T of a right circular cylinder are expressed by the formulas $S = 2\pi rh$ and $T = 2\pi r(r + h)$.

c. The lateral areas or the total areas of two similar cylinders of revolution have the same ratio as the squares of their altitudes or as the squares of the radii of their bases.

175.   *Volumes of Cylinders*

a. The volume of a circular cylinder is equal to the product of its base and altitude.

b. The volumes of two similar cylinders of revolution have the same ratio as the cubes of their altitudes or as the cubes of the radii of their bases.

WORD LIST

circular	elements	pentagonal	revolution
circumscribed	generatrix	polyhedron	section
constant	indefinitely	postulate	similar
cylinder	inscribed	prism	triangular
cylindrical	lateral	prismatic	truncated
diagonal	limits	quadrangular	variable
directrix	parallelepiped	rectangular	volume

TEST 7

True-False Statements (*Twenty Minutes*)

Copy the numbers of these statements on your paper. Then if a statement is *always* true, write T after its number. If a statement is *not always* true, write F after its number. Do not guess.

1. A prism has at least two parallel faces.

2. A parallelepiped has six lateral faces.

3. A right section of a prism is parallel to the bases.

4. The lateral faces of any prism are parallelograms.

5. Plane sections of a prism are congruent polygons.

6. Two prisms are congruent if the three faces which include a trihedral angle of one are congruent respectively to the three faces which include a trihedral angle of the other.

7. The radii of two similar cylinders of revolution are 5 and 6 respectively. If the total area of the smaller is 900, the total area of the larger is 1080.

8. The lateral area of a right prism is equal to the product of its altitude and the perimeter of its base.

9. Any face of a triangular prism is less than the sum of the other two.

10. A cylindrical tin vessel is $4\frac{1}{4}$ inches in diameter and $4\frac{1}{4}$ inches high. It contains more than one quart.

11. Any section of a right circular cylinder made by a plane through an element is a rectangle.

12. If the bases of a cylinder are equal, the cylinder is a right circular cylinder.

13. Any two diagonals of a parallelepiped bisect each other.

14. If a plane passes through two diagonally opposite edges of a parallelepiped, it divides the parallelepiped into congruent triangular prisms.

15. If the perimeter of a right section of an oblique prism is 20 inches, and a lateral edge is 8 inches, the lateral area is 80 square inches.

16. $T = 2\pi r(r + h)$ is the formula for finding the total area of a right circular cylinder whose altitude is h and whose base has a radius r.

17. If two adjacent lateral faces of a prism are rectangles, the prism is a right prism.

18. Two prisms having congruent bases and equal altitudes have equal total areas.

19. If the base of a prism is a rectangle, the prism is a right prism.

20. The volume of any parallelepiped is equal to the product of the three edges of any of its trihedral angles.

TEST 8

Completing Statements (*Twenty-two Minutes*)

On your paper write one word, and only one, for each blank to make the following statements true:

1. The least number of faces of any polyhedron is _____.

2. The least number of faces of any prism is _____.

3. A cube has _____ edges and _____ vertices.

4. The least number of lateral edges of any prism is _____.

5. A right parallelepiped has _____ rectangular faces.

6. A right section of a prism is _ _ _ _ _ _ _ to all the lateral edges.

7. The lateral faces of a right prism are _ _ _ _ _ _ _ _.

8. The least number of rectangular faces in a right prism is _ _ _ _ _ _ _.

9. Any prism has at least _ _ _ _ _ _ _ congruent faces.

10. The lateral faces of a rectangular solid are called _ _ _ _ _ _ _ _.

11. Two right prisms are congruent if they have _ _ _ _ _ _ _ _ _ _ _
_ _ _ _ _ _ _ and equal _ _ _ _ _ _ _ _.

12. The volume of any parallelepiped is equal to the product of
_ _ _ _ _ _ _ _ _ _ _ _ and _ _ _ _ _ _ _ _.

13. A hexagonal prism has _ _ _ _ _ _ _ lateral faces.

14. A parallelepiped has _ _ _ _ _ _ _ _ diagonals and _ _ _ _ _ _ _ faces.

15. The greatest number of triangular faces in a prism is _ _ _ _ _ _ _ _.

16. The opposite trihedral angles of a parallelepiped are _ _ _ _ _ _ _ _.

17. A pentagonal prism has _ _ _ _ _ _ _ _ vertices.

18. A right section of an oblique prism is _ _ _ _ _ _ _ to the lateral
faces.

19. A polyhedron whose lateral faces are parallelograms, and whose
bases are congruent, is called a _ _ _ _ _ _ _ _.

20. The _ _ _ _ _ _ _ _ faces of a parallelepiped are congruent.

21. The edge of a cube is _ _ _ _ _ _ _ _ units long if its area and its
volume are numerically equal.

22. A prism with six faces is a _ _ _ _ _ _ _ _ prism.

23. The generatrix of a cylindrical surface in any of its positions is
called _ _ _ _ _ _ _ _ _ _ _ _ _ _ _ of the _ _ _ _ _ _ _ _.

24. One of two cylinders of revolution is twice as high and has a
diameter three times as long as the other. The volume of the
larger is _ _ _ _ _ _ _ _ times as large as the smaller.

25. The lateral area of the larger cylinder (Ex. 24) is _ _ _ _ _ _ _ _
times as large as the lateral area of the smaller.

26. $V = abc$ is a formula for finding the _ _ _ _ _ _ _ _ of a _ _ _ _ _ _ _ _
_ _ _ _ _ _ _ _.

27. $V = \pi r^2 h$ is a formula for finding the _ _ _ _ _ _ _ _ of a _ _ _ _ _ _ _ _.

28. $V = e^3$ is a formula for finding the _ _ _ _ _ _ _ _ of a _ _ _ _ _ _ _ _.

29. $A = 6 e^2$ is a formula for finding the _ _ _ _ _ _ _ _ of a _ _ _ _ _ _ _ _.

Applications (*Forty Minutes*)

1. Find the area of a cube with 6-inch edges.

2. The legs of the right-triangular base of a right prism are 6 inches and 8 inches, and the altitude of the prism is 15 inches. Find the area.

3. Find the volume of a cube whose edge is 4 feet.

4. The circumference of the base of a right-circular cylinder is 28 inches, and its height is 15 inches. What is the lateral area of the cylinder?

5. The area of one face of a cube is 12 square inches. What is the area?

6. How many gallons will a rectangular tank hold if its inside dimensions are 4 feet 2 inches, 8 feet, and 37 inches?

7. The area of the base of a cylinder is 72 square inches, and the height is 20 inches. Find the volume of the cylinder.

8. The volume of a rectangular solid is 426,320 cubic inches, and its height is 80 inches. Find each side of its square base.

9. The dimensions of one rectangular solid are 4 inches, 6 inches, and 10 inches; the dimensions of another rectangular solid are 3 inches, 7 inches, and 15 inches. What is the ratio of the volume of the first solid to that of the second?

10. The dimensions of a rectangular solid are a, b, and c. Find its area.

11. Find the volume of the solid in Ex. 10.

12. Find the length of one of the diagonals of the solid in Ex. 10.

13. What is the height of a cylindrical pail 8 inches in diameter if it holds a gallon?

14. The bases of two rectangular parallelepipeds have equal areas. If their altitudes have the ratio 1 : 4, what is the ratio of their volumes?

15. What is the volume of a cube whose area is 294 square inches?

16. Find the area of a regular hexagonal prism with an altitude of 14 inches and a side of the base 5 inches.

The Great Pyramid of Khufu (Greek Cheops)

This is one of the three great pyramids at Gizeh, near Cairo. Its original height was 481 feet and its base a square 756 feet on a side. The ratio of its height to the perimeter of its base is very nearly that of a radius of a circle to its circumference

CHAPTER IV

PYRAMIDS AND CONES

176. Pyramidal Surface. A line which always intersects and completely traverses a given fixed polygon, and passes through a fixed point not in the plane of the polygon, generates a *pyramidal* (pǐ răm'ǐ dǎl) *surface*. The moving line is called the *generatrix*, and the fixed polygon the *directrix*. The moving line in any one of its positions is an *element* of the surface. In the figure, 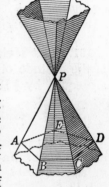 *ABCDE* is the directrix, and *P* is the *vertex* of the surface. The generatrix, moving along a side of the directrix, generates a plane determined by the vertex and a side. Why? Hence a pyramidal surface is composed of parts of three or more planes. As shown in the figure, a pyramidal surface consists of two parts separated by the vertex. Each of these parts is called a *nappe* (năp).

177. Pyramid. A *pyramid* is a solid formed by one nappe of a pyramidal surface and a plane cutting all its elements. The *base* of the pyramid is the section of the pyramidal surface made by the plane. The tri- angular faces are the *lateral faces*, and the meetings of the lateral faces are the *lateral edges*. The *vertex* of the pyramidal surface is the *vertex* of the pyramid. The *altitude* of the pyramid is the perpendicular from the vertex to the plane of the base. The *lateral area* of a pyramid is the sum of the areas of its lateral faces. The *total area* of a pyramid is the sum of the lateral area and the area of the base.

178. Pyramids Classified as to their Bases. A pyramid is *triangular, quadrangular, pentagonal,* etc., according as its base is triangular, quadrangular, pentagonal, etc. A triangular pyramid has four faces, and is often called a *tetrahedron.* Any face of a tetrahedron may be used as the base.

179. Regular Pyramid. A *regular pyramid* is a pyramid whose base is a regular polygon, and whose altitude is perpendicular to the base at its center.

180. Theorems. Properties of a regular pyramid.

a. The lateral edges of a regular pyramid are equal (use § 41).

b. The lateral faces of a regular pyramid are congruent isosceles triangles.

c. The altitudes of the triangular faces of a regular pyramid are equal.

181. Slant Height. The *slant height* of a regular pyramid is the altitude of any of the lateral faces. These altitudes are equal, by § 180 *c.*

EXERCISES. *PYRAMIDS*

1. In what respect is a pyramidal surface generated like a cylindrical surface? In what respect are the generations of the two surfaces different?

2. If the center of a cube is connected with each vertex, how many pyramids are formed?

3. Does any pyramid have a slant height?

4. How many edges has a triangular pyramid? a hexagonal pyramid? a pentagonal pyramid? a tetrahedron?

5. Find the altitude of a tetrahedron whose edges are each 8 inches.

6. A regular pyramid has a square base 6 inches on a side. Find the slant height of the pyramid if the altitude of the pyramid is 4 inches. Find the lateral area of the pyramid. What is the total area of the pyramid?

7. Find the area of a tetrahedron 3 inches on an edge.

8. Find the slant height of a regular hexagonal pyramid if one side of the base is 6 inches and the altitude is 10 inches. Find the lateral area of the pyramid.

Proposition I. Theorem (C, N)

182. *The lateral area of a regular pyramid is equal to half the product of its slant height and the perimeter of its base.*

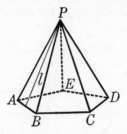

Given the regular pyramid *P-ABCDE*, with slant height *l*, perimeter of the base *p*, and lateral area *S*.

To prove that $S = \frac{1}{2} lp$.

⌈ *Selection of Method:* 1. Known methods of finding areas of solids: §§ 172, 174, 177.

 2. Method to be used: § 177. ⌋

Proof:

STATEMENTS	REASONS
1. The altitude of each lateral face is *l*.	1. § 181.
2. Area $\triangle PAB = \frac{1}{2} l \cdot AB$, area $\triangle PBC = \frac{1}{2} l \cdot BC$, area $\triangle PCD = \frac{1}{2} l \cdot CD$, etc.	2. § 28 *d*.
3. $\triangle PAB + \triangle PBC + \triangle PCD + \cdots = \frac{1}{2} l(AB + BC + CD + \cdots)$.	3. § 11 *a*.
4. But $\triangle PAB + \triangle PBC + \triangle PCD + \cdots = S$, and $AB + BC + CD + \cdots = p$.	4. § 11 *h*.
5. From (3) and (4), $S = \frac{1}{2} lp$.	5. §§ 11 *e*, 177.

EXERCISES (GROUP A)

1. Fold a piece of paper to make the pyramidal surface of a regular pyramid.

2. Find the lateral area of a hexagonal pyramid whose lateral edges are each 7 inches and whose base has sides of 6 inches each.

Proposition II. Theorem (C, N)

183. *If a pyramid is cut by a plane parallel to the base,
(a) the lateral edges and the altitude are divided proportionally,
and (b) the section is similar to the base.*

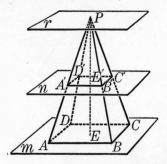

Given the pyramid *P-ABCD*, and plane *n* parallel to
plane *m* of the base, cutting the lateral edges in *A'*, *B'*, *C'*,
D', and the altitude *PE* in *E'*.

To prove that (a) $\dfrac{PA'}{PA} = \dfrac{PB'}{PB} = \dfrac{PC'}{PC} = \dfrac{PD'}{PD} = \dfrac{PE'}{PE}$;

(b) $A'B'C'D' \sim ABCD$.

> *Selection of Method:* 1. Known methods of proving
>   (a) line segments proportional: §§ 25, 67;
>   (b) polygons $\sim$: § 27.
> 2. Methods to be used: (a) § 67; (b) § 27a.

Proof:

STATEMENTS	REASONS
(a) 1. Pass plane *r* through *P* ‖ *m*.	1. § 63.
2. Then *r* ‖ *n* ‖ *m*.	2. Why?
3. Then $\dfrac{PA'}{PA} = \dfrac{PB'}{PB} = \dfrac{PC'}{PC} = \dfrac{PD'}{PD} = \dfrac{PE'}{PE}$.	3. § 67.
(b) 4. $A'B' \parallel AB$, $B'C' \parallel BC$, $C'D' \parallel CD$, $D'A' \parallel DA$.	4. Why?
5. $\angle A'B'C' = \angle ABC$, $\angle B'C'D' = \angle BCD$, etc.	5. § 66.
6. $\angle PA'B' = \angle PAB$, $\angle PB'A' = \angle PBA$, etc.	6. § 15 *i*.
7. $\triangle PA'B' \sim \triangle PAB$, $\triangle PB'C' \sim \triangle PBC$, etc.	7. § 27 *b*.

Proof: *STATEMENTS* *REASONS*

8. $\therefore \dfrac{A'B'}{AB} = \left(\dfrac{PB'}{PB}\right) = \dfrac{B'C'}{BC} = \left(\dfrac{PC'}{PC}\right) = \dfrac{C'D'}{CD}$, etc.

    8. § 27 a.

9. $\therefore \dfrac{A'B'}{AB} = \dfrac{B'C'}{BC} = \dfrac{C'D'}{CD} = \dfrac{D'A'}{DA}$.

    9. Why?

10. From (5) and (9), $A'B'C'D' \sim ABCD$.

    10. § 27 a.

184. Corollary I (N). *The area of a section of a pyramid parallel to the base is to the area of the base as the square of its distance from the vertex is to the square of the altitude of the pyramid.*

Suggestions. In the figure of Prop. II, $A'B'C'D' \sim ABCD$.

$\therefore \dfrac{A'B'C'D'}{ABCD} = \dfrac{\overline{A'B'}^2}{\overline{AB}^2}$. But $\dfrac{A'B'}{AB} = \dfrac{PA'}{PA}$ and $\dfrac{PA'}{PA} = \dfrac{PE'}{PE}$.

Then $\dfrac{A'B'}{AB} = \dfrac{PE'}{PE}$ and $\dfrac{\overline{A'B'}^2}{\overline{AB}^2} = \dfrac{\overline{PE'}^2}{\overline{PE}^2}$. $\therefore \dfrac{A'B'C'D'}{ABCD} = \dfrac{\overline{PE'}^2}{\overline{PE}^2}$.

185. Corollary II (c, n). *If two pyramids have equal altitudes and equal bases, sections of the pyramids parallel to the bases and equidistant from the vertices are equal.*

Suggestions. $ABCD = EFG$.

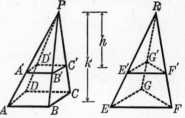

$\dfrac{A'B'C'D'}{ABCD} = \dfrac{h^2}{k^2}$ and $\dfrac{E'F'G'}{EFG} = \dfrac{h^2}{k^2}$.

$\therefore \dfrac{A'B'C'D'}{ABCD} = \dfrac{E'F'G'}{EFG}$.

$A'B'C'D' = E'F'G'$. (§ 30 f.)

186. Frustum of a Pyramid. *A frustum* (frŭs'tŭm) *of a pyramid* is the solid formed when one nappe of a pyramidal surface is intersected by two parallel planes cutting all the elements. The two sections of the pyramidal surface are called the *bases* of the frustum. The *altitude* of the frustum is the perpendicular between the bases.

187. Theorems. Properties of frustums of pyramids.

a. The lateral faces of a frustum of a pyramid are trapezoids.

b. The lateral faces of a frustum of a regular pyramid are congruent isosceles trapezoids.

c. The bases of a frustum of a pyramid are similar polygons.

Proposition III. Theorem (c, n)

188. *The lateral area of a frustum of a regular pyramid is equal to half the product of its slant height and the sum of the perimeters of the bases.*

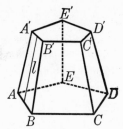

Given *BD′* a frustum of a regular pyramid, *l* the slant height, *p* the perimeter of the lower base, *p′* the perimeter of the upper base, and *S* the lateral area.

To prove that $S = \frac{1}{2} l(p + p')$.

Suggestions. Find the area of each trapezoid and add.

EXERCISES (GROUP A). *AREAS OF PYRAMIDS*

1. Find the lateral area of a regular pyramid whose slant height is 10 inches and whose base has a perimeter of 36 inches.

2. Find the lateral area of the frustum of a regular pyramid whose lower base is a square having a side of 8 inches and whose upper base is a square having a side of 6 inches, the slant height of the frustum being 12 inches.

3. The slant height of a regular pyramid is 36 inches, and the base is an equilateral triangle whose altitude is $12\sqrt{3}$ inches. Find the area of the pyramid.

4. The perimeter of the base of a regular pyramid is 60 feet, and the lateral area is 480 square feet. Find the slant height of the pyramid.

5. Find the lateral area and the total area of a regular hexagonal pyramid whose lateral edges are each 5 feet and whose base is 4 feet on each side.

6. If T represents the total area of the frustum of a regular quadrangular pyramid whose bases are s and s' on the sides and whose slant height is l, prove that $T = s^2 + 2\,l(s + s') + s'^2$.

7. The lateral area of a regular pyramid is 2048 square feet, and the perimeter of the base is 256 inches. Find the slant height.

8. The lateral area of a regular pyramid is 514.5 square inches, and the slant height is 42 inches. Find the perimeter of the base.

9. The altitude of a pyramid with a square base is 16 inches, and the area of a section parallel to the base and 6 inches from it is 56.25 square inches. Find the area of the base.

EXERCISES (GROUP B). *PYRAMIDS*

1. Find the lateral area of a regular quadrangular pyramid if each side of the base is 12 inches and the slant height forms an angle of 30° with the altitude.

2. Find the total area of a regular triangular pyramid if each side of the base is 6 inches and the slant height forms an angle of 45° with the altitude.

3. If a pyramid is cut by a plane that is parallel to the base and bisects the altitude, how does the area of the section compare with the area of the base?

4. A pyramid having an altitude of 16 feet and a base with an area of 36 square feet is cut 4 feet from the vertex by a plane that is parallel to the base. Find the area of the section.

5. The slant height of a regular quadrangular pyramid is 20 inches, and one side of the base is 32 inches. Find the lateral edge, altitude, lateral area, and total area.

6. A pyramid is cut by three planes which are parallel to the base and which divide the altitude into four equal parts. How is the slant height divided? How does the area of each section compare with the area of the base?

7. A plane parallel to the base of a pyramid divides the lateral area into equal parts. Where does the plane cut the altitude?

8. What is the slant height of a regular quadrangular pyramid having a total area of 585 square feet if each side of its base is 13 feet?

9. Two parallel planes cut sections of a pyramidal surface. One section has an area of 289 square inches, and the other an area of 169 square inches. If the smaller section is 65 inches from the vertex, how far from the vertex is the larger section?

10. A pyramid 15 feet high has a triangular base 8 feet on a side. Find the area of a section made by a plane parallel to the base at a distance of 5 feet from the vertex.

11. Find the slant height of a frustum of a regular pyramid whose bases are squares with 6-inch and 12-inch sides respectively and whose area is 543 square inches.

12. The area of the base of a pyramid is 1000 square feet. If a plane section of the pyramid parallel to the base and at a distance of 10 feet from it has an area of 700 square feet, find the altitude of the pyramid.

13. The area of a tetrahedron having equal edges is $18\sqrt{3}$. Find the length of an edge.

189. Cavalieri's Theorem. *If two solids are included between the same two parallel planes and if any plane parallel to these planes makes equal sections of the solids, the solids have equal volumes.*

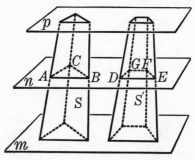

The two solids S and S' lie between the parallel planes m and p. The theorem states that if all planes such as n parallel to m and p form equal sections such as ABC and $DEFG$ of S and S', the solid S is equal to the solid S'.

We shall accept the truth of this theorem without proof.

Cavalieri's Theorem may be used to prove several theorems of mensuration, such as §§ 139 and 146.

Proposition IV.   Theorem (c, n)

190. *Two pyramids having equal altitudes and equal bases are equal.*

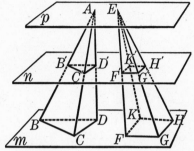

Given two pyramids *A-BCD* and *E-FGHK* having = altitudes and *BCD = FGHK*.

To prove that *A-BCD = E-FGHK*.

⎡ *Selection of Method:* 1. Known methods of proving solids =:
‏‏‎   §§ 171, 189.
‏‏‎   2. Method to be used: § 189. ⎤

Proof: STATEMENTS   REASONS

1. *A-BCD* and *E-FGHK* have = altitudes.	1. Why?
2. The pyramids can be placed so that their bases lie in a plane *m* and their vertices lie in a plane *p* ∥ *m*.	2. Give proof.
3. Pass any plane *n* ∥ *m* and *p* forming sections *B'C'D'* and *F'G'H'K'*.	3. § 63.
4. *B'C'D'* and *F'G'H'K'* are equidistant from *A* and *E* respectively.	4. § 64.
5. ∴ *B'C'D' = F'G'H'K'*.	5. § 185.
6. ∴ *A-BCD = E-FGHK*.	6. § 189.

EXERCISES (GROUP B)

1. Prove Cor. 146 using Cavalieri's Theorem.

2. The dimensions of a rectangular solid are 6, $7\frac{1}{2}$, and $16\frac{1}{5}$. What is the length of an edge of an equal cube?

Proposition V. Theorem (C, n)

191. *The volume of a triangular pyramid is equal to one third of the product of its base and altitude.*

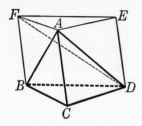 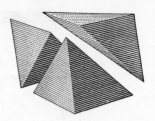

Given the triangular pyramid *A-BCD* having base *b*, altitude *h*, and volume *V*.

To prove that $V = \frac{1}{3} bh$.

⎡ *Selection of Method:* 1. Known methods of finding volumes of solids: §§ 173, 175.

2. Method to be used: § 173 *a*. ⎤

Proof: STATEMENTS   REASONS

1. With *BCD* as a base and *AC* as an edge draw a prism *AEF-CDB*.	1. § 108.
2. Draw *DF* in plane *BDEF*.	2. Why possible?
3. Pyramids *D-ABC* and *D-ABF* have the same altitude.	3. Why?
4. Base *ABC* of *D-ABC* = base *ABF* of *D-ABF*.	4. §§ 112 *a*, 13 *g*.
5. ∴ *D-ABC* = *D-ABF*.	5. § 190.
6. Pyramids *A-BCD* and *D-AEF* have the same altitude.	6. § 64.
7. Base *BCD* of *A-BCD* = base *AEF* of *D-AEF*.	7. § 115.
8. ∴ *A-BCD* = *D-AEF*.	8. § 190.
9. *A-BCD* + *D-ABF* + *D-AEF* = prism *AEF-CDB*.	9. Why?

Proof: *STATEMENTS*   *REASONS*

10. 3 A-BCD = prism AEF-CDB, or 3 V = prism AEF-$ČDB$.	10. § 11 e.
11. Volume of prism AEF-CDB = bh.	11. § 173 a.
12. 3 V = bh.	12. Why?
13. ∴ V = $\frac{1}{3} bh$.	13. Why?

Note. A model of the figure for Prop. V can be easily constructed with copper wire and solder, or with cardboard and gummed paper tape.

EXERCISES (GROUP A). *TRIANGULAR PYRAMIDS*

1. A prism and a pyramid have the same base and altitude. How do their volumes compare? Which has the greater area?

2. The area of the base of a pyramid is 84 square inches, and the altitude of the pyramid is 50 inches. Find the volume.

3. The altitude of a pyramid is 25 inches, and the base is a right triangle having a hypotenuse of 13 inches and a leg of 5 inches. Find the volume.

4. Find the volume of a triangular pyramid if the sides of the bases are 13 inches, 20 inches, and 25 inches and the altitude is 21 inches.

5. The volume of a pyramid is 336 cubic inches, and the base is a right triangle having one leg 6 inches long and the other 12 inches long. Find the altitude of the pyramid.

EXERCISES (GROUP B). *PYRAMIDS*

1. If the base of a pyramid is a parallelogram, the plane determined by the vertex of the pyramid and a diagonal of the base will divide the pyramid into two equal pyramids.

2. Find the altitude of a pyramid if the volume is 2000 cubic inches and the base is an equilateral triangle 12 inches on a side.

3. A triangular pyramid and a prism have similar bases, equal altitudes, and equal volumes. Find the ratio of one side of the base of the prism to the corresponding side of the base of the pyramid.

4. Find the edge of a cube equal to a tetrahedron whose edges are each 8 inches.

5. Find the volume of a pyramid whose altitude is 12 and whose base is a rhombus with diagonals of 6 and 8.

Proposition VI. Theorem (c, N)

192. *The volume of any pyramid is equal to one third of the product of its base and altitude.*

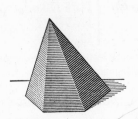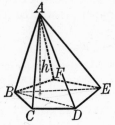

Given the pyramid *A-BCDEF* with base *b*, altitude *h*, and volume *V*.

To prove that $V = \frac{1}{3} bh$.

> *Selection of Method:* 1. Known methods of finding volumes of solids: §§ 173, 175, 191.
> 2. Method to be used: § 191.

Proof: STATEMENTS   REASONS

1. Through *B*, a vertex of the base, draw diagonals *BE* and *BD*.	1. Why possible?
2. Through the lateral edge *AB* and the diagonals of the base, pass planes separating the pyramid into triangular pyramids.	2. § 9 *e*.
3. The volume of $A\text{-}BCD = \frac{1}{3} BCD \cdot h$, the volume of $A\text{-}BDE = \frac{1}{3} BDE \cdot h$, and the volume of $A\text{-}BEF = \frac{1}{3} BEF \cdot h$.	3. § 191.
4. ∴ the sum of the volumes of the triangular pyramids $= \frac{1}{3}(BCD + BDE + BEF)h$.	4. Why?
5. But the sum of the volumes of the pyramids $= V$, and $BCD + BDE + BEF = b$.	5. Why?
6. ∴ $V = \frac{1}{3} bh$.	6. Why?

193. Corollary I (n). *Two pyramids having equal bases have the same ratio as their altitudes.*

194. Corollary II (n). *Two pyramids having equal altitudes have the same ratio as their bases.*

195. Corollary III (c, n). *Two pyramids have the same ratio as the products of their bases and altitudes.*

196. Corollary IV (n). *The volume of a frustum of a pyramid is given by the formula $V = \frac{1}{3} h(b + b' + \sqrt{bb'})$, where b and b' are the areas of the bases and h is the altitude.*

Suggestions. Produce the edges to complete the pyramid. Let P represent the volume of the whole pyramid and p the volume of the smaller pyramid.

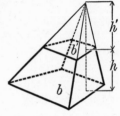

$$P = \tfrac{1}{3} b(h + h') \text{ and } p = \tfrac{1}{3} b'h'.$$

Then $V = P - p = \frac{1}{3}[bh + h'(b - b')].$

But $\dfrac{b'}{b} = \dfrac{h'^2}{(h' + h)^2},$ or $\dfrac{h'}{h' + h} = \dfrac{\sqrt{b'}}{\sqrt{b}},$

or $h' = \dfrac{h\sqrt{b'}}{\sqrt{b} - \sqrt{b'}}.$

Then $V = \dfrac{1}{3}\left[bh + \dfrac{h\sqrt{b'}}{\sqrt{b} - \sqrt{b'}}(b - b') \right] = \dfrac{1}{3} h[b + b' + \sqrt{bb'}].$

EXERCISES (GROUP A). *FINDING VOLUMES*

1. The base of one pyramid is a rectangle whose dimensions are 10 inches and 16 inches. The base of another pyramid is a square 12 inches on a side. If the pyramids have equal altitudes, compare their volumes.

2. What part of the volume of a cube is the pyramid whose base is the base of the cube and whose vertex is the center of the cube?

3. The volume of a pyramid whose lateral edges are the three edges of a parallelepiped meeting at a point is what part of the volume of the parallelepiped?

4. A marble column is in the form of a frustum of a regular pyramid having a square base. The column is 12 feet high, and the sides of the bases are 3 feet and $1\frac{1}{2}$ feet respectively. Find the weight of the column if one cubic foot of marble weighs 164 pounds.

5. A pyramid 8 feet high has a base whose area is 64 square feet. Four feet from the vertex the pyramid is cut by a plane parallel to the base. Find the volume of the frustum.

CONES

197. Conical Surface. A line which always intersects and traverses a fixed closed convex plane curve and passes through a fixed point not in the plane of the curve generates a *convex conical surface.* The moving line is called the *generatrix* and the fixed curve, the *directrix.* The moving line in any of its positions is called an *element* of the surface. A conical surface, like a pyramidal surface, is composed of two nappes, separated by the *vertex* of the surface.

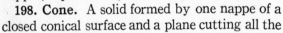

198. Cone. A solid formed by one nappe of a closed conical surface and a plane cutting all the elements is called a *cone.* The *base* of the cone is the section of the conical surface made by the plane, and the *lateral surface* is the curved part of the surface. The *lateral area* of a cone is the area of the lateral surface. The *altitude* of a cone is the perpendicular from the vertex to the plane of the base. The *radius* of a cone is the *radius of its base.*

199. Circular Cone. A *circular* cone is a cone whose base is a circle. The *axis* of a circular cone is the line segment from the vertex to the center of the base. In this text we shall study circular cones only, since the circle is the only plane curve studied in elementary geometry.

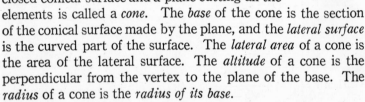

200. Right Circular Cone. A *right circular cone* is a cone whose axis is perpendicular to the plane of the base. A cone whose axis is oblique to the plane of the base is called *oblique.* Since a right circular cone has a surface which can be generated by the revolution of a right triangle about one of its legs as an axis, it is sometimes called a *cone of revolution.*

201. Frustum of a Cone. A *frustum of a cone* is the solid formed when one nappe of a conical surface is intersected by two parallel planes cutting all the elements. The two sections of the conical surface are called the *bases* of the frustum. The *altitude* of the frustum is the perpendicular between the planes of the bases.

202. Theorems. Properties of a right circular cone and a frustum of it.

a. The axis of a right circular cone is the altitude of the cone.
b. The elements of a right circular cone are equal.
c. The elements of a frustum of a right circular cone are equal.

203. Slant Height. The *slant height* of a right circular cone is the length of one of the elements.

The *slant height* of a frustum of a right circular cone is the length of one of its elements.

204. Conic Section. The section of a right circular cone made by a plane is called a *conic section*. If the cutting plane is parallel to the base of the cone, the section is a circle (Fig. 1). This will be proved in § 205. If the cutting plane

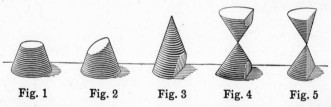

Fig. 1   Fig. 2   Fig. 3   Fig. 4   Fig. 5

is oblique to the base and cuts all the elements of the cone, the section is an ellipse (Fig. 2). If the plane is parallel to one, and only one, element of the cone, the section is a parabola (Fig. 3). If the plane is parallel to the axis of the cone, it cuts both nappes of the conical surface, resulting in a section with two branches called a hyperbola (Fig. 4). If the plane contains the axis, the section is two straight lines intersecting at the vertex (Fig. 5). Can you prove it? Conic sections are curves of the second order. That is, in general, any straight line will intersect them in two points. The equations of conic sections are of the second degree. Thus $x^2 + y^2 = 25$ is an equation of a circle, $x^2 + 4 y^2 = 25$ is an equation of an ellipse, $x^2 + 2 y = 25$ is an equation of a parabola, and $x^2 - y^2 = 25$ is an equation of a hyperbola. The circle is the only one of these curves that can be constructed by using nothing but the methods of elementary geometry.

Proposition VII. Theorem (C, N)

205. *The section of a circular cone made by a plane parallel to the base is a circle.*

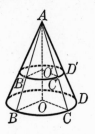

Given the circular cone A-BCD with section $B'C'D'$ made by a plane ‖ the plane of the base BCD.

To prove that $B'C'D'$ is a ⊙.

⌈ *Selection of Method:* 1. Known methods of proving that a plane ⌉
figure is a ⊙: §§ 10 q, 156.
2. Method to be used: § 10 q.
⌊ ⌋

Proof: STATEMENTS   REASONS

1. Draw the axis AO intersecting plane $B'C'D'$ at O'.	1. §§ 199, 12 a, 9 a.
2. Through any two points, B' and C', of the section draw $AB'B$ and $AC'C$.	2. § 12 a.
3. Draw OB, $O'B'$, OC, and $O'C'$.	3. Why possible?
4. OB and $O'B'$ lie in the plane of BAO, and OC and $O'C'$ lie in the plane of CAO.	4. Why?
5. ∴ OB ‖ $O'B'$ and OC ‖ $O'C'$.	5. Why?
6. ∴ △ $AB'O' \sim$ △ ABO and △ $AC'O' \sim$ △ ACO.	6. Give proof.
7. ∴ $\dfrac{O'B'}{OB} = \dfrac{AO'}{AO}$ and $\dfrac{O'C'}{OC} = \dfrac{AO'}{AO}$.	7. § 25 e.
8. ∴ $\dfrac{O'B'}{OB} = \dfrac{O'C'}{OC}$.	8. Why?

Proof: *STATEMENTS*   *REASONS*

9. But $OB = OC$.	9. Why?
10. $\therefore O'B' = O'C'$.	10. § 30 f.
11. In the same manner it may be shown that the distance from O' to any other point of $B'C'D' = O'B'$.	11. Statements 2–10.
12. $\therefore B'C'D'$ is a $\odot$.	12. § 10 q.

206. Corollary (N). *The section of a circular cone made by a plane parallel to the base is to the base as the square of its distance from the vertex is to the square of the altitude of the cone.*

MEASUREMENT OF CONES

207. Cone and Pyramid. As you remember, the measurement of the cylinder was developed by considering the cylinder as the limit of an inscribed or circumscribed prism. In the same manner we shall derive the properties of the cone by considering the cone as the limit of the inscribed or circumscribed pyramid.

208. Inscribed and Circumscribed Pyramid. A pyramid whose lateral edges are elements of a cone and whose base is inscribed in the base of the cone is said to be *inscribed* in the cone.

A pyramid whose lateral faces are tangent to a cone (i.e., each face contains only one element) and whose base is circumscribed about the base of the cone is said to be *circumscribed* about the cone.

209. Postulate on the Cone. *If a pyramid whose base is a regular polygon is inscribed in or circumscribed about a circular cone, and if the number of lateral faces of the pyramid is indefinitely increased,*

a. The lateral area of the pyramid approaches the lateral area of the cone as a limit;

b. The volume of the pyramid approaches the volume of the cone as a limit.

Proposition VIII. Theorem (c, N)

210. *The lateral area of a right circular cone is equal to half the product of its slant height and the circumference of its base.*

Given a rt. circular cone with lateral area S, slant height l, and the circumference of the base c.

To prove that $S = \frac{1}{2} cl$.

> *Selection of Method:* 1. Known methods of finding areas of solids: §§ 172, 174, 177, 182, 209.
> 2. Method to be used: §§ 182, 209.

Proof:

STATEMENTS	REASONS
1. Circumscribe about the cone a regular pyramid, denoting its lateral area by S' and the perimeter of its base by p.	1. § 208.
2. Then the slant height of the pyramid $= l$.	2. § 181.
3. $S' = \frac{1}{2} pl$.	3. § 182.
4. If the number of faces of the pyramid is increased indefinitely by successively doubling the number of faces, then $$S' \rightarrow S \quad \text{and} \quad p \rightarrow c.$$	4. §§ 209 a, 12 x.
5. Since $p \rightarrow c$, $\frac{1}{2} pl \rightarrow \frac{1}{2} cl$.	5. § 160 a.
6. From (3), (4), and (5), $S = \frac{1}{2} cl$.	6. § 160 b.

211. Corollary I (c, n). *If S denotes the lateral area, T the total area, l the slant height, and r the radius of the base of a right circular cone, then $S = \pi r l$, and $T = \pi r (l + r)$.*

212. Corollary II (c, n). *If S denotes the lateral area, l the slant height, and r and r' the radii of the bases of a frustum of a right circular cone, then $S = \pi l(r + r')$.* ✓

Suggestions. Complete the cone. $S =$ the lateral area of the large cone minus the lateral area of the small cone.

$$S = \pi r(l + l') - \pi r'l'.$$

$$S = \pi rl + \pi l'(r - r').$$

But $\dfrac{r'}{l'} = \dfrac{r}{l + l'}$. Prove it.

Solve for l' in the last equation and substitute in $S = \pi rl + \pi l'(r - r')$.

213. Corollary III. *The lateral area of the frustum of a right circular cone is equal to the circumference of a section midway between the bases, multiplied by the slant height.*

EXERCISES (GROUP A)

1. The slant height of a right circular cone is 13 inches, and the radius of the base is 5 inches. Find the lateral area and the total area.

2. A right triangle whose legs are 12 inches and 15 inches is revolved about the shorter leg as an axis. What is the area of the surface generated by the longer leg? What is the area of the surface generated by the hypotenuse?

3. The radii of the bases of a frustum of a right circular cone are 6 inches and 9 inches respectively, and the altitude is 4 inches. Find the lateral area.

4. When an irregular piece of iron is placed in a cylindrical tank partly filled with water, the water in the tank rises 1 inch. If the tank is 10 inches in diameter, what is the volume of the iron?

5. The radius of the base of a right circular cone is 15 inches, and the axis of the cone is 36 inches. Find the length of an element.

EXERCISES (GROUP B)

1. A plane is passed through the axis of a right circular cone whose altitude is 18 inches and whose slant height is 27 inches. Find the area of the section of the cone made by the plane.

2. The area of the base of a right circular cone is $144\,\pi$, and the altitude of the cone is 14. Find the slant height.

Proposition IX. Theorem (c, N)

214. *The volume of a circular cone is equal to one third of the product of its base and altitude.*

Given a circular cone with volume V, area of its base b, and altitude h.

To prove that $V = \frac{1}{3} bh$.

$\left[\begin{array}{l} \textit{Selection of Method:}\ 1.\ \text{Known methods of finding volumes of solids: §§ 173, 175, 191, 192, 196, 209.} \\ \qquad\qquad\qquad\qquad 2.\ \text{Method to be used: §§ 192, 209.} \end{array}\right]$

Proof: *STATEMENTS*   *REASONS*

1. Circumscribe about the cone a pyramid having a regular polygon for its base. Denote the volume of the pyramid by V' and the area of its base by b'.	1. § 208.
2. The altitude of the cone and pyramid $= h$.	2. Why?
3. Then $V' = \frac{1}{3} b'h$.	3. § 192.
4. If the number of faces of the pyramid is increased indefinitely by successively doubling the number of sides of its base, then $$V' \rightarrow V, \quad \text{and} \quad b' \rightarrow b.$$	4. § 209 b, 12 y.
5. Since $b' \rightarrow b$, $\frac{1}{3} b'h \rightarrow \frac{1}{3} bh$.	5. § 160 a.
6. From (3), (4), and (5), $V = \frac{1}{3} bh$.	6. § 160 b.

Note. Prop. IX may be proved by first comparing the volume of the cone with that of a pyramid having its altitude and base equal respectively to the base and altitude of the cone, and then using Cavalieri's Theorem.

215. Corollary I (c, n). *The volume of a circular cone is expressed by the formula* $V = \frac{1}{3}\pi r^2 h$, *where r is the radius of the base and h is the altitude.*

216. Corollary II (n). *The volume of a frustum of a circular cone is expressed by the formula* $V = \frac{1}{3}\pi h(r^2 + r'^2 + rr')$, *where V is the volume of the frustum, h is the altitude, and r and r' are the radii of the bases.* (Prove in a manner similar to the proof in § 196.)

EXERCISES (GROUP A). *FINDING VOLUMES*

1. The area of the base of a right circular cone is 42 square inches, and the altitude of the cone is 75 inches. Find the volume.

2. The radius of the base of a right circular cone is 14 inches, and the altitude is 16 inches. Find the volume.

3. The radius of the base of a right circular cone is 8 feet, and the altitude is 10 feet. Find the lateral area, total area, and volume of the cone.

4. The bases of the frustum of a pyramid are squares having sides of 4 inches and 9 inches respectively. Find the volume of the frustum if its altitude is $7\frac{7}{9}$ inches.

EXERCISES (GROUP B). *VOLUMES*

1. Find the volume of a regular quadrangular pyramid if a lateral edge is 101 feet and a base edge is 40 feet.

2. Find the altitude of a triangular pyramid if the volume is 30 cubic feet and the sides of its base are 3 feet, 4 feet, and 5 feet.

3. The radii of the bases of a frustum of a right circular cone are 20 inches and 15 inches respectively. Find the volume of the frustum if its slant height is $5\sqrt{10}$ inches.

4. Show that the volume of a solid formed by revolving an equilateral triangle with side s about an altitude is $\frac{1}{24}\pi s^3\sqrt{3}$.

217. Similar Cones of Revolution. *Similar cones of revolution* are cones generated by the revolution of similar right triangles about two corresponding legs as axes.

Proposition X. Theorem (c)

218. *The lateral areas or the total areas of two similar cones of revolution have the same ratio as the squares of their altitudes, or as the squares of their slant heights, or as the squares of the radii of their bases; and their volumes have the same ratio as the cubes of their altitudes, or as the cubes of their slant heights, or as the cubes of the radii of their bases.*

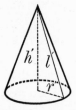

Given two ∼ cones of revolution with S and S' their lateral areas, T and T' their total areas, V and V' their volumes, r and r' the radii of their bases, l and l' their slant heights, and h and h' their altitudes.

To prove that $\dfrac{S}{S'} = \dfrac{T}{T'} = \dfrac{h^2}{h'^2} = \dfrac{l^2}{l'^2} = \dfrac{r^2}{r'^2}$

and
$$\frac{V}{V'} = \frac{h^3}{h'^3} = \frac{l^3}{l'^3} = \frac{r^3}{r'^3}.$$

Proof:

STATEMENTS	REASONS
1. $\dfrac{r}{r'} = \dfrac{h}{h'}$ and $\dfrac{r+l}{r'+l'} = \dfrac{r}{r'} = \dfrac{l}{l'} = \dfrac{h}{h'}$.	1. §§ 10 r, 30 g.
2. $S = \pi r l$ and $S' = \pi r' l'$.	2. § 211.
3. $\dfrac{S}{S'} = \dfrac{\pi r l}{\pi r' l'} = \dfrac{r}{r'} \times \dfrac{l}{l'} = \dfrac{r^2}{r'^2} = \dfrac{l^2}{l'^2} = \dfrac{h^2}{h'^2}$.	3. §§ 11 d, 11 e.
4. $T = \pi r(l + r)$ and $T' = \pi r'(l' + r')$.	4. § 211.
5. $\dfrac{T}{T'} = \dfrac{\pi r(l + r)}{\pi r'(l' + r')} = \dfrac{r}{r'} \times \dfrac{l + r}{l' + r'} = \dfrac{r}{r'} \times \dfrac{r}{r'}$ $= \dfrac{r^2}{r'^2} = \dfrac{l^2}{l'^2} = \dfrac{h^2}{h'^2}$.	5. Give reasons.

Proof: *STATEMENTS* *REASONS*

6. $V = \frac{1}{3}\pi r^2 h$ and $V' = \frac{1}{3}\pi r'^2 h'$.

6. § 215.

7. $\dfrac{V}{V'} = \dfrac{\frac{1}{3}\pi r^2 h}{\frac{1}{3}\pi r'^2 h'} = \dfrac{r^2}{r'^2} \times \dfrac{h}{h'} = \dfrac{r^2}{r'^2} \times \dfrac{r}{r'} = \dfrac{r^3}{r'^3}$

$= \dfrac{l^3}{l'^3} = \dfrac{h^3}{h'^3}$.

7. Give reasons.

EXERCISES (GROUP A). *CONES*

1. The altitude of a right circular cone is five times the altitude of a similar cone. What is the ratio of their slant heights? of the radii of their bases? of their lateral areas? of their total areas? of their volumes?

2. The lateral areas of two similar cones of revolution are 576 square inches and 1296 square inches respectively. If the altitude of the smaller cone is 18 inches, what is the altitude of the larger cone?

3. How many square feet of tin are required to make a funnel whose top and bottom have diameters of 28 inches and 4 inches respectively and whose slant height is 22 inches?

4. If two boys are similar, and one is two thirds as tall as the other, what is the ratio of their weights? What is the ratio of the length of their belts?

EXERCISES (GROUP B)

1. A piece of tin in the form of a sector of a circle of radius 12 inches is rolled into a cone. If the central angle of the sector is 210°, what is the lateral area of the resulting cone? What is the volume of the cone?

2. A plane passing through a right circular cone perpendicular to the axis and bisecting the axis separates the cone into two parts. What is the ratio of the volumes of the parts? What is the ratio of their lateral areas?

3. A circular cone has the same base and altitude as a circular cylinder. What is the ratio of their volumes?

4. A brick smokestack 100 feet high is in the shape of a frustum of a regular pyramid having square bases of 12 feet and 8 feet on a side respectively. If the smoke flue is 4 feet square, how many cubic feet of mortar and brick were used in the construction?

MISCELLANEOUS EXERCISES (GROUP A)

1. What is the locus of points at a given distance from a cylindrical surface whose right section is a circle?

2. What is the locus of straight lines that make a given angle with a given straight line at a given point in the line?

3. What is the locus of three sides of a rectangle that revolves about the fourth side?

4. A square whose side is s revolves about one diagonal as an axis. Find the locus and the area of the locus of the four sides.

5. Prove that if r is the radius of the base of a right circular cone and l the slant height, the ratio of the area of the base to the lateral area is $\frac{r}{l}$.

6. Find the volume of a right circular cone whose total area is $108\,\pi$, and whose slant height equals the diameter of the base.

Suggestions. Let $r =$ the radius of the base. Then $2r =$ the slant height. Then find the total area in terms of r.

7. What is the weight of a grindstone 2 feet 8 inches in diameter and 4 inches thick, having in the center a square hole 3 inches on a side, if 1 cubic foot of stone weighs 142 pounds?

8. Find, to the nearest square centimeter, the total area of a cylinder of revolution whose altitude is 15.2 centimeters and whose base has a diameter of 3.4 centimeters.

MISCELLANEOUS EXERCISES (GROUP B)

1. A brass cylinder is put in an open rectangular box whose interior has the same altitude as the cylinder and whose sides are tangent to the cylinder. If the altitude of the cylinder is 12 inches and the radius of its base is 5 inches, what is the weight of the water needed to fill the remaining part of the box?

2. A trench for a sewer is to be half a mile long, 16 feet deep, 6 feet wide at the top, and 4 feet wide at the bottom. How many cubic yards of earth must be removed?

3. If sewers having outside diameters of 36 inches are to be laid in the trench of Ex. 2 and the remaining space in the trench filled with earth, how many cubic yards of the earth which was removed in digging the trench remain?

4. Prove that the volume of an oblique prism is equal to the product of the area of a right section and the length of a lateral edge.

5. The altitude of a pyramid is 24 inches, and its base is a rectangle whose dimensions are 12 inches and 18 inches respectively. What is the distance from the vertex of a section parallel to the base, if the area of the section is 77.76 square inches?

6. A regular pyramid whose base is a hexagon 6 inches on a side, and whose altitude is 30 inches, is cut by a plane parallel to the base and 20 inches from its vertex. Find the volume of the frustum so formed.

7. Find the total area of the frustum in Ex. 6.

8. Show how to cut out a pattern for a tin cone that is to have a base diameter of 8 inches and a slant height of 12 inches.

9. Prove that the volume of the solid formed by revolving an equilateral triangle with side s about one side is $\frac{1}{4}\pi s^3$.

10. Prove that the volume of the solid formed by revolving a square with side a about one diagonal is $\frac{1}{6}\pi a^3\sqrt{2}$.

11. Express the lateral area of a right circular cone in terms of its altitude and the radius of its base.

REVIEW QUESTIONS

1. When is a section of a cylinder equal to the base?

2. Why are conic sections so called? Which conic section can be constructed with straightedge and compasses?

3. If the dimensions of a parallelepiped are multiplied by 3, by what is the area multiplied? the volume?

4. If two prisms have equal bases and equal altitudes, do they have the same volume? the same area?

5. If two pyramids have the same base and equal altitudes, do they have equal volumes? equal areas?

6. Do the lateral faces of a pyramid have equal altitudes?

7. What kind of pyramid has its lateral edges equal?

8. What kind of polygons are the faces of a frustum of a regular pyramid?

9. State Cavalieri's Theorem.

10. State the following formulas in words:

  a. $V = \pi r^2 h.$

  b. $V = \frac{1}{3} \pi r^2 h.$

  c. $S = \frac{1}{2} lp.$

  d. $S = \frac{1}{2} l(p + p').$

  e. $S = \pi r l.$

  f. $V = \frac{1}{3} h(b + b' + \sqrt{bb'}).$

  g. $T = \pi r(l + r).$

  h. $V = \frac{1}{3} \pi h(r^2 + r'^2 + rr').$

11. What is the name of the line segment joining the vertex and the center of the base of a right circular cone?

12. For what kind of cone may the lateral area be found by means given in this book?

13. What assumption about the lateral area of a cone was made in this chapter?

14. What is a generatrix? directrix? element? cone of revolution? prism? cylinder? pyramid? parallelepiped? frustum of a pyramid?

SUMMARY OF PRINCIPAL METHODS OF PROOF

219. *Pyramids Equal in Area*

Two pyramids having equal altitudes and equal bases are equal.

220. *Areas of Pyramids*

  a. The lateral area of a regular pyramid is equal to half the product of its slant height and the perimeter of its base.

  b. The lateral area of a frustum of a regular pyramid is equal to half the product of its slant height and the sum of the perimeters of its bases.

221. *Sections of Pyramids*

  a. If a pyramid is cut by a plane parallel to the base, the section is similar to the base.

  b. The area of a section of a pyramid parallel to the base is to the area of the base as the square of its distance from the vertex is to the square of the altitude of the pyramid.

  c. If two pyramids have equal altitudes and equal bases, sections of the pyramids parallel to the bases and equidistant from the vertices are equal.

222. *Proportional Line Segments*

If a pyramid is cut by a plane parallel to the base, the lateral
edges and the altitude are divided proportionally.

223. *Volumes of Pyramids*

a. The volume of any pyramid is equal to one third of the product of its base and altitude.

b. Two pyramids having equal bases have the same ratio as
their altitudes.

c. Two pyramids having equal altitudes have the same ratio as
their bases.

d. Two pyramids have the same ratio as the products of their
bases and altitudes.

e. The volume of a frustum of a pyramid is expressed by the
formula $V = \frac{1}{3} h(b + b' + \sqrt{bb'})$, where b and b' are the
areas of the bases and h is the altitude.

224. *Sections of Cones*

a. The section of a circular cone made by a plane parallel to the
base is a circle.

b. The section of a circular cone made by a plane parallel to the
base is to the base as the square of its distance from the
vertex is to the square of the altitude of the cone.

225. *Areas of Cones*

a. The lateral area of a right circular cone is equal to half the
product of its slant height and the circumference of its
base.

b. The lateral area S and the total area T of a right circular cone
are expressed by the formulas $S = \pi r l$ and $T = \pi r(l + r)$.

c. The lateral area S of a frustum of a right circular cone is
expressed by the formula $S = \pi l(r + r')$.

d. The lateral areas or the total areas of two similar cones of
revolution have the same ratio as the squares of their altitudes, or as the squares of their slant heights, or as the
squares of the radii of their bases.

226.   *Volumes of Cones*

   a. The volume of a circular cone is equal to one third of the product of its base and altitude.

   b. The volume of a circular cone is expressed by the formula $V = \frac{1}{3}\pi r^2 h$.

   c. The volume of a frustum of a circular cone is expressed by the formula $V = \frac{1}{3}\pi h(r^2 + r'^2 + rr')$.

   d. The volumes of two similar cones of revolution have the same ratio as the cubes of their altitudes, or as the cubes of their slant heights, or as the cubes of the radii of their bases.

WORD LIST

axis	frustum	slant height
cone	pyramid	tetrahedron
conical	pyramidal	

TEST 10

True-False Statements (*Twenty Minutes*)

Copy the numbers of these statements on your paper. If a statement is *always* true, write T after its number. If a statement is *not always* true, write F after its number. Do not guess.

1. A pyramid has only one base.

2. Any cone has a slant height.

3. A pyramid has at least three lateral edges.

4. The lateral edges of a pyramid are equal.

5. Every section of a circular cone made by a plane perpendicular to the axis of the cone is a circle.

6. The altitude of a cone of revolution is the line segment drawn from the vertex to the center of the base.

7. The lateral edges of a pyramid are parallel.

8. If a pyramid is inscribed in a right circular cone, its lateral faces are isosceles.

9. The locus of points having a given distance from a given straight line is a conical surface.

10. Cones with congruent bases and equal altitudes are congruent.

11. The slant height of a cone of revolution is $h^2 + r^2$, where r is the radius of the base and h is the altitude of the cone.

12. If a pyramid is inscribed in a right circular cone, the lateral faces are congruent.

13. The axis of a cone is perpendicular to the base.

14. If two planes are tangent to a cone, their intersection passes through the vertex of the cone.

15. If a circular cone and a circular cylinder have equal volumes and equal altitudes, the radius of the base of the cone is twice the radius of the base of the cylinder.

16. Cavalieri is a pyramid in Egypt.

17. The volume of a frustum of a pyramid or cone is given by the formula $V = \frac{1}{3} h(b + b' + \sqrt{b + b'})$.

18. The volume of a triangular pyramid whose base is an equilateral triangle with a side of 8 inches, and whose altitude is 5 inches, is $80\sqrt{3}$ cubic inches.

19. The area of the section of a cone made by a plane parallel to the base and bisecting an element is half the area of the base.

20. The volume of a cone is always less than the volume of its circumscribed pyramid.

TEST 11

Completing Statements (*Twenty Minutes*)

On your paper write one word, and only one, for each blank to make the following statements true:

1. The lateral edges of a _____ pyramid are equal.

2. A cone whose base is a circle is called a _____ cone.

3. A section of a pyramid made by a plane parallel to the base is _____ to the base.

4. The area of a section of a pyramid made by a plane bisecting an edge and parallel to the base is one _____ of the area of the base.

5. The lateral area of a regular pyramid is equal to one _____ the product of the _____ of its base and its _____ _____.

6. If a cone and a cylinder have congruent bases and equal altitudes, the volume of the cone is one _____ of the volume of the cylinder.

7. The volume of any pyramid is equal to one _____ the _____ of its _____ and _____.

8. $S = \frac{1}{2} l(p + p')$ is a formula for finding the lateral area of a _____ of a _____ pyramid.

9. $S = \frac{1}{2} lp$ is a formula for finding the _____ _____ of a _____ pyramid.

10. $V = \dfrac{\pi r^2 h}{3}$ is a formula for finding the _____ of a _____.

11. A section of a cone made by a plane through the vertex is a _____.

12. A solid cone is placed in a circular cylinder, both having equal bases and equal altitudes. If the volume of the cone is 150 cubic inches, there remain _____ cubic inches of the cylinder not occupied.

13. The circumference of a conical tent is 27 feet, and the slant height is 10 feet. The area of the tent is _____ square feet.

14. The total area of a cone of revolution is given by the formula $T = \pi r(l + \underline{\quad})$.

15. A pyramid and a prism have equal volumes. If the base of the pyramid is half the base of the prism, then the height of the pyramid is _____ times the height of the prism.

16. The two bases of a frustum of a pyramid are _____.

17. The lateral area of a pyramid is _____ than the area of the base.

18. If the base of a regular pyramid is an octagon 14 inches on a side, and the slant height is 6 inches, the lateral area of the pyramid is _____ square inches.

19. If a right triangle is revolved about one of its legs, the hypotenuse generates a _____ surface, and the other leg generates a _____ surface.

20. If S denotes the lateral area of a cone of revolution, V its volume, h its height, and r the radius of its base, then, in terms of h and V,

$$S = \frac{1}{h} \sqrt{3V} \sqrt{\underline{\quad\quad\quad}}.$$

TEST 12

Applications (*Forty Minutes*)

1. The height of a cone is 8 inches, and the area of its base is 24 square inches. Find its volume.

2. What is the volume of a regular quadrangular pyramid each side of whose base is 3 and whose altitude is 7?

3. The area of a section of a pyramid parallel to the base is one fourth of the area of the base. If the altitude of the pyramid is 10 inches, how far is the section from the vertex?

4. Find the total area of a regular pyramid whose base is a square with a side of 12 inches and whose slant height is 9 inches.

5. The area of the base of a cone is 40 square feet, and its volume is 120 cubic feet. What is its height?

6. What is the length of the side of a square base of a pyramid whose volume is 60 and whose altitude is 5?

7. Find the volume of a frustum of a triangular pyramid whose bases have areas of 4 square inches and 9 square inches respectively, if its altitude is 5 inches.

8. Find the total area of a cone whose slant height is 12 inches and whose base has a radius of 4 inches.

9. Find the total area of a square pyramid whose altitude is 3 feet, if each side of the base is 8 feet.

10. The base of a pyramid is a triangle whose sides are 9 inches, 12 inches, and 15 inches respectively. If the volume is 540 cubic inches, what is its height?

11. What is the volume of a regular tetrahedron whose edges are each 3 inches?

12. The perimeter of the base of a regular hexagonal pyramid is 12 inches, and the height of the pyramid is 3 inches. Find the volume of the pyramid.

13. The volume of a pyramid whose altitude is 15 is 2520. If the length of one diagonal of its rhombic base is 24, what is the length of the other?

14. Find the volume of a right circular cone whose total area is 124 square inches and whose base has a radius of 3 inches.

Taj Mahal, Agra, India

This domed building of white marble inlaid with precious stones is considered
by many people to be the most beautiful building in the world

CHAPTER V

SPHERES

227. A *sphere* is a closed surface all points of which are equidistant from a fixed point within called the *center*. A sphere also may be defined as the locus of points in space at a given distance from a given point.

A *radius* of a sphere is a straight line segment joining the center to any point of the sphere.

A *diameter* of a sphere is a straight line segment passing through the center and having its end points on the sphere.

228. Postulate. *One sphere, and only one, may be drawn with any given point as a center and with any given line segment as a radius.*

229. Theorems (c, n). Properties of spheres.

a. All radii of a sphere or of equal spheres are equal.

b. Spheres having equal radii are congruent.

c. All diameters of a sphere or of equal spheres are equal.

d. A point is within, on, or outside a sphere according as its distance from the center is less than, equal to, or greater than a radius.

e. A sphere may be generated by revolving a semicircle about the diameter as an axis.

EXERCISES (GROUP A)

1. If two spheres coincide, will their centers coincide?

2. What is the locus of points 3 inches from a given point?

3. What is the locus of points 2 inches from a sphere 5 inches in diameter?

4. What is the locus of points 4 inches from a sphere which has a radius of 4 inches?

5. If a line has one point inside a sphere, in how many points will it intersect the sphere?

Proposition I. Theorem (C, n)

230. *If a plane intersects a sphere, the intersection is a circle.*

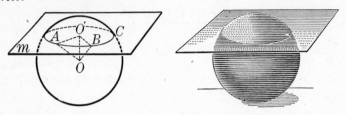

Given the sphere O intersected by plane m in the section ABC.

To prove that ABC is a $\odot$.

> *Selection of Method:* 1. Known methods of proving that a figure is a $\odot$: §§ 10 q, 156, 205.
> 2. Method to be used: § 10 q.

Proof: STATEMENTS   REASONS

1. From the center O draw $OO' \perp m$.	1. § 45.
2. From O' draw line segments to A and B, any two points of the intersection.	2. Why possible?
3. Draw radii OA and OB.	3. Why possible?
4. $OO' \perp O'A$ and $O'B$.	4. § 36.
5. $OA = OB$.	5. Why?
6. Rt. $\triangle AO'O \cong$ rt. $\triangle BO'O$.	6. § 13 f.
7. $\therefore O'A = O'B$, and the distance from A to $O' =$ the distance from any other point of intersection B to O'.	7. Why?
8. $\therefore ABC$ is a $\odot$.	8. § 10 q.

Note. If m contains O, the section is a $\odot$ whose radius is the radius of the sphere. Why?

231. Circles of a Sphere. The section of a sphere made by a plane is called a *circle of the sphere*. A *great circle of a sphere*

is the intersection of the sphere and a plane through its center. A *small circle of a sphere* is the intersection of the sphere and a plane not passing through its center.

232. Axis of a Circle. The *axis of a circle of a sphere* is the diameter of the sphere which is perpendicular to the plane of the circle. The extremities of the axis are the *poles* of the circle.

233. Corollary I (c, n). *The axis of a circle of a sphere passes through the center of the circle.* (Use the figure in § 230.)

234. Corollary II. *The center of a great circle of a sphere is the center of the sphere.*

235. Corollary III. *All great circles of a sphere are equal.* (Prove that they have equal radii.)

236. Corollary IV (c, n). *Any two great circles of a sphere bisect each other.* (The intersection of their planes passes through the center of the sphere. Why? This intersection is a diameter of each circle. Why?)

237. Corollary V (c, n). *Through any two points on a sphere that are not the extremities of a diameter one great circle of the sphere, and only one, can be drawn.*

238. Corollary VI (c, n). *Through any three points on a sphere one circle of the sphere, and only one, can be drawn.*

239. Spherical Distance. The *spherical distance* between two points of a sphere is the length of the minor arc of a great circle joining them. It can be proved (§ 316) that the spherical distance between two points is the shortest distance between them on the sphere.

240. Quadrant. A *quadrant* is one fourth of a great circle.

EXERCISES (GROUP A). *SPHERES*

1. Can a line intersect a sphere in two points? in three points?

2. In a plane what corresponds to an arc of a great circle?

3. How many spheres may intersect in three noncollinear points? in four noncoplanar points?

4. Prove that every great circle of a sphere divides the sphere into congruent parts, or hemispheres (use superposition).

5. The radius of a sphere is 20 inches. Find the area of a circle formed by a plane passing through the sphere 6 inches from the center.

6. What is the locus of points on a sphere equidistant from the ends of a diameter?

7. Find the locus of points on a sphere that are equidistant from two given points on the sphere.

8. Can you give two reasons why airplanes, airships, and steamboats, in going from the United States to England, often start in a direction north of east and reach England in a direction south of east?

9. Can two circles on a sphere intersect in two points? in three points?

10. Prove that the radius of a sphere perpendicular to a chord of the sphere bisects the chord.

11. Prove that the planes of two circles having the same axis are parallel.

12. Prove that equal chords of a sphere are equidistant from the center.

EXERCISES (GROUP B). *SPHERES*

1. The radius of a sphere is 17 inches. Find the area of a circle formed by a plane passing through the sphere 9 inches from a point on the sphere.

2. The area of a section of a sphere 10 inches from the center is 576π square inches. Find the radius of the sphere.

3. Find the spherical distance between two points on a sphere whose radius is 10 inches if the line segment joining the points is 10 inches.

4. Prove that if a plane cuts two concentric spheres, the sections are concentric circles.

5. What is the locus of points at a given distance from a given point and equidistant from two given points?

6. Prove that circles on a sphere whose planes are equidistant from the center of the sphere are equal.

7. Prove that the radius of a small circle of a sphere is less than the radius of the sphere.

Proposition II. Theorem (c, N)

241. *The spherical distances of all points on a circle of a sphere from either pole of the circle are equal.*

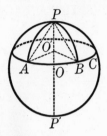 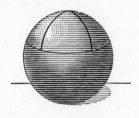

Given A and B any two points on ⊙ ABC of sphere O and P and P' the poles of ⊙ ABC.

To prove that $\widehat{PA} = \widehat{PB}$.

⎡*Selection of Method:* 1. Known methods of proving arcs =: § 22.⎤
⎣ 2. Method to be used: § 22 c. ⎦

Proof:

STATEMENTS	REASONS
1. Draw PP' intersecting plane of ABC in O'.	1. Why possible?
2. Draw AO', BO', PA, and PB.	2. Why possible?
3. PP' is the axis of ⊙ ABC.	3. § 232.
4. ∴ $PP' \perp$ the plane of ⊙ ABC.	4. § 232.
5. ∴ O' is the center of ⊙ ABC.	5. § 233.
6. ∴ $AO' = BO'$.	6. Why?
7. ∴ chord $PA =$ chord PB.	7. § 41.
8. ∴ $\widehat{PA} = \widehat{PB}$.	8. § 22 c.

242. Polar Distance of a Circle. The *polar distance* of a circle of a sphere is the spherical distance from any point on the circle to its nearest pole, or to either pole if they are equally near.

243. Corollary (c, n). *The polar distance of a great circle is a quadrant.*

Proposition III. Theorem (C, N)

244. *If a point on a sphere is at the distance of a quadrant from each of two other points on the sphere not the extremities of a diameter, then the point is a pole of the great circle passing through these two points.*

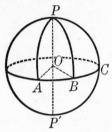

Given points *P*, *A*, and *B* on sphere *O*, $\widehat{AB}$ of a great ⊙ *ABC*, and the quadrants *PA* and *PB*.

To prove that *P* is a pole of ⊙ *ABC*.

⌈*Selection of Method:* 1. Known methods of proving that a point⌉
│   is a pole: § 232.   │
⌊   2. Method to be used: § 232.   ⌋

Proof: *STATEMENTS*   *REASONS*

1. Draw *AO*, *BO*, and diameter *POP′*.	1. Why possible?
2. $\widehat{PA}$ and $\widehat{PB}$ are quadrants.	2. Why?
3. ∴ ∠ *POA* and ∠ *POB* are rt. ∠.	3. Why?
4. ∴ *PO* ⊥ plane *ABC*.	4. Why?
5. ∴ *PP′* is the axis of ⊙ *ABC*.	5. § 232.
6. ∴ *P* is a pole of ⊙ *ABC*.	6. § 232.

245. Tangent to a Sphere. A line and a sphere, or a plane and a sphere, are tangent to each other if they have one and only one point in common. The common point is called the *point of contact* or the *point of tangency*.

246. Tangent Spheres. Two spheres are tangent to each other if they are tangent to a plane at the same point.

Proposition IV. Theorem (c, N)

247. *If a plane is perpendicular to a radius at its extremity on the sphere, it is tangent to the sphere.*

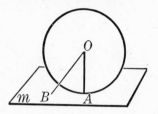

Given plane *m* ⊥ radius *OA* of sphere *O* at *A*.

To prove that *m* is tangent to sphere *O*.

⎡ *Selection of Method:* 1. Known methods of proving a plane and a
⎢   sphere tangent: § 245.
⎢   2. Method to be used: § 245.   ⎤
⎣   ⎦

Proof: STATEMENTS   REASONS

1. To *B*, any point in *m* except *A*, draw *OB*.	1. Why possible?
2. ∴ *OA* < *OB*.	2. § 43.
3. ∴ *B* or any point of *m* except *A* lies outside the sphere *O*.	3. § 229 *d*.
4. ∴ plane *m* is tangent to the sphere *O*.	4. § 245.

248. Theorem (c). *A plane tangent to a sphere is perpendicular to the radius drawn to the point of contact.*

249. Inscribed Sphere. A sphere is *inscribed* in a polyhedron if it is tangent to all the faces of the polyhedron. If the sphere is inscribed in the polyhedron, the polyhedron is *circumscribed* about the sphere.

EXERCISE

If a line is tangent to a sphere, does it touch every great circle of the sphere passing through the point of contact? Is it tangent to any of these great circles?

Proposition V. Theorem (c, N)

250. *A sphere can be inscribed in a tetrahedron.*

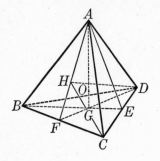 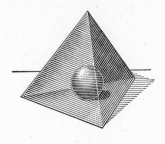

Given a tetrahedron *ABCD*.

To prove that a sphere can be inscribed in *ABCD*.

⎡ *Selection of Method:* 1. Known methods of proving that a sphere
⎢   can be inscribed: § 249.
⎣   2. Method to be used: § 249. ⎤⎦

Proof: *STATEMENTS*   *REASONS*

1. Each dihedral ∠ can be bisected by bisecting its plane ∠, etc.	1. Give proof. §§ 12 *h*, 9 *e*, 80.
2. Let plane *ABE* bisect dihedral ∠ *AB*, and plane *ADF* bisect dihedral ∠ *AD*.	2. Reason 1.
3. Then *ABE* intersects *ADF* in a st. line *AG*.	3. Give proof.
4. Any point in *AG* is equidistant from planes *ABC* and *ABD*, and equidistant from planes *ACD* and *ABD*.	4. § 89.
5. ∴ any point in *AG* is equidistant from planes *ABC*, *ABD*, and *ACD*.	5. § 11 *f*.
6. *AG* intersects in a point *O* the plane *DCH*, which bisects dihedral ∠ *DC*.	6. Why?
7. Then *O* is equidistant from planes *BCD* and *ACD*.	7. Why?

Proof: *STATEMENTS*   *REASONS*

8. From (5) and (7), *O* is equidistant from all the faces of *ABCD*.	8. § 11 *f*.
9. ∴ the sphere with center *O* and radius equal to the ⊥ from *O* to each face is tangent to each face of *ABCD*.	9. §§ 227, 247.
10. ∴ a sphere can be inscribed in *ABCD*.	10. § 249.

251. Theorem (c, n). *A cube can be circumscribed about a sphere.*

EXERCISES. *PROPERTIES OF SPHERES*

1. Do the parallels of the earth have the same poles? the same axis?

2. How many great circles of the earth pass through both New York and London?

3. How many of the parallels of the earth are great circles? Are the meridians great circles?

4. If an airplane continues to fly due east, will it follow the arc of a small circle or the arc of a great circle? In flying east, will it change its direction? In flying north, will it change its direction?

5. How can you locate on a globe the poles of a great circle?

6. What is the name of the circle on the surface of the earth at the distance of a quadrant from the north pole? at $23\frac{1}{2}°$ from the north pole? at $23\frac{1}{2}°$ from the south pole? at $23\frac{1}{2}°$ north from the equator?

7. What is the locus of points having a given distance from a given point? from a given sphere?

8. What is the locus of the center of a given sphere that is tangent to a given line?

9. What is the locus of points 3 inches from a given point and 4 inches from a second given point if the given points are 5 inches apart?

252. Circumscribed Sphere. A sphere is *circumscribed* about a polyhedron if the vertices of the polyhedron lie on the sphere. If the sphere is circumscribed about the polyhedron, the polyhedron is *inscribed* in the sphere.

Proposition VI. Theorem (C, N)

253. *A sphere can be circumscribed about a tetrahedron.*

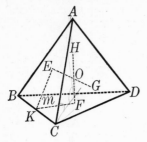
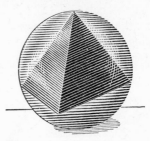

Given a tetrahedron *ABCD.*

To prove that a sphere can be circumscribed about *ABCD.*

⎡*Selection of Method:* 1. Known methods of proving that a sphere⎤
can be circumscribed : § 252.
2. Method to be used : § 252.

Proof: STATEMENTS | REASONS

1. Let *E* be the center of the ⊙ circumscribed about △ *ABC*, and *F* the center of the ⊙ circumscribed about △ *BCD*.	1. § 33 *n*.
2. Draw *GE* ⊥ *ABC* and *HF* ⊥ *BCD*.	2. § 44.
3. Any point in *GE* is equidistant from *A*, *B*, and *C*, and any point in *HF* is equidistant from *B*, *C*, and *D*.	3. § 49.
4. ∴ *GE* and *HF* both lie in plane *m*, the ⊥ bisector of *BC*.	4. § 48.
5. Plane *m* intersects plane *ABC* in *KE* and plane *BCD* in *KF*.	5. Why?
6. *GE* ⊥ *KE* and *HF* ⊥ *KF*.	6. Why?
7. Then *GE* intersects *HF* in some point *O*.	7. § 24 *a*.
8. From (3), *O* is equidistant from *A*, *B*, *C*, and *D*.	8. § 11 *f*.
9. ∴ a sphere with center *O* and radius *OA* will pass through *A*, *B*, *C*, and *D*.	9. § 227.
10. ∴ a sphere can be circumscribed about *ABCD*.	10. § 252.

254. Corollary. *A sphere can be passed through any four non-coplanar points.*

EXERCISES (GROUP B). *SPHERES*

1. Prove that a sphere can be circumscribed about a cube.

2. Prove that a sphere can be inscribed in a cube.

3. Can a sphere be inscribed in a cylinder?

4. Prove that all lines tangent to a sphere from the same point are equal.

5. Prove that circles on the same sphere are equal if they have equal polar distances.

6. State and prove the converse of Ex. 5.

7. Find the circumference of a small circle on a sphere having a diameter of 13 inches if the plane of the circle is $2\frac{1}{2}$ inches from the center.

8. Assuming that the earth is a sphere with a diameter of 8000 miles, find the length of its sixtieth parallel.

9. A sphere with a diameter of 10 inches is tangent to the faces of a trihedral angle whose face angles are right angles. Another sphere is tangent to this sphere and to the three faces. How large is the second sphere?

10. If a regular tetrahedron is 10 inches on an edge, what is the radius of its inscribed sphere? What is the radius of its circumscribed sphere?

255. Spherical Angle. A *spherical angle* is an angle formed by two intersecting arcs of great circles. A spherical angle is equal in degrees to ($\doteq$) the angle formed by the lines which are tangent to the arcs at their point of intersection.

256. Theorem (c, n). *A spherical angle is equal to the dihedral angle formed by the planes of its sides.*

$\angle EBF \doteq \angle CBD$. Why?

$\angle CBD \doteq \angle E\text{-}AB\text{-}F$. Why?

$\therefore \angle EBF \doteq \angle E\text{-}AB\text{-}F$. Why?

Proposition VII. Theorem (C, n)

257. *A spherical angle is equal in degrees to the arc of the great circle which has the vertex of the angle as a pole and is included between the sides of the angle, extended if necessary.*

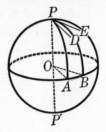

Given the spherical $\angle APB$ on sphere O, $\widehat{AB}$ of the great $\odot$ whose pole is P, and the sides PA and PB which include the spherical $\angle$.

To prove that $\angle APB \overset{\circ}{=} \widehat{AB}$.

$\Big[$*Selection of Method:* 1. Known methods of comparing ∡ and arcs: § 23.

2. Method to be used: § 23 a. $\Big]$

Proof:

STATEMENTS	REASONS
1. Draw diameter POP' and radii OA and OB of sphere O.	1. Why possible?
2. Draw PD and PE tangent to $\widehat{PA}$ and $\widehat{PB}$ respectively.	2. § 33 j.
3. $\widehat{PA}$ and $\widehat{PB}$ are quadrants.	3. § 243.
4. ∴ ∡ POA and POB are rt. ∡.	4. § 23 a.
5. ∴ $AO \perp PO$ and $BO \perp PO$.	5. Why?
6. But $DP \perp PO$ and $EP \perp PO$.	6. § 18 i.
7. ∴ $AO \parallel DP$ and $BO \parallel EP$.	7. Why?
8. ∴ $\angle AOB = \angle DPE$.	8. § 66.
9. But $\angle AOB \overset{\circ}{=} \widehat{AB}$, and	9. § 23 a.
10. $\angle DPE = \angle APB$.	10. Why?
11. ∴ $\angle APB \overset{\circ}{=} \widehat{AB}$.	11. Why?

EXERCISES (GROUP A)

1. Prove that two great circles on a sphere intersect, and that the vertical angles are equal.

2. If two spheres are tangent to each other, is their common tangent a plane perpendicular to their line of centers? What is the corresponding question in plane geometry?

3. An angle formed by two meridians on the earth's surface contains 18°. How many degrees are in the arc of the equator included by the meridians?

4. At what angle does a meridian intersect the equator?

5. What is the locus of all lines tangent to a given sphere from a given external point? to a given sphere at a point on the sphere?

6. Can a sphere be circumscribed about any tetrahedron? about any parallelepiped? about any rectangular solid?

7. If the central angle of an arc of a great circle on a sphere having a radius of 8 inches is 72°, find the length of the arc.

EXERCISES (GROUP B)

1. What is the inclination of the sun at a point on the equator at noon on March 21st? on June 21st? on September 22d? on December 22d?

2. What is the inclination of the sun here at noon on March 21st? on June 21st? on September 22d? on December 22d?

3. If two straight lines are tangent to a sphere at the same point, is their plane tangent to the sphere?

4. What is the locus of the centers of spheres which pass through three given points?

5. What is the locus of the centers of all spheres which have a given radius and are tangent to a given plane?

6. A 9-inch sphere is inscribed in a tetrahedron having equal edges. Find the volume and the area of the tetrahedron.

7. The sides of a spherical triangle on a sphere of radius 6 inches are 60°, 80°, and 100° respectively. Find the perimeter of the triangle.

8. What is the locus of the centers of spheres which pass through two given points?

Proposition VIII. Theorem (c, n)

258. *The area of the surface generated by a straight line segment revolving about an axis in its plane is equal to the product of the projection of the line segment upon the axis and the circumference of the circle whose radius is a perpendicular from the axis to the line segment at its midpoint.*

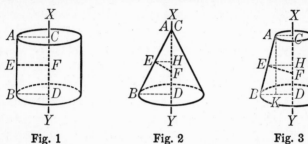

| Fig. 1 | Fig. 2 | Fig. 3 |

Given the line segment AB, CD the projection of AB on the axis XY, EF the $\perp$ bisector of AB, and the surface S generated by AB revolving about XY.

To prove that $S = CD \times 2\,\pi EF$.

⎡ *Selection of Method:* 1. Known methods of finding areas of solids: §§ 172, 174, 220, 225.

  2. Methods to be used: §§ 174 b, 225 b, c. ⎤

Proof: STATEMENTS   REASONS

1. If $AB \parallel XY$, S is the lateral surface of a rt. circular cylinder. $S = AB \cdot 2\,\pi BD$.	1. §§ 152, 174 b.
2. But $AB = CD$ and $BD = EF$.	2. § 14 f.
3. $\therefore S = CD \cdot 2\,\pi EF$.	3. Why?
4. If A lies on XY, S is the surface of a rt. circular cone.	4. Why?
5. Draw $EH \perp XY$.	5. Why possible?
6. Then $S = AB \cdot \pi BD$.	6. § 225 b.
7. But $BD = 2\,EH$.	7. § 14 j, k.
8. Then $S = AB \cdot 2\,\pi EH$.	8. Why?

Proof: *STATEMENTS*   *REASONS*

9. Rt. $\triangle ABD \sim$ rt. $\triangle EFH$.	9. Give proof.
10. $\therefore \dfrac{AB}{EF} = \dfrac{CD}{EH}$, or $AB \cdot EH = CD \cdot EF$.	10. Why?
11. From (8) and (10), $S = CD \cdot 2\,\pi EF$.	11. § 11 e.
12. If AB is not $\parallel XY$ and both A and B lie on the same side of XY, S is the surface of a frustum of a rt. circular cone.	12. Why?
13. Then $S = AB\pi(AC + BD)$.	13. § 225 c.
14. Draw $EH \perp XY$ and $AK \perp BD$.	14. Why possible?
15. Then $EH = \frac{1}{2}(AC + BD)$, or $AC + BD = 2\,EH$.	15. §§ 14 l, 11 c.
16. $\therefore S = AB \cdot 2\,\pi EH$.	16. Why?
17. Rt. $\triangle ABK \sim$ rt. $\triangle EFH$.	17. Give proof.
18. $\therefore \dfrac{AB}{EF} = \dfrac{AK}{EH}$, or $AB \cdot EH = AK \cdot EF$.	18. Why?
19. From (16) and (18), $S = AK \cdot 2\,\pi EF$.	19. Why?
20. But $AK = CD$.	20. Why?
21. $\therefore S = CD \cdot 2\,\pi EF$.	21. Why?

259. Zone. A zone is a portion of a sphere included between two parallel planes. If one of the planes is tangent to the sphere and one intersects the sphere, the zone is called a *zone of one base*. The *altitude of a zone* is the perpendicular between the planes. The *bases of a zone* are the circles formed by the intersections of the planes and the sphere. The figure at the right represents the five zones of the earth's surface.

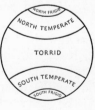

260. Postulate on Limits. If a broken line is inscribed in the generating arc of a sphere or zone and its vertices divide the arc into equal parts, and if the number of these parts is increased indefinitely, the area generated by the broken line approaches as a limit the area generated by the arc.

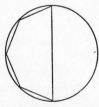

Proposition IX. Theorem (c, N)

261. *The area of a sphere with radius r is 4 πr^2.*

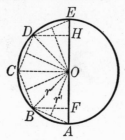

Given the sphere O with radius r and area S.

To prove that $S = 4 \pi r^2$.

> *Selection of Method:* 1. Known methods of finding areas of solids: §§ 172, 174, 220, 225, 258.
> 2. Method to be used: § 258.

Proof:

STATEMENTS	REASONS
1. Let the sphere O be generated by revolving semicircle ACE about the diameter AE.	1. § 229 e.
2. In the semicircle ACE, inscribe $ABCDE$, half of a regular polygon having an even number of sides.	2. Why possible?
3. Draw the apothems r'.	3. Why possible?
4. The apothems bisect the sides of the polygon.	4. § 14 n.
5. From B, C, and D draw ⊥s to AE.	5. Why possible?
6. The area generated by $AB = AF \cdot 2 \pi r'$, the area generated by $BC = FO \cdot 2 \pi r'$, the area generated by $CD = OH \cdot 2 \pi r'$, the area generated by $DE = HE \cdot 2 \pi r'$.	6. § 258.

7. Let S' denote the area generated by the semipolygon.
  Then $S' = (AF + FO + OH + HE)2 \pi r'$
  $= AE \cdot 2 \pi r' = 4 \pi r r'$.
	7. § 11 a, e.

Proof: *STATEMENTS*   *REASONS*

STATEMENTS	REASONS
8. If the number of sides of the polygon is increased indefinitely, $r' \to r$ and $S' \to S$ as limits.	8. §§ 12 z, 260.
9. Then $4\pi rr' \to 4\pi rr$, or $4\pi r^2$.	9. § 160 a.
10. From (7), (8), and (9), $S = 4\pi r^2$.	10. § 160 b.

262. Corollary I. *The area of a sphere is equal to the product of its diameter and the circumference of a great circle.*

263. Corollary II (c, n). *The area of a sphere is equal to four times the area of one of its great circles, or $4\pi r^2$.*

264. Corollary III. *The areas of two spheres are to each other as the squares of their radii or as the squares of their diameters.*

265. Theorem. *The area of a zone is equal to the product of its altitude and the circumference of a great circle of the sphere.*

Suggestion. Follow the method used in proving Prop. IX.

EXERCISES (GROUP A). *AREAS OF SPHERES*

1. Find the area of a sphere whose radius is 24 inches.

2. Find the area of a sphere whose diameter is 100 inches.

3. The diameter of a sphere is 36 inches. Find its area.

4. The circumference of a great circle of a sphere is 314.16 inches. Find the area of the sphere.

5. The area of a great circle of a sphere is 79 square inches. What is the area of the sphere?

6. The altitude of a zone on a sphere having a radius of 10 inches is 4 inches. Find the area of the zone. The area of the zone is what part of the area of the sphere?

7. A cylinder is circumscribed about a sphere having a diameter of 16 inches. Find the area of the sphere and the lateral area of the cylinder. Does this problem make it easier to remember the rule for finding the area of a sphere?

8. Find the radius of a sphere whose area is 225 π.

9. The areas of two spheres are 900 square inches and 1200 square inches respectively. What is the ratio of their radii?

EXERCISES (GROUP B). *AREAS OF SPHERES*

1. Derive a formula for the area of a sphere in terms of the circumference c of a great circle.

2. Two spheres have radii of 7 inches and 9 inches respectively. What is the ratio of their areas?

3. Find the cost at $2 a square foot of gilding a dome in the shape of a hemisphere whose diameter is 25 feet.

4. Find the area of a zone of one base if its altitude is 14 inches and the radius of the sphere is 20 inches.

5. A rectangle whose sides are l inches and w inches respectively is first revolved about the side l as an axis and then about the side w as an axis. Compare the areas of the two cylindrical surfaces thus generated. Compare the areas of the total surfaces generated.

6. Two spheres whose radii are r and $2r$ respectively intersect so that the larger sphere passes through the center of the smaller sphere. Find the area of the circle of intersection.

266. Theorem. *If one of two great circles passes through the pole of the other, the circles are perpendicular to each other.*

Suggestions. If P is the pole of $\odot$ *ABC*, $PO \perp$ plane *ABC*. Why? Therefore plane *PBP'* $\perp$ plane *ABC*. Why? Then $PB \perp BC$ (§ 256).

267. Spherical Polygon. A *spherical polygon* is a closed line on a sphere consisting of three or more arcs of great circles. In this text only convex spherical polygons will be studied. The arcs of the circles are the *sides* of the polygon and their points of meeting are the *vertices* of the polygon. The *angles* of the polygon are the spherical angles formed by the sides of the polygon. The figure *ABCD* on the sphere is a spherical 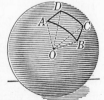 polygon, whose sides are *AB*, *BC*, *CD*, and *DA* and whose angles are $\angle ABC$, $\angle BCD$, $\angle CDA$, and $\angle DAB$. The arc of a great circle connecting any two nonconsecutive vertices of a spherical polygon is called a *diagonal* of the polygon.

268. Spherical Polygon and its Corresponding Polyhedral Angles. If the vertices of a spherical polygon are joined to the center of the sphere, a polyhedral angle is formed at the center of the sphere. The sides of the polygon correspond to the face angles of the polyhedral angle, and the angles of the polygon correspond to the dihedral angles of the polyhedral angle. In the figure of § 267, *AB*, *BC*, *CD*, and *DA* correspond respectively to ∠ *AOB*, ∠ *BOC*, ∠ *COD*, and ∠ *DOA*. Also ⊿ *ABC*, *BCD*, *CDA*, and *DAB* correspond respectively to dihedral ⊿ *OB*, *OC*, *OD*, and *OA*.

Many theorems relating to spherical polygons can be proved by using the corresponding theorems relating to polyhedral angles. Props. X and XI are proved in this manner.

269. Theorem. *The sides of a spherical polygon are equal in degrees to the corresponding face angles of the polyhedral angle* (use § 23 *a*).

270. Theorem (c, n). *The angles of a spherical polygon are equal in degrees to the corresponding dihedral angles of the polyhedral angle* (use § 256).

EXERCISES (GROUP A). *CIRCLES OF A SPHERE*

1. How many great circles can be passed through two given points on a sphere if the points are not the extremities of a diameter? if the points are the extremities of a diameter?

2. Through two points on a sphere how many small circles may be drawn?

3. In general, how many great circles can be determined by three noncollinear points on a sphere?

271. Spherical Triangle. A spherical polygon of three sides is a *spherical triangle*. The words *isosceles, equilateral, equiangular, median*, etc. have the same meaning when applied to spherical triangles as when applied to plane triangles. In the figure, *ABC* is a spherical triangle. ∠ *AOB* ≗ $\widehat{AB}$, ∠ *AOC* ≗ $\widehat{AC}$, and ∠ *BOC* ≗ $\widehat{BC}$. Why? Spherical ∠ *ABC* ≗ ∠ *A-OB-C*. Why?

Proposition X. *Theorem* (c, n)

272. *Each side of a spherical triangle is less than the sum of the other two sides.*

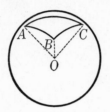

Given the spherical △ *ABC* with *AC* the longest side.

To prove that $AC < AB + BC$.

⎡ *Selection of Method:* 1. Known methods of comparing sides of spherical polygons: § 269.
2. Method to be used: § 269. ⎤

Suggestions. ∠ *AOC* < ∠ *AOB* + ∠ *BOC* (§ 95). But ∠ *AOC* ≐ $\widehat{AC}$, ∠ *AOB* ≐ $\widehat{AB}$, and ∠ *BOC* ≐ $\widehat{BC}$. Why?

Proposition XI. *Theorem* (c, n)

273. *The sum of the sides of a spherical polygon is less than 360°.*

Given the spherical polygon *ABCDE*.

To prove that $AB + BC + CD + DE + EA < 360°$.

Suggestion. ∠ *AOB* + ∠ *BOC* + ∠ *COD* + ∠ *DOE* + ∠ *EOA* < 360° (§ 96).

274. Polar Triangle. If the vertices of one spherical triangle are the poles of the sides of another spherical triangle, the second triangle is called the *polar triangle* of the first. In the figure, if A is the pole of $\overset{\frown}{B'C'}$, B is the pole of $\overset{\frown}{A'C'}$, and C is the pole of $\overset{\frown}{A'B'}$, then $\triangle A'B'C'$ is the polar triangle of $\triangle ABC$.

The properties of polar triangles were discovered independently, about 1626, by Albert Girard and Willebrord Snell, two Dutch mathematicians.

EXERCISES (GROUP A). *POLAR TRIANGLES*

1. In the figure of § 274, from what point is $\overset{\frown}{A'B'}$ a quadrant's distance? From what point is $\overset{\frown}{B'C'}$ a quadrant's distance? From what point is $\overset{\frown}{A'C'}$ a quadrant's distance?

2. If the polar triangle of $\triangle ABC$ coincides with $\triangle ABC$, what is the sum of the angles of $\triangle ABC$?

3. Can the polar triangle of a spherical $\triangle ABC$ be equilateral?

4. What do you know about $\triangle ABC$ if its polar triangle incloses it?

5. What do you know about $\triangle ABC$ if its polar triangle lies within it?

6. Is it possible to have a spherical triangle whose sides contain 70°, 90°, and 40°? whose sides contain 30°, 60°, and 100°? whose sides contain 40°, 50°, and 60°? whose sides contain 70°, 150°, and 140°?

7. In the spherical $\triangle ABC$, A is the pole of $\overset{\frown}{BC}$, which contains 130°. What is the sum of the angles of the triangle?

8. Draw a spherical triangle which intersects its polar triangle.

9. Prove that any side of a spherical triangle is a minor arc of a great circle.

EXERCISES (GROUP B)

1. Prove that a sphere is determined by any four noncoplanar points.

2. A 10-inch sphere is circumscribed about a tetrahedron having equal edges. Find the edge of the tetrahedron.

Proposition XII. Theorem (C, N)

275. *If one spherical triangle is the polar triangle of another, then the second is the polar triangle of the first.*

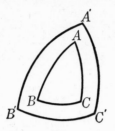

Given the spherical $\triangle$ *ABC* and its polar $\triangle$ *A'B'C'*.

To prove that $\triangle$ *ABC* is the polar $\triangle$ of *A'B'C'*.

> *Selection of Method:* 1. Known methods of proving that one $\triangle$ is the polar $\triangle$ of another: § 274.
> 2. Method to be used: § 274.

Proof: STATEMENTS · REASONS

STATEMENTS	REASONS
1. *B* is the pole of $\widehat{A'C'}$ and *C* is the pole of $\widehat{A'B'}$.	1. § 274.
2. ∴ *A'* is a quadrant's distance from *B* and *C*.	2. § 243.
3. ∴ *A'* is the pole of $\widehat{BC}$.	3. § 244.
4. Similarly, *B'* is the pole of $\widehat{AC}$ and *C'* is the pole of $\widehat{AB}$.	4. Statements 1–3.
5. ∴ *ABC* is the polar $\triangle$ of *A'B'C'*.	5. § 274.

276. Complementary and Supplementary Angles and Arcs. A spherical angle and an arc of a great circle are *complementary* when their sum is a right angle and are *supplementary* when their sum is a straight angle.

EXERCISE

Draw the polar triangle of a spherical triangle whose sides are 90°, 90°, and 60°.

Proposition XIII. Theorem (C, N)

277. *In two polar triangles each angle of one is the supplement of the opposite side of the other.*

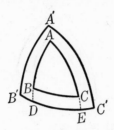

Given the polar ⩟ *ABC* and *A'B'C'* with ∠ *A* of the one opposite side *B'C'* of the other.

To prove that ∠ *A* and $\widehat{B'C'}$ are supplementary.

⌈ *Selection of Method:* 1. Known methods of comparing ⩟ and arcs : ⌉
    §§ 23, 257, 269, 276.
    2. Method to be used : § 276.
⌊   ⌋

Proof: STATEMENTS   REASONS

1. Extend $\widehat{AB}$ and $\widehat{AC}$ to meet $\widehat{B'C'}$ at *D* and *E* respectively.	1. § 236.
2. *B'* is the pole of $\widehat{ACE}$ and *C'* is the pole of $\widehat{ABD}$.	2. § 274.
3. ∴ $\widehat{B'E} = 90°$ and $\widehat{DC'} = 90°$.	3. § 243.
4. ∴ $\widehat{B'E} + \widehat{DC'} = 180°$.	4. Why?
5. ∴ $\widehat{DE} + \widehat{B'C'} = 180°$.	5. Why?
6. But $\widehat{DE} \stackrel{\circ}{=} ∠ A$.	6. § 257.
7. ∴ ∠ $A + \widehat{B'C'} = 180°$.	7. Why?
8. ∴ ∠ *A* and $\widehat{B'C'}$ are supplementary.	8. § 276.

EXERCISES (GROUP A)

1. The angles of a spherical triangle are 78°, 91°, and 45°. Find the number of degrees in each side of its polar triangle.

2. The sides of a spherical triangle contain 100°, 82°, and 94° respectively. Find the number of degrees in each angle of its polar triangle.

Proposition XIV. Theorem (C, n)

278. *The sum of the angles of a spherical triangle is greater than 180° and less than 540°.*

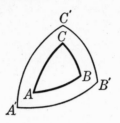

Given the spherical △ *ABC*.

To prove that $\angle A + \angle B + \angle C > 180°$ and $< 540°$.

> [*Selection of Method:* 1. Known methods of comparing ∡ and arcs:
> §§ 23, 257, 269, 276, 277.
> 2. Method to be used: § 277.]

Proof: STATEMENTS　　　　　　　　　REASONS

STATEMENTS	REASONS
1. Draw $A'B'C'$ the polar △ of *ABC*.	1. § 274.
2. $\angle A + \widehat{B'C'} = 180°,$ $\angle B + \widehat{A'C'} = 180°,$ $\angle C + \widehat{A'B'} = 180°.$	2. § 277.
3. ∴ $\angle A + \angle B + \angle C + \widehat{B'C'} + \widehat{A'C'} + \widehat{A'B'} = 540°.$	3. Why?
4. But $\widehat{B'C'} + \widehat{A'C'} + \widehat{A'B'} < 360°.$	4. § 273.
5. From (3) and (4), $\angle A + \angle B + \angle C > 180°.$	5. § 11 *l*.
6. But $\widehat{B'C'} + \widehat{A'C'} + \widehat{A'B'} > 0°.$	6. Prove by indirect method.
7. ∴ from (3) and (6), $\angle A + \angle B + \angle C < 540°.$	7. § 11 *l*.

EXERCISES (GROUP A). *SPHERICAL TRIANGLES*

1. Is a spherical triangle possible if its angles contain 70°, 60°, and 40°? if its angles contain 80°, 70°, and 100°?

2. Each side of a spherical triangle contains 90°. What are the sizes of the angles and sides of its polar triangle?

279. Kinds of Spherical Triangles. A plane triangle has, at the most, one right angle or óne obtuse angle. A spherical triangle may contain two or three right angles or two or three obtuse angles. A *birectangular* spherical triangle has two right angles, and a *trirectangular* spherical triangle has three right angles.

280. Spherical Excess. The *spherical excess* of a spherical triangle is the difference between the sum of its angles and the sum of the angles of a plane triangle. Thus the spherical excess of a triangle having angles of 70°, 80°, and 85° is (70° + 80° + 85°) − 180°, or 55°.

The *spherical excess* of a spherical polygon is the difference between the sum of its angles and the sum of the angles of a plane polygon having the same number of sides. Thus the spherical excess of a polygon having angles of 80°, 160°, 100°, and 90° is (80° + 160° + 100° + 90°) − 360°, or 70°.

EXERCISES (GROUP A). *SPHERICAL POLYGONS*

1. What is the spherical excess of a spherical triangle whose angles contain 84°, 73.2°, and 96.7°?

2. What is the spherical excess of a polygon having angles of 114°, 72° 30′, 87° 45′, and 91°?

EXERCISES (GROUP B). *SPHERICAL POLYGONS*

1. Find the perimeter and spherical excess of a trirectangular spherical triangle on a sphere having a diameter of 50 inches.

2. If three angles of a spherical quadrilateral are right angles, prove that the fourth angle is obtuse.

281. Congruent Spherical Triangles. Two spherical triangles are *congruent* if they can be made to coincide; and two spherical triangles will coincide if the sides and angles of one are equal respectively to the sides and angles of the other and are arranged in the same order. Since a definition is reversible, two spherical triangles can be made to coincide if they are congruent. Since they coincide, the corresponding sides and angles of two congruent spherical triangles are equal.

282. Symmetric Spherical Triangles. Two spherical triangles are symmetric if the sides and angles of one are equal respectively to the sides and angles of the other, but are arranged in the reverse order.

If two spherical triangles ABC and $A'B'C'$ are so situated on the same sphere that AA', BB', and CC' are diameters, it can be proved that $\widehat{AB} = \widehat{A'B'}$, $\widehat{BC} = \widehat{B'C'}$, $\widehat{AC} = \widehat{A'C'}$, $\angle A = \angle A'$, $\angle B = \angle B'$, and $\angle C = \angle C'$. Can you prove these facts? What can you say of $\triangle ABC$ and $\triangle A'B'C'$? How can you draw one triangle symmetric to another?

In general, two symmetric spherical triangles are not congruent, because of the curvature of the sides. Thus ⧍ I and II, though symmetric, are not congruent, since they cannot be made to coincide.

283. Theorem. *Two spherical triangles which are symmetric to a third triangle are congruent.*

ORAL EXERCISES

1. Here are two plane triangles having $AB = A'B'$, $BC = B'C'$, and $AC = A'C'$. Are the parts arranged in the same or in reverse order? Can $\triangle A'B'C'$ be made to coincide with $\triangle ABC$ without lifting it out of the plane and turning it over in space? Why cannot two symmetric spherical triangles be made to coincide in the same manner? Using symmetric triangles cut from an orange peel or from a rubber ball, show that, in general, it is not possible to make spherical triangles coincide.

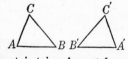

2. If two spherical triangles are mutually equiangular, what do you know about their polar triangles?

3. If two spherical triangles are mutually equilateral, what do you know about their polar triangles?

Proposition XV. Theorem (c, n)

284. *If two spherical triangles on a sphere or on equal spheres have two sides and the included angle of one equal respectively to two sides and the included angle of the other and arranged in the same order, the triangles are congruent.*

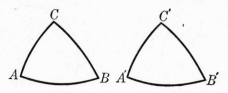

Given △ *ABC* and *A'B'C'* on = spheres with *AC = A'C'*, ∠ *C* = ∠ *C'*, *BC = B'C'*, and the parts arranged in the same order.

To prove that △ *ABC* ≅ △ *A'B'C'*.

[*Selection of Method:* 1. Known methods of proving spherical △ ≅ :
§§ 281, 283.
2. Method to be used : § 281.]

Proof: (The proof is left to the student.)

Suggestions. Place △ *ABC* on △ *A'B'C'* so that ∠ *C* coincides with its equal ∠ *C'*. *A* will fall on *A'*. Give proof. Likewise, *B* will fall on *B'*. *AB* will coincide with *A'B'*. Why?

285. Corollary (c, n). *Two symmetric isosceles spherical triangles are congruent.*

Proposition XVI. Theorem (c, n)

286. *If two spherical triangles on a sphere or on equal spheres have two angles and the included side of one equal respectively to two angles and the included side of the other and arranged in the same order, the triangles are congruent.*

(The demonstration is left to the student.)

Proposition XVII. Theorem (c, n)

287. *If two spherical triangles on a sphere or on equal spheres have two sides and the included angle of one equal respectively to two sides and the included angle of the other and arranged in the reverse order, the triangles are symmetric.*

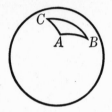 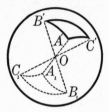

Given △ ABC and $A'B'C'$ on = spheres with $AC = A'C'$, $BC = B'C'$, $\angle C = \angle C'$, and the parts arranged in the reverse order.

To prove that △ ABC is symmetric to △ $A'B'C'$.

⎡ *Selection of Method:* 1. Known methods of proving spherical △
symmetric: § 282.
2. Method to be used: § 282. ⎤

Proof: *STATEMENTS*   *REASONS*

STATEMENTS	REASONS
1. Draw △ $A_1B_1C_1$ symmetric to △ $A'B'C'$.	1. § 282.
2. $AC = A_1C_1$, $BC = B_1C_1$, and $\angle C = \angle C_1$.	2. Give proof.
3. ∴ △ $ABC \cong$ △ $A_1B_1C_1$.	3. § 284.
4. $\angle A = \angle A'$, $\angle B = \angle B'$, and $AB = A'B'$.	4. Give proof.
5. ∴ △ ABC is symmetric to △ $A'B'C'$.	5. § 282.

Proposition XVIII. Theorem (c, n)

288. *If two spherical triangles on a sphere or on equal spheres have two angles and the included side of one equal respectively to two angles and the included side of the other and arranged in the reverse order, the triangles are symmetric.*

(The demonstration is left to the student.)

Proposition XIX. Theorem (c, n)

289. *If two spherical triangles on a sphere or on equal spheres have the three sides of one equal respectively to the three sides of the other, the triangles are either congruent or symmetric.*

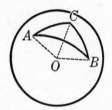 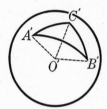 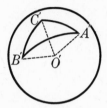

Given spherical △ *ABC* and *A'B'C'* on = spheres *O* and *O'*, with *AB* = *A'B'*, *BC* = *B'C'*, and *AC* = *A'C'*.

To prove that △ *ABC* and △ *A'B'C'* are either ≅ or symmetric.

⎡*Selection of Method:* 1. Known methods of proving spherical △ ≅ :
　　　　§§ 281, 283, 284, 285, 286; symmetric:
　　　　§§ 282, 287, 288.
　　2. Method to be used : §§ 281, 282.⎦

Proof: *STATEMENTS*　　　　　　*REASONS*

1. Draw *AO*, *BO*, *CO*, *A'O'*, *B'O'*, and *C'O'*.	1. Why possible ?
2. ∠*AOB* = ∠*A'O'B'*, ∠*BOC* = ∠*B'O'C'*, etc.	2. § 15 *n*.
3. ∴ trihedral ∠ *O-ABC* = or is symmetric to trihedral ∠ *O'-A'B'C'*.	3. § 97.
4. ∴ dihedral ∡ *AO*, *BO*, and *CO* = dihedral ∡ *A'O'*, *B'O'*, and *C'O'* respectively.	4. §§ 93, 94.
5. ∴ ∠*A* = ∠*A'*, ∠*B* = ∠*B'*, and ∠*C* = ∠*C'*.	5. §§ 270, 11 *e*.
6. ∴ △ *ABC* and *A'B'C'* are either ≅ or symmetric.	6. §§ 281, 282.

290. Corollary (c). *If two sides of a spherical triangle are equal, the angles opposite are equal.*

Proposition XX. Theorem (c, n)

291. *If two spherical triangles on a sphere or on equal spheres have the three angles of one equal respectively to the three angles of the other, the triangles are either congruent or symmetric.*

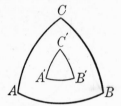 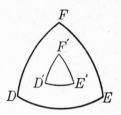

Given the spherical △ *ABC* and *DEF* on = spheres with ∠ A = ∠ D, ∠ B = ∠ E, and ∠ C = ∠ F.

To prove that △ *ABC* and △ *DEF* are either ≅ or symmetric.

> *Selection of Method:* 1. Known methods of proving spherical △ ≅:
> §§ 281, 283, 284, 285, 286, 289; symmetric: §§ 282, 287, 288, 289.
> 2. Method to be used: § 289.

Proof: *STATEMENTS*   *REASONS*

STATEMENTS	REASONS
1. Draw △ *A′B′C′*, the polar △ of △ *ABC*, and △ *D′E′F′*, the polar △ of △ *DEF*.	1. § 274.
2. ∠ A is the supplement of $\widehat{B'C'}$ and ∠ D is the supplement of $\widehat{E'F'}$.	2. § 277.
3. Since ∠ A = ∠ D, $\widehat{B'C'} = \widehat{E'F'}$.	3. § 15 c.
4. Likewise, $\widehat{A'C'} = \widehat{D'F'}$ and $\widehat{A'B'} = \widehat{D'E'}$.	4. Statements 2, 3.
5. ∴ △ *A′B′C′* and *D′E′F′* are either ≅ or symmetric.	5. § 289.
6. ∴ ∠ A′ = ∠ D′, ∠ B′ = ∠ E′ and ∠ C′ = ∠ F′.	6. §§ 281, 282.

Proof: STATEMENTS   REASONS

7. ABC is the polar $\triangle$ of $A'B'C'$ and DEF is the polar $\triangle$ of $D'E'F'$.	7. § 275.
8. But A' is the supplement of $\widehat{BC}$ and $\angle D'$ is the supplement of $\widehat{EF}$.	8. § 277.
9. ∴ $\widehat{BC} = \widehat{EF}$.	9. § 15 c.
10. Likewise, $\widehat{AC} = \widehat{DF}$ and $\widehat{AB} = \widehat{DE}$.	10. Why?
11. ∴ $\triangle ABC$ and DEF are either $\cong$ or symmetric.	11. § 289.

292. Theorem (c). *If two angles of a spherical triangle are equal, the sides opposite the angles are equal.*

Suggestions. Draw $\triangle A'B'C'$, the polar $\triangle$ of ABC. Prove that $\triangle A'B'C'$ is isosceles. Then two $\angle$ of $\triangle A'B'C'$ are $=$. Why? Then $\triangle ABC$ is isosceles? Why?

293. Theorem (c). *If two angles of a spherical triangle are unequal, the side opposite the greater angle is the greater.*

Suggestions. Let $\triangle ABC$ have $\angle A > \angle B$. Draw $\widehat{AD}$ of a great $\odot$ so that $\angle BAD = \angle B$. Then $\widehat{AD} = \widehat{BD}$ (§ 292). $\widehat{AD} + \widehat{DC} > \widehat{AC}$ (§ 272).

294. Theorem (c). *If two sides of a spherical triangle are unequal, the angle opposite the greater side is the greater.* (Use indirect method.)

295. Equal Spherical Polygons. Two spherical polygons are equal (or equivalent) if they have equal areas.

296. Theorem (c, n). *On a sphere or on equal spheres the polar distances of equal circles are equal.*

Suggestions. Prove $\triangle BOA \cong \triangle B'O'A'$. Then $BO = B'O'$ and $PB = P'B'$. Then $\triangle BAP \cong \triangle B'A'P'$.

EXERCISE (GROUP B)

If the four sides of a spherical quadrilateral are equal, prove that its diagonals bisect each other.

Proposition XXI. Theorem (c, N)

297. *Two symmetric spherical triangles are equal.*

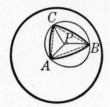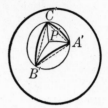

Given the symmetric spherical △ *ABC* and *A'B'C'* on
= spheres with *AB* = *A'B'*, *BC* = *B'C'*, and *AC* = *A'C'*.

To prove that △ *ABC* = △ *A'B'C'*.

⌈*Selection of Method:* 1. Known methods of proving spherical △ = :⌉
§§ 281, 295.
　　　　　　　　　2. Method to be used : § 295.
⌊　　　　　　　　　　　　　　　　　　　　　　　　　　　　　⌋

Proof:　　　STATEMENTS　　　　　　　　　　REASONS

1. Draw a ⊙ through *A*, *B*, and *C* and let *P* be its pole. Draw a ⊙ through *A'*, *B'*, and *C'* and let *P'* be its pole.	1. § 238.
2. Draw $\widehat{PA}$, $\widehat{PB}$, $\widehat{PC}$, $\widehat{P'A'}$, $\widehat{P'B'}$, and $\widehat{P'C'}$ of great ⊙s.	2. § 237.
3. $\widehat{AB} = \widehat{A'B'}$, $\widehat{BC} = \widehat{B'C'}$, and $\widehat{AC} = \widehat{A'C'}$.	3. Why?
4. Then chord *AB* = chord *A'B'*, chord *BC* = chord *B'C'*, and chord *AC* = chord *A'C'*.	4. Why?
5. ∴ plane △ *ABC* ≅ plane △ *A'B'C'*.	5. Why?
6. Since *A*, *B*, and *C* will coincide respectively with *A'*, *B'*, and *C'*, ⊙ *ABC* ≅ ⊙ *A'B'C'*.	6. Why?
7. The polar distances *PA*, *PB*, and *PC* = respectively the polar distances *P'A'*, *P'B'*, and *P'C'*.	7. § 296.
8. The isos. △ *PAB* ≅ the isos. △ *P'A'B'*.	8. §§ 289, 285.
9. Similarly, △ *PAC* ≅ △ *P'A'C'*, and △ *PBC* ≅ △ *P'B'C'*.	9. Reasons 8.
10. ∴ △ *ABC* = △ *A'B'C'*.	10. § 295.

298. Spherical Degree. A *spherical degree* is a portion of a sphere inclosed by a spherical triangle of which two sides are arcs of 90° each and the third side is an arc of 1°. From the figure it may be seen that a hemisphere contains 360 spherical degrees and a sphere contains 720 spherical degrees. Therefore, a spherical degree is $\frac{1}{720}$ of a sphere. The spherical degree is used in measuring and comparing the areas of spheri- cal surfaces on the same sphere. A spherical degree on one sphere is not equal to a spherical degree on another unequal sphere. Why?

299. Lune. A *lune* is a spherical figure composed of two great semicircles. *ABCD* is a lune composed of semicircles *ABC* and *ADC*. The *angle of a lune* is the angle formed by the semicircles. A sphere may be regarded as a lune whose angle is 360° or two straight angles. The surface of a lune is the portion of the sphere included between the semicircles. The *area of a lune* is the area of the surface of the lune.

300. Theorem (c, n). *The number of spherical degrees in the area of a lune is twice the number of degrees in the angle of the lune.*

EXERCISES (GROUP A)

1. Can two plane triangles be congruent if three sides of one are equal respectively to three sides of the other, if the sides are arranged in the reverse order and if the triangles always remain in the same plane?

2. Is a zone formed by arcs of great circles? Is a lune formed by arcs of great circles?

3. What is the name of the figure on the earth's surface formed by two meridians?

4. What is the area in spherical degrees of the earth's surface inclosed by the meridians passing through Washington, D.C., and St. Louis, Missouri?

5. Can you suggest a reason why a lune is so named?

Proposition XXII. Theorem (c, n)

301. *The number of spherical degrees in the area of a spherical triangle is equal to the number of degrees in its spherical excess.*

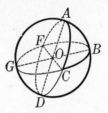

Given the spherical △ *ABC* with its spherical excess denoted by *E*.

To prove that area △ *ABC* = *E* spherical degrees.

> *Selection of Method:* 1. Known methods of finding areas expressed in spherical degrees: §§ 298, 300.
> 2. Method to be used: § 300.

Proof:

STATEMENTS	REASONS
1. Extend $\widehat{AB}, \widehat{BC},$ and $\widehat{AC}$ forming great ⑨.	1. § 237.
2. △ *ABC* + △ *ABF* = lune *CBFA* = 2 *C* spherical degrees.	2. § 11 *h*, § 300.
3. The planes of the great ⑨ *AC*, *AB*, and *BC* intersect in diameters of the sphere.	3. Give proof.
4. Draw these diameters *AD*, *BG*, and *CF*.	4. Why possible?
5. $\widehat{AB} = \widehat{GD}, \widehat{AF} = \widehat{DC},$ and $\widehat{BF} = \widehat{CG}.$	5. Give proof.
6. ∴ △ *ABF* = △ *CGD*.	6. §§ 289, 297.
7. From (2) and (6), △ *ABC* + △ *CGD* = 2 *C* spherical degrees.	7. Why?
8. △ *ABC* + △ *BCD* = lune *ACDB* = 2 *A* spherical degrees.	8. Why?
9. △ *ABC* + △ *ACG* = lune *BAGC* = 2 *B* spherical degrees.	9. Why?
10. Adding (7), (8), and (9), $3 \triangle ABC + \triangle CGD + \triangle BCD + \triangle ACG$ = 2(*A* + *B* + *C*) spherical degrees.	10. Why?

Proof: *STATEMENTS* | *REASONS*

11. Then $2 \triangle ABC + (\triangle ABC + \triangle CGD + \triangle BCD + \triangle ACG) = 2(A + B + C)$ spherical degrees.	11. Why?
12. But $\triangle ABC + \triangle CGD + \triangle BCD + \triangle ACG = 360$ spherical degrees.	12. § 298.
13. $\therefore 2 \triangle ABC + 360$ spherical degrees $= 2(A + B + C)$ spherical degrees.	13. Why?
14. $\triangle ABC + 180$ spherical degrees $= (A + B + C)$ spherical degrees.	14. Why?
15. $\triangle ABC = (A + B + C - 180)$ spherical degrees.	15. Why?
16. $\therefore \triangle ABC = E$ spherical degrees.	16. §§ 280, 11 e.

302. Corollary I. *The ratio of the area of a spherical triangle to the area of the sphere is $\dfrac{E}{720}$, where E is the spherical excess of the triangle.*

303. Corollary II (c, N). *The number of spherical degrees in the area of a spherical polygon is equal to the number of degrees in its spherical excess.*

ORAL EXERCISES

1. How many spherical degrees are in a sphere? in a hemisphere?

2. What is the spherical excess of a spherical triangle whose angles are right angles?

3. Is it possible to have a spherical triangle whose angle sum is 500°?

4. How many spherical degrees does a spherical triangle contain if its angle sum is 360°? The triangle is what part of the sphere?

5. How many spherical degrees are in a spherical triangle whose angles contain 100°, 80°, and 80° respectively?

6. If the spherical excess of a spherical triangle is $x°$, what part of the sphere is it?

7. ABC is an equiangular spherical triangle. What is the upper limit of $\angle A$? What is the lower limit of $\angle A$?

8. Is the exterior angle of a convex spherical triangle equal to the sum of the two opposite interior angles?

EXERCISES (GROUP A). *AREAS*

1. The angles of a spherical triangle contain 85°, 75°, and 135° respectively, and the radius of the sphere is 8 inches long. Find the area of the spherical triangle expressed in square inches.

2. What is the area of the surface of the earth bounded by the 77° W. longitude meridian and the 90° W. longitude meridian, assuming the diameter of the earth to be 8000 miles?

3. How much sooner does the sun rise at London than at St. Louis?

4. What part of the earth's surface is included between the parallels 30° N. latitude and 30° S. latitude?

5. Prove that the areas of two lunes have the same ratio as the angles of the lunes.

6. Show that the area of a trirectangular spherical triangle is 90 spherical degrees.

EXERCISES (GROUP B). *AREAS*

1. Prove that the areas of two zones on a sphere have the same ratio as their altitudes.

2. Find the diameter of a sphere whose area is 1 square foot.

3. Find the area of a spherical polygon on a sphere with radius of 18 inches if the angles contain 144°, 154°, 62°, and 90° respectively.

4. What is the diameter of a sphere whose area is 64 π square inches?

5. Prove that the meridians of the earth's surface are perpendicular to the equator.

6. At New York City, which is longer, a degree of longitude or a degree of latitude?

7. Find the area in square miles of the land bounded by 60° N. latitude, 45° N. latitude, 90° W. longitude, and 85° W. longitude.

304. Spherical Pyramid. A *spherical pyramid* is a solid whose base is a spherical polygon and whose vertex is the center of the sphere. In the figure, *O-ABCD* is a spherical pyramid. *ABCD* is the base and *O* the vertex of the pyramid.

305. Spherical Sector and Spherical Wedge. If a semicircle is revolved about its diameter as an axis, it generates a sphere. Any sector of the semicircle generates a *spherical sector.*

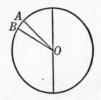 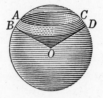

A spherical sector has a zone as its base and the center of the sphere as its vertex. The sector *AOB* generates the spherical sector *O-ABDC.*

A *spherical wedge* is a solid formed by a lune and the planes of its great circles (see figure in § 314).

306. Spherical Segment. A *spherical segment* is a solid formed by a zone and the planes of its bases.

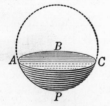 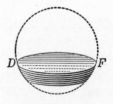

If one of the planes forming the zone is tangent to the sphere, a segment of one base, such as *APCB*, is formed.

The *altitude* of a spherical segment is the perpendicular between the planes. Does segment *DF* have one or two bases?

307. Volume of a Sphere. The *volume of a sphere* is the number of cubic units contained within it.

308. Postulate. *If a cube is circumscribed about a sphere and planes are drawn tangent to the sphere at the intersections of the sphere with lines joining the center to the vertices of the circumscribed cube, and if this process is continued indefinitely, the volume of the resulting polyhedron will approach the volume of the sphere as a limit, and the area of the resulting polyhedron will approach the area of the sphere as a limit.*

Proposition XXIII. Theorem (c, N)

309. *The volume of a sphere with radius r is $\frac{4}{3}\pi r^3$.*

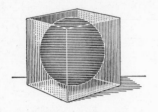 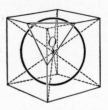

Given a sphere with center O, volume V, and radius r.

To prove that $V = \frac{4}{3}\pi r^3$.

⎡ *Selection of Method:* 1. Known methods of finding volumes of
⎢   solids: §§ 173, 175, 223, 226.
⎣   2. Method to be used: § 223 a. ⎦

Proof:

STATEMENTS	REASONS
1. Circumscribe a cube about the sphere O.	1. § 251.
2. Draw line segments from O to the vertices of the cube, forming pyramids whose bases are the faces of the cube.	2. Why possible?
3. The volume of each pyramid is $\frac{1}{3} r$ times its base.	3. § 223 a.
4. Denote the volume of the cube by V', the area of its surface by S', and the area of the sphere by S. Then $$V' = \tfrac{1}{3} r S'.$$	4. § 11 a.
5. Now continuously increase the number of faces of the circumscribed polyhedron by passing planes tangent to the sphere at the intersections of the sphere with lines joining the center to the vertices of the circumscribed polyhedron.	5. § 38.
6. Then $V' \rightarrow V$ and $S' \rightarrow S$.	6. § 308.
7. $\frac{1}{3} r S' \rightarrow \frac{1}{3} r S$.	7. § 160 a.

Proof: *STATEMENTS*   *REASONS*

8. Since $V' = \frac{1}{3} rS'$, $V' \rightarrow V$, and   8. § 160 *b*.
   $\frac{1}{3} rS' \rightarrow \frac{1}{3} rS$, then $V = \frac{1}{3} rS$.
9. But $S = 4 \pi r^2$.   9. § 263.
10. ∴ $V = \frac{1}{3} r \times 4 \pi r^2 = \frac{4}{3} \pi r^3$.   10. § 11 *e*.

310. Corollary I. *The volume of a sphere with diameter d is* $\frac{1}{6} \pi d^3$.

311. Corollary II. *The volumes of two spheres have the same ratio as the cubes of their radii or as the cubes of their diameters.*

312. Interesting Relations of the Sphere, Cone, Cylinder, and Cube. If a cylinder is circumscribed about a sphere,

 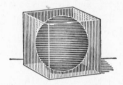

the volume of the sphere is two thirds that of the cylinder, and the area of the sphere is equal to the lateral area of the cylinder, or two thirds of the total area of the cylinder. Can you prove these statements?

If a cone has its base and height equal respectively to the base and height of this cylinder, its volume is one third that of the cylinder, or one half that of the sphere. Can you prove these facts?

If a cube is circumscribed about a sphere, the sphere has about one half the volume of the cube.

313. The Works of Archimedes. Archimedes, the greatest mathematician of antiquity and rivaled only by Newton of the modern world, was born in Syracuse, Sicily, about 287 B.C. After he had finished his studies at the university of Alexandria, Egypt, he returned to Syracuse and lived there the remainder of his life. Although he took no part in public life, his advice and help were often sought by King Hiero.

Many stories are told of his mechanical ability. It is said

that when the Romans were laying siege to the city of Syracuse, Archimedes devised catapults for throwing stones at the Roman soldiers, and by means of large lenses and mirrors set fire to their ships. Marcellus, the Roman commander, is said to have chided his own engineers with the words, "Shall we not make an end of fighting against this geometrical Briareus who, sitting at ease by the sea, plays pitch and toss with our ships to our own confusion, and by the multitude of missiles that he hurls at us outdoes the hundred-handed giants of mythology?" Syracuse finally fell, and Archimedes was killed during the sack of the city in spite of the orders of Marcellus to spare his life. It is said that a soldier entered the home of Archimedes, who was looking at a geometrical diagram drawn in sand on the floor (this was the usual way of drawing figures at that time), and as the soldier approached him, Archimedes said, "Do not disturb my diagram." The soldier, feeling insulted, slew him. Marcellus caused to be erected in his honor a tomb bearing the figure of a sphere inscribed in a cylinder.

Cicero, in his "Tusculan Disputations," relates how on his visit to Syracuse he found the tomb of Archimedes buried under rubbish.

Archimedes made many contributions to science. He discovered *the law of hydrostatics*, known as *the principle of Archimedes*, which states that a body immersed in a liquid is buoyed up by a force equal to the weight of the liquid displaced by it. He discovered the principle of the lever and invented the Archimedes screw, which was used in Egypt to drain the fields after they were inundated by the Nile. Once King Hiero of Syracuse, who had built a ship so large that it could not be launched, sought the aid of Archimedes. Archimedes overcame the difficulty by devising a system of cog wheels worked by an endless screw. At this time Archimedes said that had he a fixed fulcrum, he could move the world itself.

In the field of geometry Archimedes composed treatises on "Centers of Plane Gravities," "Quadrature of the Parabola," "Sphere and Cylinder," "The Measurement of the Circle,"

"Spirals," and "Conoids and Spheroids." Of all his discoveries he prized most highly the theorems relating to the sphere and cylinder. These theorems are as follows:

1. The area of a sphere is equal to four times that of a great circle.

2. The area of a zone of one base is equal to a circle whose radius is the line segment drawn from the vertex of the zone to the circle of its base.

3. The volume and area of a sphere are two thirds of the volume and area, respectively, of the cylinder circumscribed about the sphere.

NUMERICAL EXERCISES (GROUP A)

1. What is the volume of a sphere whose radius is 8 inches?

2. Find the volume of a sphere whose radius is 15 inches.

3. Find the radius of a sphere whose circumference is 25.1328 feet. ($\pi = 3.1416$.)

4. The diameter of one brass ball is three times the diameter of another. If the weight of the smaller is 425 pounds, what is the weight of the larger?

5. The volume of one sphere is 27 times that of another. What is the ratio of their radii? of their diameters? of their surfaces?

6. A sphere 14 inches in diameter is inscribed in a cylinder. What is the area of the sphere? the lateral area of the cylinder? What is the volume of the sphere? of the cylinder?

7. Solve the formula $S = 4 \pi r^2$ for r.

8. An iron sphere just fits into a cube. If the cube is filled with water and the sphere placed in the cube, 200 pounds of water flows out. What is the volume of the cube? (1 cubic foot of water weighs 62.4 pounds.)

9. The volume of one sphere is 36 cubic inches. What is the volume of another sphere whose radius is $2\frac{1}{3}$ times as long as the radius of the smaller sphere?

10. What is the area of a lune on a sphere with a diameter 20 inches in length if the angle of the lune is 18°?

11. Find the area of a zone on a sphere having a radius of 12 inches if the height of the zone is 4 inches.

12. The angles of a spherical polygon are 100°, 90°, 170°, and 120° respectively. The polygon is what part of the sphere?

NUMERICAL EXERCISES (GROUP B)

1. What is the volume of a sphere inscribed in a cube with an edge of 5 inches?

2. What is the radius of a sphere whose volume is 400 cubic inches? ($\frac{4}{3} \pi r^3 = 400$.)

3. Solve the formula $V = \frac{4}{3} \pi r^3$ for r.

4. If S denotes the area of a sphere and V its volume, prove that $S = \sqrt[3]{36 \pi V^2}$.

5. A spherical metal shell is $\frac{1}{2}$ inch thick. If the inside diameter of the shell is 9 inches, find the volume of metal in the shell.

6. A lune whose angle is 45° is equal in area to a zone on the same sphere. What is the ratio of the altitude of the zone to the radius of the sphere?

7. If the number of square inches in the surface of a sphere is equal to the number of cubic inches in its volume, what is the radius of the sphere?

8. What is the volume of a sphere inscribed in a regular tetrahedron each edge of which is e?

9. Find the volume of a sphere circumscribed about a regular tetrahedron each of whose edges is e.

10. Find the diameter of a 12-pound cast-iron shot if one cubic foot of the iron weighs 468 pounds.

11. Find the diameter of a 16-pound lead shot if one cubic foot of the lead weighs 706.25 pounds.

12. What is the weight of an iron spherical shell $\frac{1}{2}$ inch thick if the inside diameter of the shell is 18 inches and if a cubic foot of the iron weighs 480 pounds?

13. A sphere is placed in a cubical box, and then the remaining space of the box is filled with water. If the faces of the box are tangent to the sphere and if one gallon of water is required to fill the remaining space, what is the volume of the sphere?

MISCELLANEOUS EXERCISES (GROUP A)

1. What is the locus of a point 5 inches from a given point? 5 inches from a given line? 5 inches from a given plane?

2. Two grapefruit of the same kind have diameters of 3 inches and 4 inches respectively. If the smaller grapefruit sell at the rate of three for twenty-five cents, what should be the selling price of one of the larger kind?

3. How far from the center of a sphere of radius 10 inches should a plane be passed so as to cut from the sphere a circle having an area of 113 square inches?

4. *Prove:* If a spherical triangle is isosceles, its polar triangle is isosceles.

5. *Prove:* If a point on a sphere is equidistant from three points on a small circle of the sphere, it is the pole of the circle.

6. A 10-pound spherical iron ball is 3.6 inches in diameter. Find the diameter of a 16-pound iron ball.

7. Two spheres resting on the same table touch each other. If the radii of the spheres are 6 inches and 10 inches respectively, how far apart are the points of support?

8. If two spheres intersect, is the plane of intersection perpendicular to the line of centers?

9. Prove that if two lines are tangent to a sphere at the same point on the sphere, their plane is tangent to the sphere.

10. What part of the surface of the earth lies in the zone between the equator and the parallel 30° north?

11. What is the area in spherical degrees of a lune whose angle is 72°?

MISCELLANEOUS EXERCISES (GROUP B)

1. How many solid spheres each 2 inches in diameter can be placed in a box whose inside dimensions are 14 inches, $15\frac{3}{4}$ inches, and 8 inches?

2. If the atmosphere is clear, how many square miles of the earth's surface can be seen from an airplane 3 miles high?

3. The angles of a spherical triangle on a sphere with radius 7 inches are 140°, 130°, and 90°. The angles of another spherical triangle on a sphere with radius 9 inches are 70°, 70°, and 160°. How do the areas of the two triangles compare?

4. Show that the sum of the angles of a spherical quadrilateral is greater than 4 right angles and less than 8 right angles. (The area in spherical degrees is greater than 0° and less than 360°. Why?)

5. A sphere with a diameter of 8 inches and a right circular cone with a height of 8 inches and a base diameter of 8 inches rest on the same plane. How far from this plane must another parallel plane be placed to cut equal sections from the cone and the sphere?

6. The perimeter of a spherical triangle on a sphere with radius 12 inches is 240°. What is the area of its polar triangle?

7. The linear dimensions of a bridge are to be 1000 times as great as those of a given model. If the model weighs 2 pounds, what will be the weight of the bridge?

314. Volumes of Spherical Pyramids, Sectors, Wedges, and Segments. The following theorems are given without proof:

a. The volume of a spherical pyramid is expressed by the formula $V = \dfrac{\pi r^3 E}{540}$, where r is the radius of the sphere and E is the spherical excess of the polygon.

b. The volume of a spherical wedge is expressed by the formula $V = \dfrac{\pi r^3 A}{270}$, where r is the radius of the sphere and A is the angle of the lune that is its base.

c. The volume of a spherical sector is expressed by the formula $V = \frac{2}{3} \pi r^2 h$, where r is the radius of the sphere and h is the altitude of the zone that is its base.

d. The volume of a spherical segment is expressed by the formula $V = \frac{1}{6} \pi h(h^2 + 3 r^2 + 3 r_1{}^2)$, where h is the altitude and r and r_1 are the radii of the bases.

EXERCISES (GROUP B). *FINDING VOLUMES*

1. Find the volume of a spherical pyramid if the altitude is 20 inches and the angles of the base are 105°, 115°, 135°, and 140°.

2. Find the volume of a spherical wedge of a sphere whose radius is 12 inches if the angle of the wedge is 90°.

3. Find the volume of a spherical sector if the altitude of its zone is 9 inches and the radius of the sphere is 12 inches.

4. Find the volume of a spherical segment if the radii of the bases are 4 inches and 5 inches respectively and its altitude is 3 inches.

5. Find the volume of a spherical pyramid if the radius of the sphere is 10 inches and the base of the pyramid is a spherical triangle whose angles are 72°, 104°, and 112°.

315. Problem. *To find the diameter of a material sphere.*

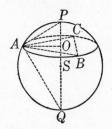 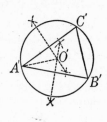 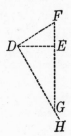

Given a material sphere S.

To find its diameter.

Construction: *STATEMENTS* *REASONS*

1. With any point P on the sphere as a pole draw a convenient small $\odot$ ABC, and let its center be O.	1. Why possible?
2. In a plane construct the $\triangle$ $A'B'C'$ whose sides are respectively $=$ the chords AB, BC, and CA. (Chord AB is measured by adjusting the compasses so that the end points of the legs rest on points A and B of the sphere.)	2. Why possible?
3. Circumscribe a $\odot$ O' about $\triangle$ $A'B'C'$.	3. Why possible?
4. Draw $A'O'$, the radius of $\odot$ O'.	4. Why possible?
5. Construct rt. $\triangle$ DEF with hypotenuse $DF = AP$ and leg $DE = A'O'$.	5. Give in full.
6. At D construct $DH \perp DF$.	6. Why possible?
7. Extend FE to intersect DH at G.	7. Why possible?

Then FG is the diameter of the sphere S.

Proof: *STATEMENTS* *REASONS*

1. Draw diameter PQ of the sphere.	1. Why possible?
2. Draw QA and OA.	2. Why possible?
3. $\triangle$ $DEF \cong \triangle$ AOP and $\triangle$ $FDG \cong \triangle$ PAQ.	3. Give proof.
4. $\therefore FG = PQ$.	4. Give proof.

MISCELLANEOUS EXERCISES

1. Find the diameter of some conveniently large sphere such as a spherical-blackboard or a basket ball.

2. If a micrometer is available from your physics laboratory, find the diameter of a marble, or some sphere of like size.

3. In the third century B.C. Eratosthenes determined a method for measuring the circumference of the earth. He found that when the sun's rays were vertical at Syene, they made an angle of 7° 12′ with a vertical pole *AE* at Alexandria. Then assuming that the sun's rays are parallel, ∠ *DAE* = ∠ *BOA*. Why? Knowing the distance *AS* and ∠ *DAE*, he computed the 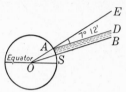 length of a degree on the earth's surface. How did he do this? From the length of a degree, how did he find the circumference of the earth? Can Eratosthenes' method be employed using Chicago and St. Louis? using Baltimore and Indianapolis?

4. A spherical shell 3 inches thick contains the same amount of material as a solid sphere whose radius is 8 inches. Find the radius of the outer surface of the shell.

5. Find the volume of a sphere circumscribed about a rectangular solid whose edges are 3 inches, 4 inches, and 12 inches.

6. A cube and a sphere have equal areas. What is the ratio of their volumes?

7. A hole ¼ inch in diameter was bored through a lead ball 2 inches in diameter. Find the weight of the ball if a cubic foot of the lead weighs 712.5 pounds.

8. Show that the sum of the angles of a spherical pentagon is greater than 6 right angles and less than 10 right angles.

9. Prove that the volume of a tetrahedron is equal to one third of the product of its area and the radius of the inscribed sphere.

10. Find the radius of a sphere equal in volume to a cube whose diagonal is 1 foot.

11. A cylindrical tank 4 feet in diameter, partly filled with water, is lying on its side. If the greatest depth of the water is 3 feet 4 inches, what part of the tank is filled with water?

316. Theorem (c). *The shortest line between two points on a sphere is the minor arc of a great circle through these points.*

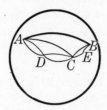

Given two points A and B on a sphere, with AB the minor arc of a great ⊙ through them.

To prove that $\overarc{AB}$ is the shortest line between A and B on the sphere.

Proof:

STATEMENTS	REASONS
1. Let $ADCEB$ be any other line on the sphere joining A and B, and C a point not on $\overarc{AB}$. Draw $\overarc{AC}$ and $\overarc{BC}$ of great ⊚.	1. Why possible?
2. $\overarc{AB} < \overarc{AC} + \overarc{CB}$.	2. § 272.
3. If line $ADCEB$ coincides with $\overarc{AC}$ and $\overarc{CB}$, the theorem is proved.	3. Statements 1 and 2.
4. If line $ADCEB$ does not coincide with $\overarc{AC}$ and $\overarc{CB}$, select the point D of $ADCEB$ not on $\overarc{AC}$ or $\overarc{CB}$ and draw $\overarc{AD}$ and $\overarc{DC}$ of great ⊚.	4. § 237.
5. Then $\overarc{AC} < \overarc{AD} + \overarc{DC}$.	5. § 272.
6. ∴ $\overarc{AB} < \overarc{AD} + \overarc{DC} + \overarc{CB}$.	6. § 11 e.
7. In like manner, we can take any number of points on line $ADCEB$, and $\overarc{AB}$ will be less than the sum of the arcs through these points.	7. Statements 2–6.
8. ∴ $\overarc{AB}$ is the shortest line between A and B on the sphere.	8. § 11 j.

EXERCISE

What postulate in plane geometry corresponds to § 316?

REVIEW QUESTIONS

1. What is the locus of a point 7 inches from a given point?

2. What is the name of a circle on a sphere whose center is the center of the sphere?

3. What is the axis of a circle on a sphere? What is the name of each of its ends?

4. Can two circles on a sphere have the same center? the same poles?

5. Do all circles of a sphere bisect each other?

6. Can a plane intersect a sphere in a circle?

7. Can a sphere be circumscribed about any tetrahedron? about any cube? about any rectangular solid? about any parallelepiped?

8. Can a sphere be passed through any two points? through any three points? through any four points? Explain each answer.

9. Will two meridians and the 45° N. parallel form a spherical triangle on the earth's surface?

10. How does the sum of the angles of a spherical triangle compare with the sum of the angles of a plane triangle?

11. Are two spherical triangles congruent if the three sides of one are equal respectively to the three sides of the other?

12. Are two spherical triangles congruent if the three angles of one are equal respectively to the three angles of the other?

13. What is a quadrant? a pole? polar distance?

14. How do you find (*a*) the area of a circle? (*b*) the area of a sphere? (*c*) the area of a zone? (*d*) the area of a lune? (*e*) the area of a spherical triangle?

15. How many spherical degrees are there in a hemisphere?

16. Through two points on a sphere how many small circles may be passed? how many great circles?

17. A stone of irregular shape was placed in a cylindrical pail filled with water. The stone was then removed from the water and it was found that the pail lacked 2 inches of being full. Find the volume of the stone if the pail was 10 inches high and 8 inches in diameter.

18. How do you find (*a*) the volume of a pyramid? (*b*) the volume of a cylinder? (*c*) the volume of a sphere? (*d*) the volume of a prism?

SUMMARY OF PRINCIPAL METHODS OF PROOF

317. *Great Circles of a Sphere*

 a. The center of a great circle of a sphere is the center of the sphere.
 b. All great circles of a sphere are equal.
 c. Any two great circles of a sphere bisect each other.
 d. Through any two points on a sphere that are not the extremities of a diameter one great circle of the sphere, and only one, can be drawn.

318. *Spherical Distances*

 a. The spherical distances of all points on a circle of a sphere from either pole of the circle are equal.
 b. The polar distance of a great circle is a quadrant.
 c. On a sphere or on equal spheres the polar distances of equal circles are equal.

319. *Spherical Angles*

 a. A spherical angle is equal to the dihedral angle formed by the planes of its sides.
 b. A spherical angle is equal in degrees to the arc of the great circle which has the vertex of the angle as a pole and is included between the sides of the angle, extended if necessary.

320. *Spherical Areas*

 a. The area of a sphere with radius r is $4\pi r^2$.
 b. The area of a sphere is equal to the product of its diameter and the circumference of a great circle.
 c. The areas of two spheres are to each other as the squares of their radii or as the squares of their diameters.
 d. The area of a zone is equal to the product of its altitude and the circumference of a great circle of the sphere.
 e. The number of spherical degrees in the area of a lune is twice the number of degrees in the angle of the lune.
 f. The number of spherical degrees in the area of a spherical triangle is equal to the number of degrees in its spherical excess.

g. The ratio of the area of a spherical triangle to the area of the sphere is $E : 720$, where E is the spherical excess of the triangle.

h. The number of spherical degrees in the area of a spherical polygon is equal to the number of degrees in its spherical excess.

321. *Spherical Polygons*

a. The sides of a spherical polygon are equal in degrees to the corresponding face angles of the polyhedral angle.

b. The angles of a spherical polygon are equal in degrees to the corresponding dihedral angles of the polyhedral angle.

c. The sum of the sides of a spherical polygon is less than $360°$.

322. *Spherical Triangles*

a. Each side of a spherical triangle is less than the sum of the other two sides.

b. If two sides of a spherical triangle are equal, the angles opposite the sides are equal.

c. If two angles of a spherical triangle are equal, the sides opposite the angles are equal.

d. If two angles of a spherical triangle are unequal, the side opposite the greater angle is the greater.

e. If two sides of a spherical triangle are unequal, the angle opposite the greater side is the greater.

f. Two symmetric spherical triangles are equal in area.

g. If one spherical triangle is the polar triangle of another, then the second is the polar triangle of the first.

h. In two polar triangles, each angle of one is the supplement of the opposite side of the other.

323. *Two Spherical Triangles Congruent or Symmetric*

a. If two spherical triangles on a sphere or on equal spheres have the sides and angles of one equal respectively to the sides and angles of the other, they are either congruent or symmetric.

b. Two spherical triangles which are symmetric to a third triangle are congruent.

c. If two spherical triangles on a sphere or on equal spheres have two sides and the included angle of one equal respectively to two sides and the included angle of the other and arranged in the same order, the triangles are congruent.

d. Two symmetric isosceles spherical triangles are congruent.

e. If two spherical triangles on a sphere or on equal spheres have two angles and the included side of one equal respectively to two angles and the included side of the other and arranged in the same order, the triangles are congruent.

f. If two spherical triangles on a sphere or on equal spheres have the three sides of one equal respectively to the three sides of the other, the triangles are either congruent or symmetric.

g. If two spherical triangles on a sphere or on equal spheres have the three angles of one equal respectively to the three angles of the other, the triangles are either congruent or symmetric.

h. If two spherical triangles on a sphere or on equal spheres have two sides and the included angle of one equal respectively to two sides and the included angle of the other and arranged in the reverse order, the triangles are symmetric.

i. If two spherical triangles on a sphere or on equal spheres have two angles and the included side of one equal respectively to two angles and the included side of the other and arranged in the reverse order, the triangles are symmetric.

324.   *Volumes of Spheres*

a. The volume of a sphere with radius r is $\frac{4}{3}\pi r^3$.

b. The volume of a sphere with diameter d is $\frac{1}{6}\pi d^3$.

c. The volumes of two spheres have the same ratio as the cubes of their radii or as the cubes of their diameters.

WORD LIST

birectangular	pole	symmetric
excess	quadrant	trirectangular
lune	sphere	zone
polar	spherical	

True-False Statements (*Fifteen Minutes*)

Copy the numbers of these statements on your paper. Then if a statement is *always* true, write T after its number. If a statement is *not always* true, write F after its number. Do not guess.

1. If a circle of a sphere has an axis, the circle is a great circle.
2. The equator is a great circle of the earth.
3. A plane tangent to a sphere is perpendicular to the radius drawn to the point of tangency.
4. The area of a sphere is 2 if its diameter is 2.
5. A sphere may be passed through any four points which are not coplanar.
6. All great circles of a sphere are equal.
7. The area of a lune whose angle is 60° is 60 spherical degrees.
8. Only great circles have polar distances.
9. If the angles of one spherical triangle are 70°, 80°, and 90°, the sides of its polar triangle are 110°, 80°, and 90°.
10. Not more than one sphere can be passed through three points which are not in the same straight line.
11. If two lines are tangent to a sphere at a given point on the sphere, the plane of these lines is tangent to the sphere at that point.
12. The polar distance of a great circle is 90°.
13. If the planes of two great circles of a sphere are perpendicular to each other, each circle passes through the poles of the other.
14. All points on a small circle of a sphere are equidistant from either of its poles.
15. A sphere is said to be circumscribed about a polyhedron if the vertices of the polyhedron are points of the sphere.
16. Through any two points on a sphere there can be one circle, and only one, drawn on the sphere.
17. Two sides of a spherical triangle are 75° and 80°. The third side may be 5°.
18. A zone on the earth's surface is bounded by two great circles.

TEST 14

Completing Statements (*Fifteen Minutes*)

On your paper write one word, and only one, for each blank to make the following statements true:

1. A _____ is the locus of points at a given distance from a given point.

2. A quadrant of a circle contains _____ degrees.

3. The greatest number of spheres that can be passed through 4 noncoplanar points is _____.

4. The _____ distance of the arctic circle is $23\frac{1}{2}°$.

5. The locus of points of the lines tangent to a sphere from a given point is a _____ _____.

6. A sphere may be inscribed in an irregular _____.

7. If a sphere can be inscribed in a rectangular solid, the solid is a _____.

8. All the circles on a sphere are equal if they have equal _____ distances.

9. A spherical angle is formed by two _____ circles on a sphere.

10. If the angle of a lune is 40°, its area is _____ spherical degrees.

11. $A = 4 \pi r^2$ is the formula for finding the _____ of a _____.

12. A boy has two solid iron balls. If the diameter of one is 3 times the diameter of the other, the volume of the larger is _____ times that of the smaller.

13. When going from New York to London, airplanes usually follow the _____ of a _____ circle.

14. Two great circles of a sphere will bisect _____ _____.

15. A plane tangent to a sphere is _____ to the radius drawn to the point of contact.

16. The areas of two spheres are to each other as _____ _____ _____ _____ _____.

17. Each side of a spherical triangle is _____ _____ the sum of the other two sides.

18. In two polar triangles each angle of one is _____ _____ _____ the opposite side of the other.

TEST 15

Applications (*Forty-five Minutes*)

1. Find the area of a sphere whose diameter is 7 inches. ($\pi = \frac{22}{7}$.)

2. Find the volume of a sphere whose diameter is 14 inches. ($\pi = \frac{22}{7}$.)

3. Find the circumference of a small circle on a sphere whose radius is 10 inches if the plane of the circle is 8 inches from the center.

4. The ratio of the radii of two spheres is 2 : 3. What is the ratio of their volumes?

5. What is the ratio of the areas of the spheres in Ex. 4?

6. A sphere is inscribed in a cube. The sphere is what per cent of the cube?

7. What is the spherical excess of a spherical triangle whose angles are 85°, 65°, and 75°?

8. An angle of a lune is 30°, and the radius of the sphere is 10 inches. What is the area of the lune?

9. What is the diameter of a sphere whose volume is 64 π?

10. The volume of a right circular cylinder is 120. A sphere just fits in the cylinder. What is the volume of the sphere?

11. Find the radius of a sphere whose area is 100 square inches.

12. The altitude of a zone on a sphere of radius 16 inches is 3 inches. Find the area of the zone.

13. The radius of a sphere is 6 inches. The angles of a spherical triangle on the sphere are 79°, 86°, and 60°. Find the area of the triangle.

14. The angles of one spherical triangle are 90°, 70°, and 80°. Find the sides of its polar triangle.

15. The angles of a spherical polygon on a 10-inch sphere are 100°, 120°, 120°, and 140°. What is the area of the polygon?

16. Find the area of a sphere whose volume is 288 π.

17. Find the volume of a sphere whose area is 64.

18. If a ball 3 inches in diameter weighs 15 pounds, what is the diameter of a ball of the same material weighing 120 pounds?

19. The angles of a triangle are 70°, 80°, and 100°. Find the angle of a lune of equal area.

CHAPTER VI

GENERAL POLYHEDRONS

325. Polyhedrons Classified as to Faces. A polyhedron of four faces is a *tetrahedron*; one of six faces, a *hexahedron*; one of eight faces, an *octahedron*; one of twelve faces, a *dodecahedron*; and one of twenty faces, an *icosahedron* (ī kŏ så hē′drŏn).

326. Regular Polyhedron. A *regular polyhedron* is a polyhedron whose faces are congruent regular polygons and whose polyhedral angles are congruent.

It will be proved in § 327 that there cannot be more than five regular polyhedrons. These five regular polyhedrons are shown in the illustration below in the order in which they are mentioned in § 325.

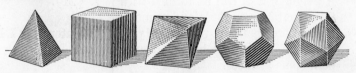

When certain liquids are solidified, either by cooling or by evaporation, crystals with definite shapes are formed. When brine is evaporated, the salt crystals formed are regular hexahedrons (cubes). Most minerals of the earth occur in crystalline form. Diamonds and certain compounds of copper are in the form of regular octahedrons.

EXERCISES (GROUP A)

1. Find the area of a regular dodecahedron if the area of each face is 14 square inches.

2. Find the area of a regular hexahedron 8 inches on an edge.

3. Find the area of a regular octahedron 6 inches on an edge.

Proposition I. Theorem (c, n)

327. *There can be no more than five regular polyhedrons.*

Proof:

STATEMENTS	REASONS
1. A polyhedral ∠ has at least three faces.	1. § 91.
2. The sum of the face ⩞ of a polyhedral ∠ is less than 360°.	2. § 96.
3. ∴ a polyhedral ∠ can be formed with three, four, or five equilateral ⩞ as faces, and no more.	3. § 21 *f*.
4. ∴ no more than three regular polyhedrons can be formed having equilateral ⩞ as faces.	4. Statements 1–3.
5. A polyhedral ∠ can be formed with three squares as faces, and no more.	5. § 21 *f*.
6. ∴ no more than one regular polyhedron can be formed having squares as faces.	6. Statements 1, 2, 5.
7. A polyhedral ∠ can be formed with three pentagons as faces, and no more.	7. § 21 *f*.
8. ∴ no more than one regular polyhedron can be formed having regular pentagons as faces.	8. Statements 1, 2, 7.
9. A polyhedral ∠ cannot be formed with regular polygons of more than five faces.	9. Why?
10. Hence there can be no more than five regular polyhedrons.	10. Statements 4, 6, 8, 9.

328. The Five Regular Polyhedrons. It was not proved in § 327 that there are five regular polyhedrons, but it is possible to prove their existence and construct them. The existence of the five regular polyhedrons has been known since early times. Pythagoras (6th century B.C.) knew of all the regular polyhedrons except the dodecahedron, which was discovered by Hippasus (5th century B.C.).

Models of the regular polyhedrons can easily be made as follows:

1. Draw on stiff paper the diagrams shown below.
2. Cut along the solid lines and fold along the dotted lines.
3. Fasten the edges that meet with gummed paper.

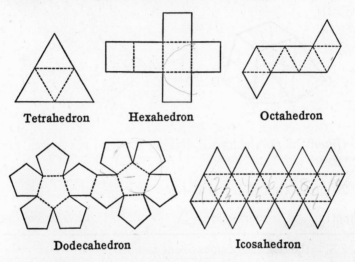

| Tetrahedron | Hexahedron | Octahedron |

| Dodecahedron | Icosahedron |

EXERCISES (GROUP A)

1. Construct models of the five regular polyhedrons shown above.

2. Copy the table below and fill in the blank spaces, referring to the models of Ex. 1:

Name	No. of faces	Form of faces	No. of edges	No. of vertices	No. of faces at each vertex	Sum of face ⁄s
Tetrahedron						
Hexahedron						
Octahedron						
Dodecahedron						
Icosahedron						

Proposition II. Theorem (Euler's) (n)

329. *If the number of edges of a polyhedron is denoted by E, the number of vertices by V, and the number of faces by F, then $E + 2 = V + F$.*

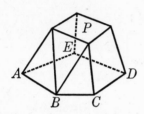
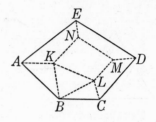

Given the polyhedron P, having E edges, V vertices, and F faces.

To prove that $E + 2 = V + F$.

Proof: STATEMENTS   REASONS

Let $S_1 =$ the number of sides of one face AD,
    $S_2 =$ the number of sides of a second face,

. . . . ,

and $S_F =$ the number of sides of the last face.

1. The sum of the $\measuredangle$ of $P = (S_1 - 2)$ st. $\measuredangle$ $+ (S_2 - 2)$ st. $\measuredangle + \cdots + (S_F - 2)$ st. $\measuredangle = (S_1 + S_2 + \cdots + S_F)$ st. $\measuredangle - 2 F$ st. $\measuredangle$.   1. §§ 21 *e*, 11 *a*.

2. $S_1 + S_2 + \cdots + S_F = 2 E$.   2. Why?

3. ∴ the sum of all the $\measuredangle$ of $P = 2 E$ st. $\measuredangle - 2 F$ st. $\measuredangle$, or $(E - F) 2$ st. $\measuredangle$.   3. Why?

From some point outside P project the several faces on $ABCDE$ as shown in the figure at the right above.

4. Then the sum of the $\measuredangle$ of $P =$ the sum of the $\measuredangle$ of $ABCDE$ and of the polygons projected on $ABCDE$.   4. §§ 21 *e*, 11 *a*.

Proof: *STATEMENTS*   *REASONS*

5. Then the sum of the $\angle$ of $P =$ the sum of the $\angle$ of $ABCDE +$ the sum of the $\angle$ of $ABCDE +$ the sum of the $\angle$ at K, L, M, etc.	5. § 11 e.
6. The sum of the $\angle$ at each point K, L, M, etc. is 2 st. $\angle$.	6. § 21 a.
7. The number of vertices of $P = V$, and the number of vertices of $ABCDE = S_1$.	7. Why?
8. The number of vertices of K, L, M, etc. $= V - S_1$.	8. § 11 b.
9. $\therefore$ the sum of the $\angle$ of $P = (S_1 - 2)$ st. $\angle$ $+ (S_1 - 2)$ st. $\angle + (V - S_1)$ 2 st. $\angle =$ $(V - 2)$ 2 st. $\angle$.	9. § 11 e.
10. $\therefore (E - F)$ 2 st. $\angle = (V - 2)$ 2 st. $\angle$.	10. § 11 f.
11. $\therefore E - F = V - 2$, or $E + 2 = V + F$.	11. Why?

Note. This theorem is called Euler's Theorem in honor of Leonhard Euler, one of the greatest mathematicians of the eighteenth century.

EXERCISES (GROUP A)

1. If a polyhedron has 7 faces and 10 vertices, how many edges does it have?

2. If a polyhedron has 9 faces and 5 more vertices than it has faces, how many edges does it have?

3. If a polyhedron has 12 edges and 8 vertices, how many faces does it have?

4. If a polyhedron has 36 edges and two thirds as many vertices as edges, how many faces does it have?

5. If a polyhedron has 8 faces and 2 more than twice as many edges, how many vertices does it have?

6. What is another name for a tetrahedron?

7. A plane cuts off a corner of a given polyhedron by cutting only the edges of one of its trihedral angles. Compare the number of edges of the resulting polyhedron with the number of edges of the given polyhedron. Compare the number of vertices. Compare the number of faces.

Proposition III. Theorem

330. *If the number of edges of a polyhedron is denoted by E, the number of vertices by V, the number of faces by F, and the sum of the face angles by S, then S = (V − 2) 2 st. ∡.*

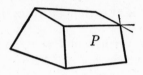

Given the polyhedron *P*, having *E* edges, *V* vertices, *F* faces, and the sum of the face ∡ = *S*.

To prove that *S* = (*V* − 2) 2 st. ∡.

Proof:

STATEMENTS	REASONS
1. Since each edge is common to two polygons, the number of sides of the faces equals 2 *E*.	1. § 9 *b*, 11 *c*.
2. Let an ext. ∠ be formed at each vertex of every polygon. Then the sum of an int. ∠ and an ext. ∠ at each vertex is one st. ∠.	2. § 16 *b*.
3. The sum of the ext. and int. ∡ of all faces is 2 *E* st. ∡, since the polygons have the same number of vertices as sides.	3. Why?
4. The sum of the ext. ∡ of each face is 2 st. ∡, and the sum of the ext. ∡ of *F* faces is 2 *F* st. ∡.	4. Why?
5. ∴ *S* = 2 *E* st. ∡ − 2 *F* st. ∡, or (*E* − *F*) 2 st. ∡.	5. § 11 *b*.
6. But *E* + 2 = *V* + *F*, or *E* − *F* = *V* − 2.	6. § 329.
7. ∴ *S* = (*V* − 2) 2 st. ∡.	7. § 11 *e*.

How does the above theorem compare with § 21 *e*?

331. Similar Polyhedrons. *Two polyhedrons are similar* if they have the same number of faces similar each to each and similarly placed, and have their corresponding polyhedral angles equal.

Proposition IV. Theorem (c, n)

332. *Two tetrahedrons are similar if the three faces which include a trihedral angle of one are similar respectively to the three faces which include a trihedral angle of the other, and are similarly placed.*

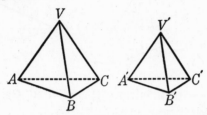

Given the tetrahedrons V-ABC and V'-$A'B'C'$ with $\triangle VAB \sim \triangle V'A'B'$, $\triangle VBC \sim \triangle V'B'C'$, $\triangle VAC \sim \triangle V'A'C'$, and the faces similarly placed.

To prove that V-$ABC \sim V'$-$A'B'C'$.

Proof:

STATEMENTS	REASONS
1. $\triangle VAB \sim \triangle V'A'B'$, $\triangle VBC \sim \triangle V'B'C'$, $\triangle VAC \sim \triangle V'A'C'$.	1. Why?
2. $\dfrac{AB}{A'B'} = \left(\dfrac{VB}{V'B'}\right) = \dfrac{BC}{B'C'} = \left(\dfrac{VC}{V'C'}\right) = \dfrac{AC}{A'C'}$.	2. Why?
3. $\therefore \dfrac{AB}{A'B'} = \dfrac{BC}{B'C'} = \dfrac{AC}{A'C'}$.	3. Why?
4. $\therefore \triangle ABC \sim \triangle A'B'C'$.	4. § 27 f.
5. $\angle AVB = \angle A'V'B'$, $\angle BVC = \angle B'V'C'$, $\angle AVC = \angle A'V'C'$.	5. Why?
6. These $\angle$ are similarly placed.	6. Given.
7. $\therefore$ trihedral $\angle V =$ trihedral $\angle V'$.	7. § 97.
8. Similarly, the other corresponding trihedral $\angle$ are $=$.	8. Statements 4-6.
9. The faces of V-ABC and V'-$A'B'C'$ are similarly placed.	9. Given.
10. $\therefore V$-$ABC \sim V'$-$A'B'C'$.	10. § 331.

Proposition V. Theorem (c, n)

333. *The volumes of two similar tetrahedrons have the same ratio as the cubes of any two corresponding edges.*

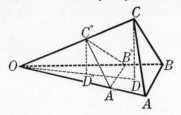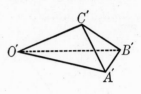

Given two ∼ tetrahedrons $O\text{-}ABC$ and $O'\text{-}A'B'C'$, with volumes V and V' respectively.

To prove that $\dfrac{V}{V'} = \dfrac{\overline{OC}^3}{\overline{O'C'}^3}$.

Proof:

STATEMENTS	REASONS
1. Place $O'\text{-}A'B'C'$ on $O\text{-}ABC$ so that trihedral $\angle O'$ coincides with trihedral $\angle O$, taking the position $O\text{-}A''B''C''$.	1. §§ 12f, 331.
2. Draw CD and $C''D''$ each $\perp$ plane OAB.	2. Why possible?
3. Then CD and $C''D''$ determine a plane intersecting plane OAB in OD and also $\perp$ plane OAB.	3. §§ 9 f, 9 b, 81.
4. $\triangle OCD \sim \triangle OC''D''$.	4. Give proof,
5. $\dfrac{CD}{C''D''} = \dfrac{OC}{OC''}$.	5. Why?
6. $\dfrac{V}{V'} = \dfrac{OAB \cdot CD}{OA''B'' \cdot C''D''} = \dfrac{OAB}{OA''B''} \cdot \dfrac{CD}{C''D''}$.	6. § 195.
7. $\dfrac{OAB}{OA''B''} = \dfrac{\overline{OA}^2}{\overline{OA''}^2}$ and $\dfrac{\overline{OA}^2}{\overline{OA''}^2} = \dfrac{\overline{OC}^2}{\overline{OC''}^2}$.	7. Give proof.
8. $\therefore \dfrac{OAB}{OA''B''} = \dfrac{\overline{OC}^2}{\overline{OC''}^2}$.	8. Why?
9. Then $\dfrac{V}{V'} = \dfrac{\overline{OC}^2}{\overline{OC''}^2} \cdot \dfrac{OC}{OC''} = \dfrac{\overline{OC}^3}{\overline{OC''}^3}$.	9. Why?

EXERCISES (GROUP A)

1. Find the area of a regular tetrahedron 4 inches on an edge; of a regular hexahedron 4 inches on an edge; of a regular octahedron 4 inches on an edge.

2. Find the volume of a tetrahedron each edge of which is 12 inches.

3. Two corresponding edges of two similar tetrahedrons are 3 inches and 5 inches respectively. Compare their volumes.

4. Find the diagonal of a regular octahedron with an edge of 16 inches.

5. Find the volume of a regular octahedron with an edge of 20 inches.

6. One edge of a tetrahedron is 7 inches and the corresponding edge of a similar tetrahedron is 11 inches. If the volume of the smaller tetrahedron is 294 cubic inches, what is the volume of the larger?

EXERCISES (GROUP B)

1. Find the volume of a regular tetrahedron whose slant height is $4\sqrt{3}$.

2. The volume of a tetrahedron with equal edges is 100 cubic inches. Find the length of an edge.

3. Find the volume of a regular tetrahedron whose area is 108 square inches.

4. Find the edge of a cube whose area is numerically equal to its diagonal.

5. If the edge of a regular tetrahedron is e, prove that its volume is given by the formula $V = \frac{1}{12} e^3 \sqrt{2}$.

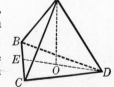

Suggestions. $V = \frac{1}{3} AO \cdot$ area of BCD. Why? $DE = \frac{1}{2} e\sqrt{3}$. Why? $OD = \frac{2}{3} DE$. Why? Find the length of AO from rt. $\triangle AOD$.

6. Prove that the volume of a sphere is to the volume of the inscribed cube as π is to $\frac{2}{3} \sqrt{3}$.

7. Prove that the section of a regular tetrahedron formed by a plane parallel to a face is an equilateral triangle.

8. Find the volume of a regular octahedron whose diagonal is 20 inches.

Proposition VI. Theorem (c, n)

334. *Two similar polyhedrons can be separated into the same number of tetrahedrons, similar each to each and similarly placed.*

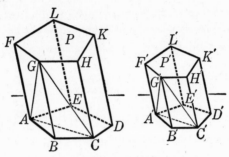

Given two ∼ polyhedrons P and P'.

To prove that P and P' can be separated into the same number of tetrahedrons, ∼ each to each and similarly placed.

Proof:

STATEMENTS	REASONS
1. Pass planes through G, A, and C and G', A', and C', forming tetrahedrons $G\text{-}ABC$ and $G'\text{-}A'B'C'$.	1. §9 c.
2. $\triangle ABG \sim \triangle A'B'G'$, $\triangle ABC \sim \triangle A'B'C'$, and $\triangle BGC \sim \triangle B'G'C'$.	2. § 27 h.
3. Trihedral $\angle B =$ trihedral $\angle B'$.	3. Given.
4. Tetrahedron $G\text{-}ABC \sim$ tetrahedron $G'\text{-}A'B'C'$.	4. § 332.
5. $\triangle ACG \sim \triangle A'C'G'$.	5. § 331.
6. Polygons FAG, GHC, and $ACDE$ ∼ polygons $F'A'G'$, $G'H'C'$, and $A'C'D'E'$ respectively.	6. Give proof, using §§ 27 h, 27 i.
7. Polyhedral ∡ A, C, and $G =$ polyhedral ∡ A', C', and G' respectively.	7. Given.

Proof: *STATEMENTS* *REASONS*

8. $\angle A\text{-}GBC = \angle A'\text{-}G'B'C'$, $\angle C\text{-}BAG = \angle C'\text{-}B'A'G'$, and $\angle G\text{-}ABC = \angle G'\text{-}A'B'C'$.	8. § 331.
9. ∴ when the tetrahedrons $G\text{-}ABC$ and $G'\text{-}A'B'C'$ are removed, the poly-hedral ∡ remaining at G, A, and C and G', A', and C' are respectively =.	9. § 11 *b*.
10. ∴ the remaining polyhedrons are ∼.	10. § 331 and given.
11. Two similar tetrahedrons can be cut off from the remainders, etc.	11. Statements 1–10.
12. ∴ P and P' can be separated into the same number of tetrahedrons ∼ each to each and similarly placed.	12. Why?

335. Corollary I. *Any two corresponding line segments of two similar polyhedrons have the same ratio as any two corresponding edges.*

336. Corollary II. *The areas of any two corresponding faces of two similar polyhedrons have the same ratio as the squares of any two corresponding line segments.*

337. Corollary III (c). *The total areas of two similar poly-hedrons have the same ratio as the squares of any two correspond-ing line segments.*

338. Corollary IV (c, n). *The volumes of any two similar polyhedrons have the same ratio as the cubes of any two correspond-ing line segments.* (Use §§ 334, 333, and 335.)

339. Prismatoid. A *prismatoid* is a polyhedron all of whose vertices lie in two parallel planes. The faces that lie in the parallel planes are called the *bases*. Prisms, pyramids, and frustums of pyramids are all special cases of the prismatoid. The *altitude* of a prismatoid is the distance between the parallel planes. The *midsection* of a prismatoid is the sec-tion made by a plane parallel to the bases and midway be-tween them.

Proposition VII. Theorem (n)

340. *The volume of a prismatoid equals the product of one sixth the altitude and the sum of the upper base, the lower base, and four times the midsection.*

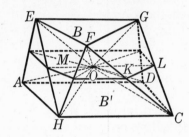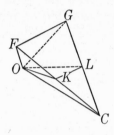

Given the prismatoid *AHCD-EFG* with altitude *h*, upper base *B*, lower base *B′*, and midsection *M*.

To prove that $V = \frac{1}{6} h(B + B' + 4 M)$.

Proof: *STATEMENTS*   *REASONS*

1. Join *0*, any point in the midsection, with the vertices of both bases and the midsection by straight line segments.	1. Why possible?
2. Pass planes through these lines dividing the prismatoid into pyramids with a common vertex at *0*.	2. Why possible?
3. Volume $0\text{-}EFG = \frac{1}{3} \cdot \frac{1}{2} h \cdot B = \frac{1}{6} hB$.	3. Why?
4. Volume $0\text{-}AHCD = \frac{1}{3} \cdot \frac{1}{2} h \cdot B' = \frac{1}{6} hB'$.	4. Why?
5. (*a*) Volume $0\text{-}FCG$ is divided into two parts by the midsection.	5. (*a*) Why?
(*b*) $\triangle KLC = \frac{1}{4} \triangle FCG$.	(*b*) § 26 *d*.
(*c*) Volume $0\text{-}KLC = \frac{1}{4}$ volume $0\text{-}FCG$.	(*c*) § 195.
(*d*) But $0\text{-}KLC = C\text{-}OKL = \frac{1}{3} \cdot \frac{1}{2} h (\triangle OKL) = \frac{1}{6} h(\triangle OKL)$.	(*d*) Why?
(*e*) ∴ volume $0\text{-}FCG = \frac{4}{6} h(\triangle OKL)$.	(*e*) Why?
(*f*) In like manner, the volume of each of the other pyramids having lateral	(*f*) Why?

Proof: *STATEMENTS*   *REASONS*

faces for bases can be shown to equal $\frac{4}{6} h$ times the area of the midsection included in it. If any pyramid is not triangular it can be divided into triangular pyramids.

(g) ∴ the volumes of the pyramids having lateral faces for bases is $\frac{4}{6} hM$.   (g) § 11 *a*.

6. ∴ $V = \frac{1}{6} hB + \frac{1}{6} hB' + \frac{4}{6} hM = \frac{1}{6} h(B + B' + 4M)$.   6. § 11 *a*.

Note. The prismatoid formula was introduced into geometry by Ernst Ferdinand August about 1850.

EXERCISES (GROUP B). *FINDING VOLUMES*

1. Derive the formulas for the volumes of a prism, pyramid, cylinder, and cone from the formula for the volume of a prismatoid.

2. Derive the formula for the volume of a frustum of a pyramid, using the formula for the volume of a prismatoid.

Suggestions. Since it is to be proved that $\frac{1}{6} h(B + B' + 4 M) = \frac{1}{3} h(B + B' + \sqrt{BB'})$, it is necessary to express M in terms of B and B'. If s and s' represent corresponding sides of B and B', then $\frac{1}{2}(s + s')$ is the corresponding side of M. Why?

$$\frac{s^2}{[\frac{1}{2}(s + s')]^2} = \frac{B}{M} \quad \text{and} \quad \frac{s'^2}{[\frac{1}{2}(s + s')]^2} = \frac{B'}{M},$$

or

$$\frac{s}{\frac{1}{2}(s + s')} = \frac{\sqrt{B}}{\sqrt{M}} \quad \text{and} \quad \frac{s'}{\frac{1}{2}(s + s')} = \frac{\sqrt{B'}}{\sqrt{M}}.$$

Add the corresponding members of the last two equations and solve for M. Then find $4 M$.

3. Using the prismatoid formula, find the volume of the frustum of a square pyramid if the lower base is 10 feet on a side, the upper base 6 feet on a side, and the altitude 16 feet. Also find its volume, using the frustum formula.

4. Using the prismatoid formula, find the volume of a frustum of a triangular pyramid if the lower base is an equilateral triangle 9 feet on a side, the upper base is an equilateral triangle 4 feet on a side, and the altitude is 20 feet.

Proposition VIII. Theorem

341. *The volume of any truncated triangular prism is equal to one third the area of a right section multiplied by the sum of the lateral edges.*

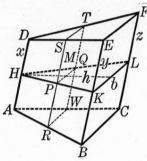

Given the truncated triangular prism *ABC-DEF*, with edges *x*, *y*, and *z*, and rt. section *HKL* whose base is *b* and whose altitude is *h*.

To prove that $V = \frac{1}{6} hb(x + y + z)$.

Proof:

STATEMENTS	REASONS
1. Through the midpoints of *AB* and *DE* pass a plane *RSTW* ∥ to plane *BCFE*.	1. Why possible?
2. The section *M* of the truncated prism made by plane *RSTW* is the midsection of prismatoid *AD-BCFE*, which has altitude *h*, one base *BCFE*, and the vertices *A* and *D* in line *AD* ∥ plane *BCFE*.	2. Give proof.
3. Area of trapezoid $BCFE = \frac{1}{2} b(y + z)$.	3. Why?
4. $RS = \frac{1}{2}(x + y)$, $TW = \frac{1}{2}(x + z)$, $PQ = \frac{1}{2} b$.	4. Give proof.
5. Area $M = \frac{1}{2} \cdot \frac{1}{2} b [\frac{1}{2}(x + y) + \frac{1}{2}(x + z)]$, or $M = \frac{1}{4} b(x + \frac{1}{2} y + \frac{1}{2} z)$ and $4M = b(x + \frac{1}{2} y + \frac{1}{2} z)$.	5. Why?
6. $V = \frac{1}{6} h[BCFE + 0 + 4M]$.	6. § 340.
7. ∴ $V = \frac{1}{6} h[\frac{1}{2} b(y + z) + b(x + \frac{1}{2} y + \frac{1}{2} z)]$, or $V = \frac{1}{6} hb(x + y + z)$.	7. § 11 *e*.

EXERCISES (GROUP A). *POLYHEDRONS*

1. Find the volume of a truncated right triangular prism, the sides of whose base are 8, 15, and 17 and whose lateral edges are 3, 4, and 5 respectively.

2. Find the volume of a truncated right triangular prism, the sides of whose base are 10 inches, 10 inches, and 6 inches, and whose lateral edges are 7 inches, 9 inches, and 11 inches respectively.

3. Find the volume of a polyhedron whose base is a rectangle 10 by 14 inches and whose lateral edges are perpendicular to the base, if the lengths of the lateral edges are 3, 5, 7, and 8 inches respectively.

Suggestion. Divide the polyhedron into two triangular truncated prisms by passing a plane through two diagonally opposite edges.

4. The corresponding edges of three similar tetrahedrons are 2, 4, and 5 respectively. Find the corresponding edge of a similar tetrahedron equal in volume to their sum.

5. Prove that the sum of two opposite lateral edges of a truncated parallelepiped is equal to the sum of the other two lateral edges.

6. The volumes of two similar polyhedrons are 64 cubic feet and 125 cubic feet respectively. If the area of the smaller is 160 square feet, what is the area of the larger?

7. Two wheat bins are similar in shape, one containing 270 bushels and the other 500 bushels. If the smaller bin is 9 feet deep, how deep is the larger?

8. The corresponding edges of two similar polyhedrons are 3 inches and 5 inches respectively. If the volume of the smaller is 512 cubic inches, find the volume of the larger.

EXERCISES (GROUP B). *POLYHEDRONS*

1. If the edge of a regular octahedron is e, prove that its volume is given by the formula $V = \frac{1}{3} e^3 \sqrt{2}$.

2. Find the volume of a regular octahedron whose edge is 8 inches.

3. Find the area and volume of a regular tetrahedron having an edge of 6 inches.

4. Find the volume of a regular tetrahedron that has an altitude of 4 inches.

5. Find the area of a regular dodecahedron whose edge is 3.

6. The edge of a regular icosahedron is 2. Find the edge of a similar icosahedron five times as large.

7. Find the difference between the number of edges and the number of vertices of an icosahedron.

8. The breast of a dam made of reënforced concrete has a cross section in the form of a trapezoid whose depth is 40 feet, the width of whose base is 90 feet, and whose sides make an angle of 45° with the base. If the breast of the dam is 1200 feet long, find the number of cubic yards of concrete in it.

SUMMARY OF PRINCIPAL METHODS OF PROOF

342. *Similar Polyhedrons*

a. Two tetrahedrons are similar if the three faces which include a trihedral angle of one are similar respectively to the three faces which include a trihedral angle of the other, and are similarly placed.

b. The volumes of two similar tetrahedrons have the same ratio as the cubes of any two corresponding edges.

c. Two similar polyhedrons can be separated into the same number of tetrahedrons, similar each to each and similarly placed.

d. Any two corresponding line segments of two similar polyhedrons have the same ratio as any two corresponding edges.

e. The areas of any two corresponding faces of two similar polyhedrons have the same ratio as the squares of any two corresponding line segments.

f. The total areas of two similar polyhedrons have the same ratio as the squares of any two corresponding line segments.

g. The volumes of any two similar polyhedrons have the same ratio as the cubes of any two corresponding line segments.

343. *Miscellaneous Theorems*

a. If the number of edges of a polyhedron is denoted by E, the number of vertices by V, and the number of faces by F, then $E + 2 = V + F$.

b. If the number of edges of a polyhedron is denoted by E, the number of vertices by V, the number of faces by F, and the sum of the face angles by S, then $S = (V - 2)\, 2$ st. $\angle$.

c. There can be no more than five regular polyhedrons.

344. *Volumes of a Prismatoid and a Truncated Triangular Prism*

 a. The volume of a prismatoid equals the product of one sixth the altitude and the sum of the upper base, the lower base, and four times the midsection.

 b. The volume of any truncated triangular prism is equal to one third the area of a right section multiplied by the sum of the lateral edges.

WORD LIST

dodecahedron	midsection	tetrahedron
hexahedron	octahedron	truncated
icosahedron	prismatoid	

TEST 16

True-False Statements (*Eight Minutes*)

Copy the numbers of these statements on your paper. Then if a statement is *always* true, write T after its number. If a statement is *not always* true, write F after its number. Do not guess.

1. A regular triangular pyramid is a regular tetrahedron.

2. A polyhedron of fifteen faces is called an icosahedron.

3. A hexahedron has six vertices and six faces.

4. A regular polyhedron may have any number of faces greater than three.

5. Euler's Theorem is given by the formula $E + 2 = V + F$.

6. Two tetrahedrons are equal if three faces which include a trihedral angle of one are similar, respectively, to three faces which include a trihedral angle of the other and are similarly placed.

7. The volumes of two similar tetrahedrons have the same ratio as the cubes of any two corresponding edges.

8. The formula for the volume of a truncated triangular prism is $V = \frac{1}{6}\, hb(x + y + z)$.

TEST 17

Completing Statements (*Ten Minutes*)

On your paper write one word, and only one, for each blank to make the following statements true:

1. A regular polyhedron of twelve faces is called a _____.
2. There can be no more than _____ regular polyhedrons.
3. A regular tetrahedron has four vertices and _____ edges.
4. The sum of the face angles of any octahedron is equal to _____ degrees.
5. The volumes of two similar tetrahedrons have the same ratio as the _____ of their corresponding edges.
6. The total areas of any two similar polyhedrons have the same ratio as the _____ of any two corresponding line segments.
7. $V = \frac{1}{6} h(B + B' + 4M)$ is the formula for the volume of _____ _____.
8. The corresponding edges of two similar polyhedrons are 2 inches and 3 inches. If the volume of the smaller is 36 cubic inches, the volume of the larger is _____ cubic inches.

TEST 18

Applications (*Twenty Minutes*)

1. If a polyhedron has seven vertices and eight faces, how many edges does it have?
2. Find the sum of the face angles of a polyhedron of five faces.
3. The volumes of two similar tetrahedrons are 108 cubic inches and 500 cubic inches respectively. If one edge of the smaller tetrahedron is 3 inches, find the corresponding edge of the larger tetrahedron.
4. Two similar polyhedrons have corresponding diagonals that are in the ratio of 2 to 7. If the total area of the smaller polyhedron is 40 square inches, what is the total area of the larger?
5. Find the volume of a truncated right triangular prism the sides of whose base are 3, 4, and 5 and whose lateral edges are 8, 15, and 17 respectively.
6. Find the volume of a regular octahedron whose edge is 6.
7. Find the volume of a regular tetrahedron whose edge is 8.

MISCELLANEOUS EXERCISES

CHAPTER I

1. If three concurrent lines are each cut by a fourth line that does not pass through the point of concurrence, all four lines are coplanar.

2. If a line is perpendicular to a plane, all the perpendiculars from the given line to a line of the plane are concurrent.

3. If a plane contains one of the diagonals of a parallelogram, the perpendiculars to the plane from the end points of the other diagonal are equal.

4. If three planes intersect in pairs, their lines of intersection are either parallel or concurrent.

5. If perpendiculars are drawn to a plane from the vertices of a triangle that lies outside the plane, their sum is equal to three times the perpendicular to the plane from the centroid of the triangle.

6. If perpendiculars are drawn to a plane from the vertices of a parallelogram that lies outside the plane, their sum is equal to four times the perpendicular to the plane from the intersection of the diagonals.

7. If a plane contains one side of a triangle, and a second plane, parallel to the first, intersects the other two sides, the second plane divides the two sides of the triangle proportionally.

8. If three noncoplanar line segments are parallel and equal, the triangles formed by connecting their end points are congruent.

9. If a line is perpendicular to the plane of a circle at its center and a tangent is drawn to the circle, the line joining the point of tangency to any point in the perpendicular is perpendicular to the tangent.

10. If two perpendiculars extend from a given external point to a plane and to a line in that plane respectively, prove that the line joining the feet of the two perpendiculars is perpendicular to the given line.

CHAPTER II

1. If two planes intersect, the planes which bisect two adjacent dihedral angles are perpendicular.

2. If from any point within a dihedral angle lines are drawn perpendicular to the faces, the angle between these lines is the supplement of the plane angle of the dihedral angle.

3. If two face angles of a trihedral angle are equal, the opposite dihedral angles are equal.

4. In any trihedral angle, the planes which bisect the three face angles and are perpendicular to those faces, respectively, intersect in the same straight line.

5. If the base of an isosceles triangle lies in a plane, the equal sides of the triangle are equally inclined to the plane.

6. If two lines intersect at an angle of 60° and each makes an angle of 45° with a plane, the projections of these lines on a plane are perpendicular to each other.

7. If a line segment joining the faces of a dihedral angle is perpendicular to the plane bisecting the dihedral angle, it is bisected by this plane.

8. If perpendiculars are drawn to the faces of a dihedral angle from any point not in either face of the angle, the plane determined by these lines is perpendicular to the edge of the dihedral angle.

9. If a plane intersects two parallel planes, the interior dihedral angles on the same side of the intersecting plane are supplementary.

10. If two lines are parallel and each intersect the same plane, they make equal angles with the plane.

11. The projection of a line segment on a plane equals the length of the line segment multiplied by the cosine of the angle formed by the line segment and its projection.

12. If six lines, no three of which lie in the same plane, are concurrent, how many planes are determined by these lines?

13. Prove that the planes that bisect the dihedral angles of a trihedral angle intersect in the same straight line.

14. If a line in one face of a dihedral angle is parallel to one in the other face, each is parallel to the edge of the angle.

CHAPTER III

1. The volume of a right triangular prism is equal to one half the product of any lateral face and its distance from the opposite edge.

2. Find the edge of a cube whose area is numerically equal to half its volume.

3. A log is 30 feet long and 2 feet in diameter at the smaller end. Find the dimensions of the largest piece of square timber that can be cut from the log.

4. Find the diagonal of a cube if the area of one of its faces is 3 square inches.

5. What is the depth of a cubical box that holds one bushel?

6. Given the three dimensions of a rectangular solid, construct a line segment equal to a diagonal.

7. Find the diameter of a cylinder of revolution in which the volume and lateral area have the same numerical value.

8. Show geometrically that $(a + b)^3 = a^3 + 3\,a^2b + 3\,ab^2 + b^3$.

9. A cylindrical vessel holds 1 cubic foot of water. What are the dimensions of the vessel if the diameter is equal to the altitude?

10. The volume of a regular prism is equal to the product of its lateral area and one half the apothem of its base.

11. If the bases of a prism are trapezoids, a section made by a plane cutting all the lateral edges is a trapezoid.

12. The volume of a right circular cylinder is equal to the product of its lateral area and one half the radius of the base.

13. Derive a formula for the circumference of the base of a cylinder of revolution in terms of the altitude and lateral area.

14. Prove that the right triangle whose two legs are equal respectively to the diagonal and edge of a cube is a 30°–60° right triangle.

15. The diagonals of a parallelepiped are concurrent.

16. How many cubic feet of concrete will be required to make a watering trough if the inside dimensions are 2 feet, 8 feet, and $1\frac{1}{2}$ feet, and the concrete is to be 4 inches thick?

17. How many gallons of water pour in 24 hours from a $\frac{1}{2}$-inch pipe if the rate of flow is 50 feet a minute?

18. The length and width of a rectangular solid are 9 inches and 8 inches respectively. Find the height if the diagonal is 17 inches.

19. A silo in the form of a right circular cylinder is 12 feet in diameter and 20 feet high (inside measurements). How many cubic feet of concrete did it take to build it if the floor and wall are each 6 inches thick and the foundation wall is 9 inches thick and 6 feet deep?

20. How high must a cylindrical can 6 inches in diameter be in order to hold a gallon?

21. If the volume of a given cube is denoted by V, find the volume of a cube whose edge is three times as large.

22. The edge of a cube is e. Find the area of a section made by a plane through two diagonally opposite edges.

23. Prove that a right section of an oblique cylinder is not a circle.

24. Find the largest number of tin cans having an outside diameter of 3 inches and a height of 5 inches that can be packed in a rectangular box whose inside dimensions are 27 inches, 24 inches, and 5 inches respectively.

25. How many feet of copper wire $\frac{1}{10}$ inch in diameter can be made from 1 cubic foot of the metal?

26. A trunk is 3 feet long and 2 feet wide. How high must it be so that a rifle 4 feet long may be placed inside?

27. Prove that the sum of the squares of the four diagonals of a parallelepiped is equal to the sum of the squares of the twelve edges.

28. The lateral area of a cylinder of revolution is $60\,\pi$, and the area of its base is $18\,\pi$. Find the altitude.

CHAPTER IV

1. Find the volume of a solid generated when a right triangle whose legs are a and b is revolved about the hypotenuse.

2. Find the volume of a regular quadrangular pyramid if a side of the base is s and a lateral edge is e.

3. The planes determined by the diagonals of a parallelepiped divide the parallelepiped into six pyramids equal in volume.

4. If r is the radius of the base of a right circular cone and l the slant height, the ratio of the area of the base and the lateral area is $\frac{r}{l}$.

5. If a right circular cylinder and a right circular cone have equal bases, and the altitude of the cylinder is equal to the slant height of the cone, the total area of the cylinder is equal to twice the total area of the cone.

6. What per cent of a square stick is wasted if the largest possible conical stick is turned out of it on a lathe?

7. Find the volume of a circular cone if its axis is 13 inches, the radius of the base is 5 inches, and the projection of the axis on the plane of the base is 12 inches.

8. If a circular cylinder and a circular cone have equal bases and equal volumes, compare their altitudes.

9. A cone of revolution 18 inches high and 20 inches in diameter at the base is cut by a plane parallel to the base and 8 inches from the vertex. Find the area of the frustum.

10. If the four faces of a triangular pyramid are equilateral triangles, the sum of the perpendiculars drawn from any point within the pyramid to the four faces is equal to an altitude of the pyramid.

CHAPTER V

1. If the arc of a great circle passes through the pole of another great circle, the planes of these two circles are perpendicular to each other.

2. What is the name of a spherical triangle that is its own polar triangle?

3. If the centers of two intersecting spheres are 10 inches apart, and the radii of the spheres are 6 inches and 10 inches respectively, what is the area of the circle formed by their intersection?

4. Find the diameter of a bowl in the form of a hemisphere that will hold 1 gallon.

5. The radii of two concentric spheres are 3 inches and 5 inches respectively. If a plane is tangent to the inner sphere, find the area of the section of the outer sphere made by the plane.

6. Find the volume of a sphere inscribed in a cone of revolution whose altitude is 16 inches and the radius of whose base is 4 inches.

7. What is the diameter of a sphere whose area and volume have the same numerical value?

8. How far from the center of a sphere of radius r must the eye of an observer be so that one third of the surface of the sphere is visible?

9. Derive a formula for the area of a zone on a sphere of radius r which is illuminated by a light at the height h above the sphere.

10. A sphere is inscribed in a right circular cylinder. In the same cylinder are placed two cones of revolution whose vertices are the center of the sphere and whose bases are the bases of the cylinder. If a plane is passed through the cylinder parallel to a base, prove that the area of the ring between the section of the cylinder and the section of the cone is equal to the area of the section of the sphere.

CHAPTER VI

EXERCISES. *TETRAHEDRONS*

1. Find the area of a regular tetrahedron 4 inches on an edge; of a regular hexahedron 4 inches on an edge; of a regular octahedron 4 inches on an edge.

2. Two corresponding edges of two similar tetrahedrons are 3 inches and 5 inches respectively. Compare their areas and volumes.

3. Two similar bins contain 625 bushels and 1372 bushels of oats respectively. If the smaller bin is 5 feet long, find the length of the larger.

4. The area of a tetrahedron is 192 square inches, and its volume is 768 cubic inches. If the area of a similar tetrahedron is 96 square inches, what is its volume?

5. Prove that the line segments connecting the middle points of the opposite edges of a tetrahedron bisect one another.

6. Find the volume of a truncated right triangular prism the sides of whose base are 5, 12, and 13 and whose lateral edges are 10, 12, and 15 respectively.

7. Find the area of a regular icosahedron whose edge is 5.

8. Find the difference between the number of edges and the number of vertices of a dodecahedron.

9. The edge of a regular dodecahedron is 2. Find the edge of a similar dodecahedron five times as large.

10. If a tetrahedron is cut by a plane parallel to one of its faces, the tetrahedron cut off is similar to the given tetrahedron.

SUMMARY OF PRINCIPAL METHODS OF PROOF OF SOLID GEOMETRY

345. *A Line Perpendicular to a Plane*

a. A line is perpendicular to a plane if it is perpendicular to every line in the plane passing through its foot.

b. If a line is perpendicular to each of two intersecting lines at their point of intersection, it is perpendicular to the plane of the two lines.

c. Through a given point there can be one plane, and only one, perpendicular to a given line.

d. The perpendicular is the shortest line segment from a point to a plane.

e. Through a given point there can be drawn one, and only one, perpendicular to the plane.

f. If one of two parallel lines is perpendicular to a plane, the other is also perpendicular to the plane.

g. A line perpendicular to one of two parallel planes is perpendicular to the other.

h. If two planes are perpendicular to each other, a line drawn in one of them perpendicular to their intersection is perpendicular to the other.

i. If two intersecting planes are perpendicular to a third plane, their intersection is also perpendicular to that plane.

346. *A Line Parallel to a Plane*

a. A line and a plane are parallel if they do not meet even if extended.

b. If two lines are parallel, every plane containing one of the lines, and only one, is parallel to the other.

c. Through either of two skew lines there can be one plane, and only one, parallel to the other line.

d. Through a given point in space there can be one plane, and only one, parallel to each of two skew lines, or else parallel to one line and containing the other.

347. *Two Planes Parallel*

a. Two planes are parallel if they do not meet even if extended.
b. Two planes perpendicular to the same line are parallel.
c. Through a point outside a plane there can be one plane, and only one, parallel to a given plane.
d. If two intersecting lines are each parallel to a plane, the plane of these lines is parallel to that plane.
e. If two angles not in the same plane have their sides parallel and extending in the same direction, their planes are parallel.

348. *Two Lines Parallel*

a. Two lines perpendicular to the same plane are parallel.
b. If two lines are parallel to a third line, they are parallel to each other.
c. If a line is parallel to a plane, it is parallel to the intersection of that plane with any plane through the line.
d. If two parallel planes are cut by a third plane, the lines of intersection are parallel.

349. *Two Line Segments Equal*

a. Oblique lines drawn from a point to a plane meeting the plane at equal distances from the foot of the perpendicular are equal.
b. Two parallel planes are everywhere equidistant.

350. *Loci*

a. The locus of points equidistant from two given points is the plane perpendicular to the line joining them, at its midpoint.
b. The locus of points equidistant from the vertices of a triangle is the line through the center of the circumcircle, perpendicular to the plane of the triangle.
c. The locus of points equidistant from the faces of a dihedral angle is the plane bisecting the dihedral angle.

351. *Planes Perpendicular*

a. Two planes are perpendicular if the plane angle of their dihedral angle is a right angle.

b. If a line is perpendicular to a given plane, every plane which contains this line is perpendicular to the given plane.

c. Through a line not perpendicular to a plane there can be one plane, and only one, perpendicular to the given plane.

352. *Dihedral Angles Equal*

a. Two dihedral angles are equal (or congruent) if they can be made to coincide.

b. Two dihedral angles are equal if their plane angles are equal.

353. *Trihedral Angles Equal or Symmetric*

Two trihedral angles are either equal or symmetric if the three face angles of one are equal respectively to the three face angles of the other.

354. *Sum of Face Angles of Polyhedral Angles*

a. The sum of any two face angles of a trihedral angle is greater than the third face angle.

b. The sum of the face angles of any convex polyhedral angle is less than 360°.

355. *Sections of Solids*

a. The sections of a prism made by parallel planes intersecting all the lateral edges are congruent polygons.

b. The bases of a prism are congruent polygons.

c. Every section of a prism made by a plane parallel to the base is congruent to the base.

d. The opposite faces of a parallelepiped are congruent.

e. If a pyramid is cut by a plane parallel to the base, the section is similar to the base.

f. The area of a section of a pyramid parallel to the base is to the area of the base as the square of its distance from the vertex is to the square of the altitude of the pyramid.

g. If two pyramids have equal altitudes and equal bases, sections of the pyramids parallel to the bases and equidistant from the vertices are equal in area.

h. The section of a circular cone made by a plane parallel to the base is a circle.

i. The section of a circular cone made by a plane parallel to the
base is to the base as the square of its distance from the
vertex is to the square of the altitude of the cone.

j. If a plane intersects a sphere, the intersection is a circle.

356.   *Congruent and Equal Solids*

a. Two prisms are congruent if they can be made to coincide.

b. Two prisms are congruent if the three faces which include a
trihedral angle of one are congruent respectively to the
three faces which include a trihedral angle of the other,
and are similarly placed.

c. Two right prisms are congruent if they have congruent bases
and equal altitudes.

d. Two truncated prisms are congruent if the three faces which
include a trihedral angle of one are congruent respectively
to the three faces which include a trihedral angle of the
other, and are similarly placed.

e. Two prisms are equal if they have equal volumes.¹

f. An oblique prism is equal to a right prism whose base is a right
section of the oblique prism and whose altitude is equal to
a lateral edge of the oblique prism.

g. The plane passed through two diagonally opposite edges of a
parallelepiped divides it into equal triangular prisms.

h. Two parallelepipeds having equal bases and equal altitudes
are equal.

i. Two pyramids having equal altitudes and equal bases are
equal.

357.   *Areas*

a. The lateral area of a prism is the sum of the areas of the lateral faces.

b. The lateral area of a prism is equal to the product of a lateral
edge and the perimeter of a right section. ($S = ep$.)

c. The lateral area of a right prism is equal to the product of its
altitude and the perimeter of its base.

d. The lateral area of a circular cylinder is equal to the product
of an element and the perimeter of a right section.

e. The lateral area S and the total area T of a right circular
cylinder are expressed by the formulas $S = 2\pi r h$ and
$T = 2\pi r(r + h)$.

f. The lateral areas or the total areas of two similar cylinders of revolution have the same ratio as the squares of their altitudes or as the squares of the radii of their bases.

g. The lateral area of a regular pyramid is equal to half the product of its slant height and the perimeter of its base.

h. The lateral area of a frustum of a regular pyramid is equal to half the product of its slant height and the sum of the perimeters of the bases.

i. The lateral area of a right circular cone is equal to half the product of its slant height and the circumference of its base.

j. The lateral area S and the total area T of a right circular cone are expressed by the formulas $S = \pi r l$ and $T = \pi r (l + r)$.

k. The lateral area S of a frustum of a right circular cone is expressed by the formula $S = \pi l (r + r')$.

l. The lateral areas or the total areas of two similar cones of revolution have the same ratio as the squares of their altitudes, or as the squares of their slant heights, or as the squares of the radii of their bases.

m. The area of a sphere with radius r is $4 \pi r^2$.

n. The area of a sphere is equal to the product of its diameter and the circumference of a great circle.

o. The areas of two spheres are to each other as the squares of their radii or as the squares of their diameters.

p. The area of a zone is equal to the product of its altitude and a circumference of a great circle of the sphere.

q. The number of spherical degrees in the area of a lune is twice the number of degrees in the angle of the lune.

r. The number of spherical degrees in the area of a spherical triangle is equal to the number of degrees in its spherical excess.

s. The ratio of the area of a spherical triangle to the area of the sphere is $E : 720$, where E is the spherical excess of the triangle.

t. The number of spherical degrees in the area of a spherical polygon is equal to the number of degrees in its spherical excess.

358.   *Volumes*

a. The volume of any prism is equal to the product of its base and altitude.

b. The volume of a cube is equal to the cube of an edge.

c. Two parallelepipeds having equal bases have the same ratio as their altitudes.

d. Two parallelepipeds having equal altitudes have the same ratio as their bases.

e. Two parallelepipeds have the same ratio as the products of their three dimensions.

f. The volume of a circular cylinder is equal to the product of its base and altitude.

g. The volumes of two similar cylinders of revolution have the same ratio as the cubes of their altitudes or as the cubes of the radii of their bases.

h. The volume of any pyramid is equal to one third the product of its base and altitude.

i. Two pyramids having equal bases have the same ratio as their altitudes.

j. Two pyramids having equal altitudes have the same ratio as their bases.

k. Two pyramids have the same ratio as the product of their bases and altitudes.

l. The volume of a frustum of a pyramid is expressed by the formula $V = \frac{1}{3} h(b + b' + \sqrt{bb'})$, where b and b' are the areas of the bases and h is the altitude.

m. The volume of a circular cone is equal to one third the product of its base and altitude.

n. The volume of a circular cone is expressed by the formula $V = \frac{1}{3} \pi r^2 h$.

o. The volume of a frustum of a circular cone is expressed by the formula $V = \frac{1}{3} \pi h(r^2 + r'^2 + rr')$.

p. The volumes of two similar cones of revolution have the same ratio as the cubes of their altitudes, or as the cubes of their slant heights, or as the cubes of the radii of their bases.

q. The volume of a sphere with radius r is expressed by the formula $V = \frac{4}{3} \pi r^3$.

r. The volume of a sphere with diameter d is expressed by the formula $V = \frac{1}{6} \pi d^3$.

s. The volumes of two spheres have the same ratio as the cubes of their radii, or as the cubes of their diameters.

t. The volume of a prismatoid equals the product of one sixth the altitude and the sum of the upper base, the lower base, and four times the midsection.

u. The volume of any truncated triangular prism is equal to one third the area of a right section multiplied by the sum of the lateral edges.

v. The volumes of two similar tetrahedrons have the same ratio as the cubes of any two corresponding edges.

w. The volumes of any two similar polyhedrons have the same ratio as the cubes of any two corresponding line segments.

359.   *Great Circles of a Sphere*

a. The center of a great circle of a sphere is the center of the sphere.

b. All great circles of a sphere are equal.

c. Any two great circles of a sphere bisect each other.

d. Through any two points on a sphere that are not the extremities of a diameter one great circle of a sphere, and only one, can be drawn.

360.   *Spherical Distances*

a. The spherical distances of all points on a circle of a sphere from either pole of the circle are equal.

b. The polar distance of a great circle is a quadrant.

c. On a sphere or on equal spheres the polar distances of equal circles are equal.

361.   *Spherical Angles*

a. A spherical angle is equal to the dihedral angle formed by the planes of its sides.

b. A spherical angle is equal in degrees to the arc of the great circle which has the vertex of the angle as a pole and is included between the sides of the angle, extended if necessary.

362.   *Spherical Polygons*

a. The sides of a spherical polygon are equal in degrees to the corresponding face angles of the polyhedral angle.

b. The angles of a spherical polygon are equal in degrees to the corresponding dihedral angles of the polyhedral angle.

c. The sum of the sides of a spherical polygon is less than 360°.

d. Each side of a spherical triangle is less than the sum of the other two sides.

e. If two sides of a spherical triangle are equal, the angles opposite these sides are equal.

f. If two angles of a spherical triangle are equal, the sides opposite these angles are equal.

g. If two angles of a spherical triangle are unequal, the side opposite the greater angle is the greater.

h. If two sides of a spherical triangle are unequal, the angle opposite the greater side is the greater.

i. Two symmetric spherical triangles are equal in area.

j. If one spherical triangle is the polar triangle of another, then the second is the polar triangle of the first.

k. In two polar triangles, each angle of one is the supplement of the opposite side of the other.

363. *Two Spherical Triangles Congruent*
or Symmetric

a. Two spherical triangles on a sphere or on equal spheres are congruent if the sides and angles of one are equal respectively to the sides and angles of the other and are arranged in the same order.

b. Two spherical triangles which are symmetric to a third triangle are congruent.

c. If two spherical triangles on a sphere or on equal spheres have two sides and the included angle of one equal respectively to two sides and the included angle of the other and arranged in the same order, the triangles are congruent.

d. Two symmetric isosceles spherical triangles are congruent.

e. If two spherical triangles on a sphere or on equal spheres have two angles and the included side of one equal respectively to two angles and the included side of the other and arranged in the same order, the triangles are congruent.

f. If two spherical triangles on a sphere or on equal spheres have the three sides of one equal respectively to the three sides of the other, the triangles are either congruent or symmetric.

g. If two spherical triangles on a sphere or on equal spheres have the three angles of one equal respectively to the three angles of the other, the triangles are either congruent or symmetric.

h. If two spherical triangles on a sphere or on equal spheres have two sides and the included angle of one equal respectively to two sides and the included angle of the other and arranged in the reverse order, the triangles are symmetric.

i. If two spherical triangles on a sphere or on equal spheres have two angles and the included side of one equal respectively to two angles and the included side of the other and arranged in the reverse order, the triangles are symmetric.

364. *Similar Polyhedrons*

a. Two tetrahedrons are similar if the three faces which include a trihedral angle of one are similar respectively to the three faces which include a trihedral angle of the other, and are similarly placed.

b. The volumes of two similar tetrahedrons have the same ratio as the cubes of any two corresponding edges.

c. Two similar polyhedrons can be separated into the same number of tetrahedrons, similar each to each and similarly placed.

d. Any two corresponding line segments of two similar polyhedrons have the same ratio as any two corresponding edges.

e. The areas of any two corresponding faces of two similar polyhedrons have the same ratio as the squares of any two corresponding line segments.

f. The total areas of two similar polyhedrons have the same ratio as the squares of any two corresponding line segments.

g. The volumes of any two similar polyhedrons have the same ratio as the cubes of any two corresponding line segments.

365. *Miscellaneous Theorems*

a. If a pyramid is cut by a plane parallel to the base, the lateral edges and the altitude are divided proportionally.

b. If the number of edges of a polyhedron is denoted by E, the number of vertices by V, and the number of faces by F, then $E + 2 = V + F$.

c. If the number of edges of a polyhedron is denoted by E, the number of vertices by V, the number of faces by F, and the sum of the face angles by S, then $S = (V - 2) 2$ st. $\angle$.

d. There can be no more than five regular polyhedrons.

TABLE I. SQUARE ROOTS AND CUBE ROOTS

N	$\sqrt{N}$	$\sqrt[3]{N}$	N	$\sqrt{N}$	$\sqrt[3]{N}$	N	$\sqrt{N}$	$\sqrt[3]{N}$	N	$\sqrt{N}$	$\sqrt[3]{N}$
1	1.000	1.000	51	7.141	3.708	101	10.050	4.657	151	12.288	5.325
2	1.414	1.260	52	7.211	3.733	102	10.100	4.672	152	12.329	5.337
3	1.732	1.442	53	7.280	3.756	103	10.149	4.688	153	12.369	5.348
4	2.000	1.587	54	7.348	3.780	104	10.198	4.703	154	12.410	5.360
5	2.236	1.710	55	7.416	3.803	105	10.247	4.718	155	12.450	5.372
6	2.449	1.817	56	7.483	3.826	106	10.296	4.733	156	12.490	5.383
7	2.646	1.913	57	7.550	3.849	107	10.344	4.747	157	12.530	5.395
8	2.828	2.000	58	7.616	3.871	108	10.392	4.762	158	12.570	5.406
9	3.000	2.080	59	7.681	3.893	109	10.440	4.777	159	12.610	5.418
10	3.162	2.154	60	7.746	3.915	110	10.488	4.791	160	12.649	5.429
11	3.317	2.224	61	7.810	3.936	111	10.536	4.806	161	12.689	5.440
12	3.464	2.289	62	7.874	3.958	112	10.583	4.820	162	12.728	5.451
13	3.606	2.351	63	7.937	3.979	113	10.630	4.835	163	12.767	5.463
14	3.742	2.410	64	8.000	4.000	114	10.677	4.849	164	12.806	5.474
15	3.873	2.466	65	8.062	4.021	115	10.724	4.863	165	12.845	5.485
16	4.000	2.520	66	8.124	4.041	116	10.770	4.877	166	12.884	5.496
17	4.123	2.571	67	8.185	4.062	117	10.817	4.891	167	12.923	5.507
18	4.243	2.621	68	8.246	4.082	118	10.863	4.905	168	12.962	5.518
19	4.359	2.668	69	8.307	4.102	119	10.909	4.919	169	13.000	5.529
20	4.472	2.714	70	8.367	4.121	120	10.955	4.932	170	13.038	5.540
21	4.583	2.759	71	8.426	4.147	121	11.000	4.946	171	13.077	5.550
22	4.690	2.802	72	8.485	4.160	122	11.045	4.960	172	13.115	5.561
23	4.796	2.844	73	8.544	4.179	123	11.091	4.973	173	13.153	5.572
24	4.899	2.884	74	8.602	4.198	124	11.136	4.987	174	13.191	5.583
25	5.000	2.925	75	8.660	4.217	125	11.180	5.000	175	13.229	5.593
26	5.099	2.962	76	8.718	4.236	126	11.225	5.013	176	13.267	5.604
27	5.196	3.000	77	8.775	4.254	127	11.269	5.027	177	13.304	5.615
28	5.292	3.037	78	8.832	4.273	128	11.314	5.040	178	13.342	5.625
29	5.385	3.072	79	8.888	4.291	129	11.358	5.053	179	13.379	5.636
30	5.477	3.107	80	8.944	4.309	130	11.402	5.066	180	13.416	5.646
31	5.568	3.141	81	9.000	4.327	131	11.446	5.079	181	13.454	5.657
32	5.657	3.175	82	9.055	4.344	132	11.489	5.092	182	13.491	5.667
33	5.745	3.208	83	9.110	4.362	133	11.533	5.104	183	13.528	5.677
34	5.831	3.240	84	9.165	4.380	134	11.576	5.117	184	13.565	5.688
35	5.916	3.271	85	9.220	4.397	135	11.619	5.130	185	13.602	5.698
36	6.000	3.302	86	9.274	4.414	136	11.662	5.143	186	13.638	5.708
37	6.083	3.332	87	9.327	4.431	137	11.705	5.155	187	13.675	5.718
38	6.164	3.362	88	9.381	4.448	138	11.747	5.168	188	13.711	5.729
39	6.245	3.391	89	9.434	4.465	139	11.790	5.180	189	13.748	5.739
40	6.325	3.420	90	9.487	4.481	140	11.832	5.192	190	13.784	5.749
41	6.403	3.448	91	9.539	4.498	141	11.874	5.205	191	13.820	5.759
42	6.481	3.476	92	9.592	4.514	142	11.916	5.217	192	13.856	5.769
43	6.557	3.503	93	9.644	4.531	143	11.958	5.229	193	13.892	5.779
44	6.633	3.530	94	9.695	4.547	144	12.000	5.241	194	13.928	5.789
45	6.708	3.557	95	9.747	4.563	145	12.042	5.254	195	13.964	5.799
46	6.782	3.583	96	9.798	4.579	146	12.083	5.266	196	14.000	5.809
47	6.856	3.609	97	9.849	4.595	147	12.124	5.278	197	14.036	5.819
48	6.928	3.634	98	9.899	4.610	148	12.166	5.290	198	14.071	5.828
49	7.000	3.659	99	9.950	4.626	149	12.207	5.301	199	14.107	5.838
50	7.071	3.684	100	10.000	4.642	150	12.247	5.313	200	14.142	5.848

SUPPLEMENTARY TOPICS

BRIEF EXPLANATION OF LOGARITHMS

Logarithm, an Exponent

A *logarithm* of a given number is the power to which a number (such as 10) must be raised to equal the given number. Thus the logarithm of 1000 is 3, since $10^3 = 1000$.

Since logarithms are exponents, the processes of multiplication, division, and finding powers and roots are reduced to addition, subtraction, multiplication, and division respectively.

Finding the Logarithm of a Number

The logarithm of a number consists of an integer and a decimal fraction. The number which precedes the decimal point is called the *characteristic*, and the decimal part is called the *mantissa*. The characteristic is found by the following rules:

---

1. The characteristic of the logarithm of a number greater than 1 is positive, and is one less than the number of integral places in the number.

2. The characteristic of the logarithm of a number between 0 and 1 is negative, and is numerically one more than the number of zeros immediately following the decimal point.

Examples. log 634.72 = 2 + (some mantissa).
log 0.724 = − 1 + (some mantissa).
log 0.072 = − 2 + (some mantissa).

We can therefore tell the characteristic of a logarithm of a number by inspection. To find the mantissa we must use the tables on pages 242 and 243. How to find the logarithm of a number will be illustrated by the following examples:

Example 1. Find the logarithm of 3.56.

Solution. The characteristic is 0. To find the mantissa, we look on page 242 under the column headed N for 35 and then follow along the horizontal line 35 to column 6; we find 5514. Then log 3.56 = 0.5514.

Example 2. Find the logarithm of 27.42.

Solution. The characteristic is 1. From the table the mantissa of 27.40 is .4378 and the mantissa of 27.50 is .4393; that is,

$$\log 27.50 = 1.4393$$
$$\underline{\log 27.40 = 1.4378}$$
$$\text{difference} = .0015$$

Since 27.42 is $\frac{1}{5}$ of the way between 27.40 and 27.50, we take $\frac{1}{5}$ of .0015, or .0003, and add it to log 27.40. Then 1.4378 + .0003 = 1.4381; that is, log 27.42 = 1.4381.

Finding a Number when its Logarithm is Given

The number which corresponds to a given logarithm is called an *antilogarithm*. We find an antilogarithm by reversing the method of finding the logarithm of a number.

Example. Find the antilogarithm of 2.5445.

Solution. Since the characteristic is 2, there are 3 figures before the decimal point of the number. Looking through the mantissas in the table we find that the mantissa 5445 is not given, but we do find the mantissas 5441 and 5453 between which it lies. We proceed to find the required number in this manner:

$$\log 351.0 = 2.5453$$
$$\underline{\log 350.0 = 2.5441}$$
$$\text{difference} = .0012$$

The difference between 2.5441 and the given logarithm 2.5445 is .0004. Hence the number is $\frac{.0004}{.0012}$, or $\frac{1}{3}$, of the way between 350.0 and 351.0. Then $\frac{1}{3}$ of 1 = .3. Hence we add .3 to 350.0 and find the required number to be 350.3.

Logarithm of a Product. $\log ab = \log a + \log b$.

Example. Find 0.057×79.4 by logarithms.

Solution. $\log (0.057 \times 79.4) = \log 0.057 + \log 79.4$.

$$\log 0.057 = 8.7559 - 10$$
$$\underline{\log 79.4 = 1.8998}$$
$$\log \text{ product} = 10.6557 - 10$$

or   0.6557

antilog 0.6557 = 4.526.

Hence $0.057 \times 79.4 = 4.526$.

Since the characteristic of log 0.057 is negative 2, it is written 8.7559 − 10 instead of $\bar{2}.7559$, to make the addition easier.

Logarithm of a Quotient. $\log \frac{a}{b} = \log a - \log b$.

Example. Find $23.02 \div 0.092$ by logarithms.

Solution. $\log (23.02 \div 0.092) = \log 23.02 - \log 0.092$.

$$\log 23.02 = 11.3621 - 10$$
$$\log 0.092 = 8.9638 - 10$$
$$\overline{\log \text{quotient} = 2.3983}$$
$$\text{antilog } 2.3983 = 250.2.$$

Hence $23.02 \div 0.092 = 250.2.$

The logarithm of 23.02 is 1.3621, but is written $11.3621 - 10$ to make the subtraction easier.

Logarithm of a Power. $\log a^p = p \log a$.

Example. Find the value of $(3.04)^3$ by logarithms.

Solution. $\log (3.04)^3 = 3 \log 3.04$.

$$\log 3.04 = 0.4829$$
$$3 \log 3.04 = 1.4487$$
$$\text{antilog } 1.4487 = 28.10.$$

Hence $(3.04)^3 = 28.10.$

Logarithm of a Root. $\log \sqrt[r]{a} = \frac{1}{r} \log a$.

Example. Find $\sqrt[3]{672}$ by logarithms.

Solution. $\log \sqrt[3]{672} = \frac{1}{3} \log 672$.

$$\log 672 = 2.8274$$
$$\tfrac{1}{3} \log 672 = 0.9425$$
$$\text{antilog } 0.9425 = 8.76.$$

Hence $\sqrt[3]{672} = 8.76.$

EXERCISES

Find the values of the following by the use of logarithms:

1. 67×106.
2. 9×3.1416.
3. $83.42 \div 678$.
4. $\overline{315}^2$.
5. $0.624 \div 13.6$.
6. $\overline{61}^3$.

7. $\sqrt{62.66}$.
8. $\sqrt{439}$.
9. $\sqrt[3]{500}$.
10. $\sqrt[3]{2372}$.
11. $\pi (13)^2$.
12. $\pi \sqrt[3]{324}$.

13. $\dfrac{16 \times 23.04}{3.1416}$.

14. $\sqrt{\dfrac{86.92}{36.1}}$.

15. $\sqrt[8]{\dfrac{3.1416 \times 0.072}{0.119}}$.

TABLE II. MANTISSAS

$\log \pi = .4971$ $\log 4\pi = 1.0992$ $\log \frac{4}{3}\pi = .6221$

N	0	1	2	3	4	5	6	7	8	9
10	0000	0043	0086	0128	0170	0212	0253	0294	0334	0374
11	0414	0453	0492	0531	0569	0607	0645	0682	0719	0755
12	0792	0828	0864	0899	0934	0969	1004	1038	1072	1106
13	1139	1173	1206	1239	1271	1303	1335	1367	1399	1430
14	1461	1492	1523	1553	1584	1614	1644	1673	1703	1732
15	1761	1790	1818	1847	1875	1903	1931	1959	1987	2014
16	2041	2068	2095	2122	2148	2175	2201	2227	2253	2279
17	2304	2330	2355	2380	2405	2430	2455	2480	2504	2529
18	2553	2577	2601	2625	2648	2672	2695	2718	2742	2765
19	2788	2810	2833	2856	2878	2900	2923	2945	2967	2989
20	3010	3032	3054	3075	3096	3118	3139	3160	3181	3201
21	3222	3243	3263	3284	3304	3324	3345	3365	3385	3404
22	3424	3444	3464	3483	3502	3522	3541	3560	3579	3598
23	3617	3636	3655	3674	3692	3711	3729	3747	3766	3784
24	3802	3820	3838	3856	3874	3892	3909	3927	3945	3962
25	3979	3997	4014	4031	4048	4065	4082	4099	4116	4133
26	4150	4166	4183	4200	4216	4232	4249	4265	4281	4298
27	4314	4330	4346	4362	4378	4393	4409	4425	4440	4456
28	4472	4487	4502	4518	4533	4548	4564	4579	4594	4609
29	4624	4639	4654	4669	4683	4698	4713	4728	4742	4757
30	4771	4786	4800	4814	4829	4843	4857	4871	4886	4900
31	4914	4928	4942	4955	4969	4983	4997	5011	5024	5038
32	5051	5065	5079	5092	5105	5119	5132	5145	5159	5172
33	5185	5198	5211	5224	5237	5250	5263	5276	5289	5302
34	5315	5328	5340	5353	5366	5378	5391	5403	5416	5428
35	5441	5453	5465	5478	5490	5502	5514	5527	5539	5551
36	5563	5575	5587	5599	5611	5623	5635	5647	5658	5670
37	5682	5694	5705	5717	5729	5740	5752	5763	5775	5786
38	5798	5809	5821	5832	5843	5855	5866	5877	5888	5899
39	5911	5922	5933	5944	5955	5966	5977	5988	5999	6010
40	6021	6031	6042	6053	6064	6075	6085	6096	6107	6117
41	6128	6138	6149	6160	6170	6180	6191	6201	6212	6222
42	6232	6243	6253	6263	6274	6284	6294	6304	6314	6325
43	6335	6345	6355	6365	6375	6385	6395	6405	6415	6425
44	6435	6444	6454	6464	6474	6484	6493	6503	6513	6522
45	6532	6542	6551	6561	6571	6580	6590	6599	6609	6618
46	6628	6637	6646	6656	6665	6675	6684	6693	6702	6712
47	6721	6730	6739	6749	6758	6767	6776	6785	6794	6803
48	6812	6821	6830	6839	6848	6857	6866	6875	6884	6893
49	6902	6911	6920	6928	6937	6946	6955	6964	6972	6981
50	6990	6998	7007	7016	7024	7033	7042	7050	7059	7067
51	7076	7084	7093	7101	7110	7118	7126	7135	7143	7152
52	7160	7168	7177	7185	7193	7202	7210	7218	7226	7235
53	7243	7251	7259	7267	7275	7284	7292	7300	7308	7316
54	7324	7332	7340	7348	7356	7364	7372	7380	7388	7396
N	0	1	2	3	4	5	6	7	8	9

TABLE II. MANTISSAS

$\log \pi = .4971$ $\log 4\pi = 1.0992$ $\log \frac{4}{3}\pi = .6221$

N	0	1	2	3	4	5	6	7	8	9
55	7404	7412	7419	7427	7435	7443	7451	7459	7466	7474
56	7482	7490	7497	7505	7513	7520	7528	7536	7543	7551
57	7559	7566	7574	7582	7589	7597	7604	7612	7619	7627
58	7634	7642	7649	7657	7664	7672	7679	7686	7694	7701
59	7709	7716	7723	7731	7738	7745	7752	7760	7767	7774
60	7782	7789	7796	7803	7810	7818	7825	7832	7839	7846
61	7853	7860	7868	7875	7882	7889	7896	7903	7910	7917
62	7924	7931	7938	7945	7952	7959	7966	7973	7980	7987
63	7993	8000	8007	8014	8021	8028	8035	8041	8048	8055
64	8062	8069	8075	8082	8089	8096	8102	8109	8116	8122
65	8129	8136	8142	8149	8156	8162	8169	8176	8182	8189
66	8195	8202	8209	8215	8222	8228	8235	8241	8248	8254
67	8261	8267	8274	8280	8287	8293	8299	8306	8312	8319
68	8325	8331	8338	8344	8351	8357	8363	8370	8376	8382
69	8388	8395	8401	8407	8414	8420	8426	8432	8439	8445
70	8451	8457	8463	8470	8476	8482	8488	8494	8500	8506
71	8513	8519	8525	8531	8537	8543	8549	8555	8561	8567
72	8573	8579	8585	8591	8597	8603	8609	8615	8621	8627
73	8633	8639	8645	8651	8657	8663	8669	8675	8681	8686
74	8692	8698	8704	8710	8716	8722	8727	8733	8739	8745
75	8751	8756	8762	8768	8774	8779	8785	8791	8797	8802
76	8808	8814	8820	8825	8831	8837	8842	8848	8854	8859
77	8865	8871	8876	8882	8887	8893	8899	8904	8910	8915
78	8921	8927	8932	8938	8943	8949	8954	8960	8965	8971
79	8976	8982	8987	8993	8998	9004	9009	9015	9020	9025
80	9031	9036	9042	9047	9053	9058	9063	9069	9074	9079
81	9085	9090	9096	9101	9106	9112	9117	9122	9128	9133
82	9138	9143	9149	9154	9159	9165	9170	9175	9180	9186
83	9191	9196	9201	9206	9212	9217	9222	9227	9232	9238
84	9243	9248	9253	9258	9263	9269	9274	9279	9284	9289
85	9294	9299	9304	9309	9315	9320	9325	9330	9335	9340
86	9345	9350	9355	9360	9365	9370	9375	9380	9385	9390
87	9395	9400	9405	9410	9415	9420	9425	9430	9435	9440
88	9445	9450	9455	9460	9465	9469	9474	9479	9484	9489
89	9494	9499	9504	9509	9513	9518	9523	9528	9533	9538
90	9542	9547	9552	9557	9562	9566	9571	9576	9581	9586
91	9590	9595	9600	9605	9609	9614	9619	9624	9628	9633
92	9638	9643	9647	9652	9657	9661	9666	9671	9675	9680
93	9685	9689	9694	9699	9703	9708	9713	9717	9722	9727
94	9731	9736	9741	9745	9750	9754	9759	9763	9768	9773
95	9777	9782	9786	9791	9795	9800	9805	9809	9814	9818
96	9823	9827	9832	9836	9841	9845	9850	9854	9859	9863
97	9868	9872	9877	9881	9886	9890	9894	9899	9903	9908
98	9912	9917	9921	9926	9930	9934	9939	9943	9948	9952
99	9956	9961	9965	9969	9974	9978	9983	9987	9991	9996
N	0	1	2	3	4	5	6	7	8	9

APPLICATIONS OF TRIGONOMETRY

Trigonometric Functions

Trigonometric functions are the ratios of the sides of a right triangle.

The *sine* of an acute angle of a right triangle is the ratio of the opposite side to the hypotenuse. In rt. $\triangle ABC$, the sine of $\angle A$ (written $\sin A$) $= \dfrac{\text{opposite side}}{\text{hypotenuse}} = \dfrac{a}{c}$.

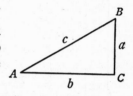

The *cosine* of an acute angle of a right triangle is the ratio of the adjacent side to the hypotenuse. In rt. $\triangle ABC$, the cosine of $\angle A$ (written $\cos A$) $= \dfrac{\text{adjacent side}}{\text{hypotenuse}} = \dfrac{b}{c}$.

The *tangent* of an acute angle of a right triangle is the ratio of the opposite side to the adjacent side. In rt. $\triangle ABC$, the tangent of $\angle A$ (written $\tan A$) $= \dfrac{\text{opposite side}}{\text{adjacent side}} = \dfrac{a}{b}$.

In the above triangle $\angle A$ and $\angle B$ are complementary. Notice that the sine of $\angle A$ is equal to the cosine of $\angle B$ and that the cosine of $\angle A$ is equal to the sine of $\angle B$. The *cotangent* of $\angle A$ is the reciprocal of the tangent of $\angle A$ and is equal to the tangent of $\angle B$. In the figure above

$$\cot A = \frac{b}{a} = \tan B.$$

EXERCISES

1. Give the values of the sine, cosine, tangent, and cotangent of each acute angle in the following right triangles:

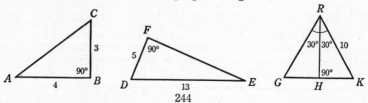

2. Draw any rt. $\triangle ABC$ with $\angle C = 90°$. Construct $\triangle A'B'C' \sim \triangle ABC$. What is sin A? sin A'? cos A? cos A'? tan A? tan A'? Why does sin $A = $ sin A'? Why does cos $A = $ cos A'? Why does tan $A = $ tan A'?

3. When $\angle A$ increases how does sin A change?

4. When $\angle A$ increases how does cos A change?

5. When $\angle A$ increases how does tan A change?

How to Use Tables III and IV

On page 249 is a table of trigonometric ratios. These ratios are given for angles with intervals of one degree. To find the sine of any angle, say sin 76°, look for the number 76 in the angle columns. Then in the sin column, to the right of and next to the angle column containing the number 76, find the number .9703 in the same horizontal line with 76. The number .9703 is the sine of 76°. The cosine and tangent of an angle are found in the same manner.

Table IV on pages 250–252 is a table of the logarithms of trigonometric ratios. To find the logarithm of the sine, cosine, tangent, or cotangent of an angle less than 45°, use the columns as they are headed at the *top*. To find the functions of an angle greater than 45°, use the columns as they are headed at the *bottom*.

Since the values of all sines and cosines are less than 1, their logarithms have negative characteristics. In this table the number -10 is understood to follow each logarithm in the log sin and log cos columns.

Likewise, since the tangent of an angle less than 45° is less than 1, its logarithm is negative and -10 is understood to follow the logarithm given in the table. For angles greater than 45° the characteristic is given in the table.

To find the logarithm of the cotangent of an angle greater than 45° add -10 to the logarithm given in the table.

Example. Find log tan 18° 40′.

Solution. Find 18° 40′ in the left-hand column headed *angle* at the top. Then in the column headed *log tan* at the top find the number 9.5287, which is in the same horizontal line with 18° 40′. Since 18° 40′ is less than 45°, -10 must be added to 9.5287. Then log tan 18° 40′ = 9.5287 − 10.

EXERCISES

From Table IV find the following:

1. log sin 18° 20′.
2. log tan 47° 15′.
3. log tan 8° 40′.

4. log cot 19° 15′.
5. log sin 7° 50′.
6. log cos 7° 30′.

7. log tan 75°.
8. log sin 51° 45′.
9. log cos 86° 30′.

Find ∠x when:

10. log sin x = 8.8436 − 10.
11. log cos x = 9.9866 − 10.
12. log tan x = 9.3020 − 10.
13. log sin x = 9.8444 − 10.

14. log tan x = 9.7802 − 10.
15. log tan x = .0736.
16. log sin x = 9.9248 − 10.
17. log cos x = 9.5477 − 10.

Solving Geometry Problems by Trigonometry

Tables II, III, and IV are correct to four significant figures. For this reason the results should not contain more than four significant figures.

The problems given on pages 247–248 are to be solved by trigonometry, using either Table III or Table IV. The following example illustrates the two methods of solution:

Example. Find the volume of a circular cylinder if the radius of its base is 8 inches and if one of its elements is 15 inches and makes an angle of 42° 10′ with the plane of the base.

Solution 1. Since the elements are parallel, they make equal angles with the base.

$$\frac{h}{15} = \sin 42° 10′.$$
$$h = 15 \sin 42° 10′.$$
$$V = \pi r^2 h.$$
$$V = 3.1416 \times 64 \times 15 \times .6713.$$
$$V = 2025.$$

Solution 2. $\frac{h}{15} = \sin 42° 10′.$
$$h = 15 \sin 42° 10′.$$
$$V = \pi r^2 h.$$
$$V = \pi r^2 \, 15 \sin 42° 10′.$$

$$\log \pi = \quad .4971$$
$$\log 64 = \quad 1.8062$$
$$\log 15 = \quad 1.1761$$
$$\log \sin 42° 10′ = \quad \underline{9.8269 - 10}$$
$$\log (2024) = 13.3063 - 10, \text{ or } 3.3063.$$
Then $\qquad V = 2024.$

EXERCISES

1. A vertical pole 70 feet high is set on level ground and has three guy wires which reach from its top to the ground. What angles do the wires make with the ground if their lengths are 100 feet, 110 feet, and 115 feet?

2. A line segment 18 feet long makes an angle of 16° 20′ with a plane. What is the length of its projection on the plane?

3. Two planes form a dihedral angle of 36° 40′. A point in the bisector of the angle is 10 inches from the edge of the angle. How far is the point from either face?

4. Two base edges of a parallelepiped are 8 inches and 10 inches in length and form an angle of 33°. Find the volume of the parallelepiped if its height is 6.2 inches.

5. What is the size of each of the angles that the diagonal of a cube makes with the faces of the cube?

6. The projection on a plane of a line segment 10 inches long is 8 inches. What is the size of the angle formed by the line and the plane?

7. The projection of a line segment on a plane is 22 inches long. If the line segment makes an angle of 38° with the plane, how long is the segment?

8. A point in the plane bisecting a dihedral angle is 6 feet 3 inches from each face of the angle and 7 feet from the edge of the angle. How large is the angle?

9. *Given* $PE \perp$ plane m at E, $EC \perp$ line DC in m, $PE = 60$ feet, $\angle PCE = 64° 20′$, and $\angle PDC = 84° 10′$. *Find* PD and $\angle PDE$.

10. In pyramid $ABCD$, AB is $\perp$ face BCD, CD is $\perp$ face ABD, $BC = 20$, $\angle BCD = 41°$, and $\angle BAD = 28°$. Find AB.

11. Each edge of the base of a regular pyramid with a square base is 6 inches. Find its volume if a lateral edge makes an angle of 72° with the plane of the base.

12. Each side of the base of a regular triangular prism is 8 inches. Find the volume of the prism if a lateral edge is 18.1 inches and makes an angle of 25° with the altitude.

13. Find the volume of a parallelepiped if its base contains an angle of 36° with including sides of 22 inches and 28 inches and its altitude is 15 inches.

14. Find the volume of a parallelepiped if its base is a rectangle 10 by 24 and if one of its lateral edges is 12 inches long and makes an angle of 76° with the plane of the base.

15. Find the volume of a circular cylinder if the radius of its base is 5 and if one of its elements is 12 inches long and makes an angle of 59° with the plane of its base.

16. The slant height of a right circular cone is 18 inches and makes an angle of 18° with the altitude of the cone. Find the lateral area of the cone.

17. Find the total area of right prism ABC-$A'B'C'$ if $\angle ACB = 90°$, $\angle BAC = 26° \, 30'$, $AB = 27$ inches, and $AA' = 46$ inches.

18. Find the volume of a prism whose base is a square 16 inches on a side and has a lateral edge 18 inches long making an angle of 63° with the plane of the base.

19. Assuming the radius of the earth to be 4000 miles, find the area of the north temperate zone which is bounded on the north by the arctic circle 66° 30′ N. latitude and on the south by the tropic of Cancer 23° 30′ N. latitude.

20. Find the total surface of a parallelepiped $ABCD$-$EFGH$ if $AB = 14$, $BC = 8$, $BF = 10$, $\angle ABC = 120°$, $\angle FBC = 100°$, and $\angle ABF = 80°$.

21. An element of a right circular cone is 252 inches and it makes an angle of 36° 10′ with the plane of the base. Find the volume and total area of the cone.

22. A sheet-metal worker wishes to use some sheet metal to make a right circular cone that will hold a gallon. Find the length of its element x if an element must form an angle of 22° with the altitude. What is the size of $\angle y$, disregarding the lapping of the joint?

23. A filling station has a cylindrical gas tank 20 feet long and 8 feet in diameter. The tank is buried in the ground in a horizontal position. How many gallons of gasoline are in the tank when it is filled to a depth of 27 inches counting $7\frac{1}{2}$ gallons to the cubic foot?

TABLE III. TRIGONOMETRIC RATIOS

Angle	sin	cos	tan	Angle	sin	cos	tan
0°	.0000	1.0000	.0000	45°	.7071	.7071	1.0000
1°	.0175	.9998	.0175	46°	.7193	.6947	1.0355
2°	.0349	.9994	.0349	47°	.7314	.6820	1.0724
3°	.0523	.9986	.0524	48°	.7431	.6691	1.1106
4°	.0698	.9976	.0699	49°	.7547	.6561	1.1504
5°	.0872	.9962	.0875	50°	.7660	.6428	1.1918
6°	.1045	.9945	.1051	51°	.7771	.6293	1.2349
7°	.1219	.9925	.1228	52°	.7880	.6157	1.2799
8°	.1392	.9903	.1405	53°	.7986	.6018	1.3270
9°	.1564	.9877	.1584	54°	.8090	.5878	1.3764
10°	.1736	.9848	.1763	55°	.8192	.5736	1.4281
11°	.1908	.9816	.1944	56°	.8290	.5592	1.4826
12°	.2079	.9781	.2126	57°	.8387	.5446	1.5399
13°	.2250	.9744	.2309	58°	.8480	.5299	1.6003
14°	.2419	.9703	.2493	59°	.8572	.5150	1.6643
15°	.2588	.9659	.2679	60°	.8660	.5000	1.7321
16°	.2756	.9613	.2867	61°	.8746	.4848	1.8040
17°	.2924	.9563	.3057	62°	.8829	.4695	1.8807
18°	.3090	.9511	.3249	63°	.8910	.4540	1.9626
19°	.3256	.9455	.3443	64°	.8988	.4384	2.0503
20°	.3420	.9397	.3640	65°	.9063	.4226	2.1445
21°	.3584	.9336	.3839	66°	.9135	.4067	2.2460
22°	.3746	.9272	.4040	67°	.9205	.3907	2.3559
23°	.3907	.9205	.4245	68°	.9272	.3746	2.4751
24°	.4067	.9135	.4452	69°	.9336	.3584	2.6051
25°	.4226	.9063	.4663	70°	.9397	.3420	2.7475
26°	.4384	.8988	.4877	71°	.9455	.3256	2.9042
27°	.4540	.8910	.5095	72°	.9511	.3090	3.0777
28°	.4695	.8829	.5317	73°	.9563	.2924	3.2709
29°	.4848	.8746	.5543	74°	.9613	.2756	3.4874
30°	.5000	.8660	.5774	75°	.9659	.2588	3.7321
31°	.5150	.8572	.6009	76°	.9703	.2419	4.0108
32°	.5299	.8480	.6249	77°	.9744	.2250	4.3315
33°	.5446	.8387	.6494	78°	.9781	.2079	4.7046
34°	.5592	.8290	.6745	79°	.9816	.1908	5.1446
35°	.5736	.8192	.7002	80°	.9848	.1736	5.6713
36°	.5878	.8090	.7265	81°	.9877	.1564	6.3138
37°	.6018	.7986	.7536	82°	.9903	.1392	7.1154
38°	.6157	.7880	.7813	83°	.9925	.1219	8.1443
39°	.6293	.7771	.8098	84°	.9945	.1045	9.5144
40°	.6428	.7660	.8391	85°	.9962	.0872	11.4301
41°	.6561	.7547	.8693	86°	.9976	.0698	14.3007
42°	.6691	.7431	.9004	87°	.9986	.0523	19.0811
43°	.6820	.7314	.9325	88°	.9994	.0349	28.6363
44°	.6947	.7193	.9657	89°	.9998	.0175	57.2900
45°	.7071	.7071	1.0000	90°	1.0000	.0000	∞

TABLE IV. LOGARITHMS OF TRIGONOMETRIC RATIOS

Angle	Log Sin	Log Tan	Log Cot	Log Cos	Angle
0° 0'	—	—	—	10.000	90° 0'
10	7.4637	7.4637	2.5363	10.000	50
20	7.7648	7.7648	2.2352	10.000	40
30	7.9408	7.9409	2.0591	10.000	30
40	8.0658	8.0658	1.9342	10.000	20
50	8.1627	8.1627	1.8373	10.000	10
1° 0'	8.2419	8.2419	1.7581	9.9999	89° 0'
10	8.3088	8.3089	1.6911	9.9999	50
20	8.3668	8.3669	1.6331	9.9999	40
30	8.4179	8.4181	1.5819	9.9999	30
40	8.4637	8.4638	1.5362	9.9998	20
50	8.5050	8.5053	1.4947	9.9998	10
2° 0'	8.5428	8.5431	1.4569	9.9997	88° 0'
10	8.5776	8.5779	1.4221	9.9997	50
20	8.6097	8.6101	1.3899	9.9996	40
30	8.6397	8.6401	1.3599	9.9996	30
40	8.6677	8.6682	1.3318	9.9995	20
50	8.6940	8.6945	1.3055	9.9995	10
3° 0'	8.7188	8.7194	1.2806	9.9994	87° 0'
10	8.7423	8.7429	1.2571	9.9993	50
20	8.7645	8.7652	1.2348	9.9993	40
30	8.7857	8.7865	1.2135	9.9992	30
40	8.8059	8.8067	1.1933	9.9991	20
50	8.8251	8.8261	1.1739	9.9990	10
4° 0'	8.8436	8.8446	1.1554	9.9989	86° 0'
10	8.8613	8.8624	1.1376	9.9989	50
20	8.8783	8.8795	1.1205	9.9988	40
30	8.8946	8.8960	1.1040	9.9987	30
40	8.9104	8.9118	1.0882	9.9986	20
50	8.9256	8.9272	1.0728	9.9985	10
5° 0'	8.9403	8.9420	1.0580	9.9983	85° 0'
10	8.9545	8.9563	1.0437	9.9982	50
20	8.9682	8.9701	1.0299	9.9981	40
30	8.9816	8.9836	1.0164	9.9980	30
40	8.9945	8.9966	1.0034	9.9979	20
50	9.0070	9.0093	0.9907	9.9977	10
6° 0'	9.0192	9.0216	0.9784	9.9976	84° 0'
10	9.0311	9.0336	0.9664	9.9975	50
20	9.0426	9.0453	0.9547	9.9973	40
30	9.0539	9.0567	0.9433	9.9972	30
40	9.0648	9.0678	0.9322	9.9971	20
50	9.0755	9.0786	0.9214	9.9969	10
7° 0'	9.0859	9.0891	0.9109	9.9968	83° 0'
10	9.0961	9.0995	0.9005	9.9966	50
20	9.1060	9.1096	0.8904	9.9964	40
30	9.1157	9.1194	0.8806	9.9963	30
Angle	Log Cos	Log Cot	Log Tan	Log Sin	Angle

Angle	Log Sin	Log Tan	Log Cot	Log Cos	Angle
7° 30'	9.1157	9.1194	0.8806	9.9963	82° 30'
40	9.1252	9.1291	0.8709	9.9961	20
50	9.1345	9.1385	0.8615	9.9959	10
8° 0'	9.1436	9.1478	0.8522	9.9958	82° 0'
10	9.1525	9.1569	0.8431	9.9956	50
20	9.1612	9.1658	0.8342	9.9954	40
30	9.1697	9.1745	0.8255	9.9952	30
40	9.1781	9.1831	0.8169	9.9950	20
50	9.1863	9.1915	0.8085	9.9948	10
9° 0'	9.1943	9.1997	0.8003	9.9946	81° 0'
10	9.2022	9.2078	0.7922	9.9944	50
20	9.2100	9.2158	0.7842	9.9942	40
30	9.2176	9.2236	0.7764	9.9940	30
40	9.2251	9.2313	0.7687	9.9938	20
50	9.2324	9.2389	0.7611	9.9936	10
10° 0'	9.2397	9.2463	0.7537	9.9934	80° 0'
10	9.2468	9.2536	0.7464	9.9931	50
20	9.2538	9.2609	0.7391	9.9929	40
30	9.2606	9.2680	0.7320	9.9927	30
40	9.2674	9.2750	0.7250	9.9924	20
50	9.2740	9.2819	0.7181	9.9922	10
11° 0'	9.2806	9.2887	0.7113	9.9919	79° 0'
10	9.2870	9.2953	0.7047	9.9917	50
20	9.2934	9.3020	0.6980	9.9914	40
30	9.2997	9.3085	0.6915	9.9912	30
40	9.3058	9.3149	0.6851	9.9909	20
50	9.3119	9.3212	0.6788	9.9907	10
12° 0'	9.3179	9.3275	0.6725	9.9904	78° 0'
10	9.3238	9.3336	0.6664	9.9901	50
20	9.3296	9.3397	0.6603	9.9899	40
30	9.3353	9.3458	0.6542	9.9896	30
40	9.3410	9.3517	0.6483	9.9893	20
50	9.3466	9.3576	0.6424	9.9890	10
13° 0'	9.3521	9.3634	0.6366	9.9887	77° 0'
10	9.3575	9.3691	0.6309	9.9884	50
20	9.3629	9.3748	0.6252	9.9881	40
30	9.3682	9.3804	0.6196	9.9878	30
40	9.3734	9.3859	0.6141	9.9875	20
50	9.3786	9.3914	0.6086	9.9872	10
14° 0'	9.3837	9.3968	0.6032	9.9869	76° 0'
10	9.3887	9.4021	0.5979	9.9866	50
20	9.3937	9.4074	0.5926	9.9863	40
30	9.3986	9.4127	0.5873	9.9859	30
40	9.4035	9.4178	0.5822	9.9856	20
50	9.4083	9.4230	0.5770	9.9853	10
15° 0	9.4130	9.4281	0.5719	9.9849	75° 0'
Angle	Log Cos	Log Cot	Log Tan	Log Sin	Angle

TABLE IV. LOGARITHMS OF TRIGONOMETRIC RATIOS

ANGLE	LOG SIN	LOG TAN	LOG COT	LOG COS	ANGLE
15° 0′	9.4130	9.4281	0.5719	9.9849	75° 0′
10	9.4177	9.4331	0.5669	9.9846	50
20	9.4223	9.4381	0.5619	9.9843	40
30	9.4269	9.4430	0.5570	9.9839	30
40	9.4314	9.4479	0.5521	9.9836	20
50	9.4359	9.4527	0.5473	9.9832	10
16° 0′	9.4403	9.4575	0.5425	9.9828	74° 0′
10	9.4447	9.4622	0.5378	9.9825	50
20	9.4491	9.4669	0.5331	9.9821	40
30	9.4533	9.4716	0.5284	9.9817	30
40	9.4576	9.4762	0.5238	9.9814	20
50	9.4618	9.4808	0.5192	9.9810	10
17° 0′	9.4659	9.4853	0.5147	9.9806	73° 0′
10	9.4700	9.4898	0.5102	9.9802	50
20	9.4741	9.4943	0.5057	9.9798	40
30	9.4781	9.4987	0.5013	9.9794	30
40	9.4821	9.5031	0.4969	9.9790	20
50	9.4861	9.5075	0.4925	9.9786	10
18° 0′	9.4900	9.5118	0.4882	9.9782	72° 0′
10	9.4939	9.5161	0.4839	9.9778	50
20	9.4977	9.5203	0.4797	9.9774	40
30	9.5015	9.5245	0.4755	9.9770	30
40	9.5052	9.5287	0.4713	9.9765	20
50	9.5090	9.5329	0.4671	9.9761	10
19° 0′	9.5126	9.5370	0.4630	9.9757	71° 0′
10	9.5163	9.5411	0.4589	9.9752	50
20	9.5199	9.5451	0.4549	9.9748	40
30	9.5235	9.5491	0.4509	9.9743	30
40	9.5270	9.5531	0.4469	9.9739	20
50	9.5306	9.5571	0.4429	9.9734	10
20° 0′	9.5341	9.5611	0.4389	9.9730	70° 0′
10	9.5375	9.5650	0.4350	9.9725	50
20	9.5409	9.5689	0.4311	9.9721	40
30	9.5443	9.5727	0.4273	9.9716	30
40	9.5477	9.5766	0.4234	9.9711	20
50	9.5510	9.5804	0.4196	9.9706	10
21° 0′	9.5543	9.5842	0.4158	9.9702	69° 0′
10	9.5576	9.5879	0.4121	9.9697	50
20	9.5609	9.5917	0.4083	9.9692	40
30	9.5641	9.5954	0.4046	9.9687	30
40	9.5673	9.5991	0.4009	9.9682	20
50	9.5704	9.6028	0.3972	9.9677	10
22° 0′	9.5736	9.6064	0.3936	9.9672	68° 0′
10	9.5767	9.6100	0.3900	9.9667	50
20	9.5798	9.6136	0.3864	9.9661	40
30	9.5828	9.6172	0.3828	9.9656	30

ANGLE	LOG SIN	LOG TAN	LOG COT	LOG COS	ANGLE
22° 30′	9.5828	9.6172	0.3828	9.9656	67° 30′
40	9.5859	9.6208	0.3792	9.9651	20
50	9.5889	9.6243	0.3757	9.9646	10
23° 0′	9.5919	9.6279	0.3721	9.9640	67° 0′
10	9.5948	9.6314	0.3686	9.9635	50
20	9.5978	9.6348	0.3652	9.9629	40
30	9.6007	9.6383	0.3617	9.9624	30
40	9.6036	9.6417	0.3583	9.9618	20
50	9.6065	9.6452	0.3548	9.9613	10
24° 0′	9.6093	9.6486	0.3514	9.9607	66° 0′
10	9.6121	9.6520	0.3480	9.9602	50
20	9.6149	9.6553	0.3447	9.9596	40
30	9.6177	9.6587	0.3413	9.9590	30
40	9.6205	9.6620	0.3380	9.9584	20
50	9.6232	9.6654	0.3346	9.9579	10
25° 0′	9.6259	9.6687	0.3313	9.9573	65° 0′
10	9.6286	9.6720	0.3280	9.9567	50
20	9.6313	9.6752	0.3248	9.9561	40
30	9.6340	9.6785	0.3215	9.9555	30
40	9.6366	9.6817	0.3183	9.9549	20
50	9.6392	9.6850	0.3150	9.9543	10
26° 0′	9.6418	9.6882	0.3118	9.9537	64° 0′
10	9.6444	9.6914	0.3086	9.9530	50
20	9.6470	9.6946	0.3054	9.9524	40
30	9.6495	9.6977	0.3023	9.9518	30
40	9.6521	9.7009	0.2991	9.9512	20
50	9.6546	9.7040	0.2960	9.9505	10
27° 0′	9.6570	9.7072	0.2928	9.9499	63° 0′
10	9.6595	9.7103	0.2897	9.9492	50
20	9.6620	9.7134	0.2866	9.9486	40
30	9.6644	9.7165	0.2835	9.9479	30
40	9.6668	9.7196	0.2804	9.9473	20
50	9.6692	9.7226	0.2774	9.9466	10
28° 0′	9.6716	9.7257	0.2743	9.9459	62° 0′
10	9.6740	9.7287	0.2713	9.9453	50
20	9.6763	9.7317	0.2683	9.9446	40
30	9.6787	9.7348	0.2652	9.9439	30
40	9.6810	9.7378	0.2622	9.9432	20
50	9.6833	9.7408	0.2592	9.9425	10
29° 0′	9.6856	9.7438	0.2562	9.9418	61° 0′
10	9.6878	9.7467	0.2533	9.9411	50
20	9.6901	9.7497	0.2503	9.9404	40
30	9.6923	9.7526	0.2474	9.9397	30
40	9.6946	9.7556	0.2444	9.9390	20
50	9.6968	9.7585	0.2415	9.9383	10
30° 0′	9.6990	9.7614	0.2386	9.9375	60° 0′

ANGLE	LOG COS	LOG COT	LOG TAN	LOG SIN	ANGLE

TABLE IV. LOGARITHMS OF TRIGONOMETRIC RATIOS

Angle	Log Sin	Log Tan	Log Cot	Log Cos	Angle
30° 0'	9.6990	9.7614	0.2386	9.9375	60° 0'
10	9.7012	9.7644	0.2356	9.9368	50
20	9.7033	9.7673	0.2327	9.9361	40
30	9.7055	9.7701	0.2299	9.9353	30
40	9.7076	9.7730	0.2270	9.9346	20
50	9.7097	9.7759	0.2241	9.9338	10
31° 0'	9.7118	9.7788	0.2212	9.9331	59° 0'
10	9.7139	9.7816	0.2184	9.9323	50
20	9.7160	9.7845	0.2155	9.9315	40
30	9.7181	9.7873	0.2127	9.9308	30
40	9.7201	9.7902	0.2098	9.9300	20
50	9.7222	9.7930	0.2070	9.9292	10
32° 0'	9.7242	9.7958	0.2042	9.9284	58° 0'
10	9.7262	9.7986	0.2014	9.9276	50
20	9.7282	9.8014	0.1986	9.9268	40
30	9.7302	9.8042	0.1958	9.9260	30
40	9.7322	9.8070	0.1930	9.9252	20
50	9.7342	9.8097	0.1903	9.9244	10
33° 0'	9.7361	9.8125	0.1875	9.9236	57° 0'
10	9.7380	9.8153	0.1847	9.9228	50
20	9.7400	9.8180	0.1820	9.9219	40
30	9.7419	9.8208	0.1792	9.9211	30
40	9.7438	9.8235	0.1765	9.9203	20
50	9.7457	9.8263	0.1737	9.9194	10
34° 0'	9.7476	9.8290	0.1710	9.9186	56° 0'
10	9.7494	9.8317	0.1683	9.9177	50
20	9.7513	9.8344	0.1656	9.9169	40
30	9.7531	9.8371	0.1629	9.9160	30
40	9.7550	9.8398	0.1602	9.9151	20
50	9.7568	9.8425	0.1575	9.9142	10
35° 0'	9.7586	9.8452	0.1548	9.9134	55° 0'
10	9.7604	9.8479	0.1521	9.9125	50
20	9.7622	9.8506	0.1494	9.9116	40
30	9.7640	9.8533	0.1467	9.9107	30
40	9.7657	9.8559	0.1441	9.9098	20
50	9.7675	9.8586	0.1414	9.9089	10
36° 0'	9.7692	9.8613	0.1387	9.9080	54° 0'
10	9.7710	9.8639	0.1361	9.9070	50
20	9.7727	9.8666	0.1334	9.9061	40
30	9.7744	9.8692	0.1308	9.9052	30
40	9.7761	9.8718	0.1282	9.9042	20
50	9.7778	9.8745	0.1255	9.9033	10
37° 0'	9.7795	9.8771	0.1229	9.9023	53° 0'
10	9.7811	9.8797	0.1203	9.9014	50
20	9.7828	9.8824	0.1176	9.9004	40
30	9.7844	9.8850	0.1150	9.8995	30
Angle	Log Cos	Log Cot	Log Tan	Log Sin	Angle

Angle	Log Sin	Log Tan	Log Cot	Log Cos	Angle
37° 30'	9.7844	9.8850	0.1150	9.8995	52° 30'
40	9.7861	9.8876	0.1124	9.8985	20
50	9.7877	9.8902	0.1098	9.8975	10
38° 0'	9.7893	9.8928	0.1072	9.8965	52° 0'
10	9.7910	9.8954	0.1046	9.8955	50
20	9.7926	9.8980	0.1020	9.8945	40
30	9.7941	9.9006	0.0994	9.8935	30
40	9.7957	9.9032	0.0968	9.8925	20
50	9.7973	9.9058	0.0942	9.8915	10
39° 0'	9.7989	9.9084	0.0916	9.8905	51° 0'
10	9.8004	9.9110	0.0890	9.8895	50
20	9.8020	9.9135	0.0865	9.8884	40
30	9.8035	9.9161	0.0839	9.8874	30
40	9.8050	9.9187	0.0813	9.8864	20
50	9.8066	9.9212	0.0788	9.8853	10
40° 0'	9.8081	9.9238	0.0762	9.8843	50° 0'
10	9.8096	9.9264	0.0736	9.8832	50
20	9.8111	9.9289	0.0711	9.8821	40
30	9.8125	9.9315	0.0685	9.8810	30
40	9.8140	9.9341	0.0659	9.8800	20
50	9.8155	9.9366	0.0634	9.8789	10
41° 0'	9.8169	9.9392	0.0608	9.8778	49° 0'
10	9.8184	9.9417	0.0583	9.8767	50
20	9.8198	9.9443	0.0557	9.8756	40
30	9.8213	9.9468	0.0532	9.8745	30
40	9.8227	9.9494	0.0506	9.8733	20
50	9.8241	9.9519	0.0481	9.8722	10
42° 0'	9.8255	9.9544	0.0456	9.8711	48° 0'
10	9.8269	9.9570	0.0430	9.8699	50
20	9.8283	9.9595	0.0405	9.8688	40
30	9.8297	9.9621	0.0379	9.8676	30
40	9.8311	9.9646	0.0354	9.8665	20
50	9.8324	9.9671	0.0329	9.8653	10
43° 0'	9.8338	9.9697	0.0303	9.8641	47° 0'
10	9.8351	9.9722	0.0278	9.8629	50
20	9.8365	9.9747	0.0253	9.8618	40
30	9.8378	9.9772	0.0228	9.8606	30
40	9.8391	9.9798	0.0202	9.8594	20
50	9.8405	9.9823	0.0177	9.8582	10
44° 0'	9.8418	9.9848	0.0152	9.8569	46° 0'
10	9.8431	9.9874	0.0126	9.8557	50
20	9.8444	9.9899	0.0101	9.8545	40
30	9.8457	9.9924	0.0076	9.8532	30
40	9.8469	9.9949	0.0051	9.8520	20
50	9.8482	9.9975	0.0025	9.8507	10
45° 0'	9.8495	0.0000	0.0000	9.8495	45° 0'
Angle	Log Cos	Log Cot	Log Tan	Log Sin	Angle

TABLES FOR REFERENCE

LINEAR MEASURE

12 in. = 1 ft. (1′)
3 ft. = 1 yd.
16.5 ft. = 1 rd.
320 rd. = 1 mi.
5280 ft. = 1 mi.

SQUARE MEASURE

144 sq. in. = 1 sq. ft.
9 sq. ft. = 1 sq. yd.
272.25 sq. ft. = 1 sq. rd.
160 sq. rd. = 1 acre
100 sq. ft. = 1 square

CUBIC MEASURE

1728 cu. in. = 1 cu. ft.
27 cu. ft. = 1 cu. yd.

AVOIRDUPOIS WEIGHT

16 oz. = 1 lb.
2000 lb. = 1 ton

MISCELLANEOUS

$\pi = 3.1416$, or 3.14, or $\frac{22}{7}$ 1 cu. ft. contains 7.5 gal. approximately
1 cu. ft. of water weighs 62.4 lb. 1 meter = 39.37 in.
1 gal. contains 231 cu. in.   1 kilogram = 2.2 lb. approximately
1 bu. contains 2150.42 cu. in.   1 bbl. contains 31.5 gal.

FORMULAS OF PLANE GEOMETRY

Notation

a, apothem of a regular polygon
a, b, c, sides of $\triangle ABC$
A, area
b, b', bases
c, circumference

h, altitude
p, perimeter
r, radius
s, semiperimeter, side

Formulas

Circle:	$c = 2\pi r$, $A = \pi r^2$
Equilateral triangle:	$A = \frac{1}{4} s^2 \sqrt{3}$, $h = \frac{1}{2} s \sqrt{3}$
Parallelogram:	$A = bh$
Regular polygon:	$A = \frac{1}{2} ap$
Trapezoid:	$A = \frac{1}{2} h(b + b')$
Triangle:	$A = \frac{1}{2} bh$, $A = \sqrt{s(s-a)(s-b)(s-c)}$

253

FORMULAS OF SOLID GEOMETRY

Notation

A, angle of lune
B, B', b, b', area of bases
c, circumference
e, element, lateral edge
E, spherical excess
h, altitude
l, slant height

M, area of midsection
p, p', perimeters
r, r', r_1, radii
S, lateral area or area of curved surface
T, total area
V, volume

Formulas

Cone of revolution:	$S = \frac{1}{2} cl$, $S = \pi r l$, $T = \pi r(l + r)$, $V = \frac{1}{3} \pi r^2 h$
Cylinder of revolution:	$S = 2\pi r h$, $T = 2\pi r(r + h)$, $V = \pi r^2 h$
Cone and pyramid:	$V = \frac{1}{3} bh$
Cylinder and prism:	$S = ep$, $V = bh$
Frustum	
of cone of revolution:	$S = \pi l(r + r')$, $V = \frac{1}{3} \pi h(r^2 + r'^2 + rr')$
of a regular pyramid:	$S = \frac{1}{2} l(p + p')$, $V = \frac{1}{3} h(b + b' + \sqrt{bb'})$
of a cone or pyramid:	$V = \frac{1}{3} h(b + b' + \sqrt{bb'})$
Lune:	$S = \dfrac{\pi r^2 A}{90}$
Prismatoid:	$V = \frac{1}{6} h(B + B' + 4M)$
Regular pyramid:	$S = \frac{1}{2} lp$, $V = \frac{1}{3} bh$
Regular tetrahedron:	$S = e^2\sqrt{3}$, $V = \dfrac{e^3}{12}\sqrt{2}$, $h = \dfrac{e}{3}\sqrt{6}$
Sphere:	$S = 4\pi r^2$, $V = \frac{4}{3}\pi r^3$
Spherical polygon:	$S = \dfrac{\pi r^2 E}{180}$
Spherical pyramid:	$V = \dfrac{\pi r^3 E}{540}$
Spherical sector:	$V = \frac{2}{3}\pi r^2 h$
Spherical segment:	$V = \frac{1}{6}\pi h(h^2 + 3r^2 + 3r_1^2)$
Wedge:	$V = \dfrac{\pi r^3 A}{270}$
Zone:	$S = 2\pi r h$

INDEX

PAGE

Abbreviations xii

Altitude
  of a cone 132
  of a cylinder 100
  of a frustum 123, 132
  of a prism 82
  of a prismatoid 215
  of a pyramid 119
  of a spherical segment . . . 187
  of a zone 165

Angle
  dihedral 55
  face 67
  hexahedral 67
  between a line and a plane . 61
  of a lune 183
  octahedral 67
  pentahedral 67
  plane 55
  polyhedral 67, 169
  spherical 161
  tetrahedral 67
  trihedral 67

Area
  lateral, of a cylinder . . 105, 108
  lateral, of a prism 82, 89
  lateral, of a pyramid . . 119, 121
  lateral, of a right circular
    cone 136, 137
  of a lune 183
  of a sphere 166, 167
  of a spherical polygon . . . 185
  of a spherical triangle . . . 184
  total, of a cone 136
  total, of a cylinder . . 105, 108
  total, of a prism 82

PAGE

Area
  of a zone 167

Axis
  of a circle of a sphere . . . 153
  of a circular cone 132

Base
  of a cone 132
  of a pyramid 119

Bases
  of a cylinder 100
  of a frustum 123, 132
  of a prism 82
  of a prismatoid 215
  of a zone 165

Cavalieri's Theorem 126

Center of a sphere 151

Circle of a sphere 152
  axis of a 153
  great 152, 153
  poles of a 153
  small 153

Cone 132
  altitude of a 132
  axis of a circular 132
  base of a 132
  circular 132
  circumscribed 135
  element of a 132
  frustum of a 132
  inscribed 135
  lateral area of a right circular
             136, 137
  oblique 132
  radius of a 132

255

PAGE

Cone
of revolution 132
right circular 132
slant height of a 133
total area of a 136
vertex of a 132
volume of a circular . . 138, 139
Cones, similar 139
Conic section 133
Cube 91
duplication of 96
Cylinder 100
altitude of a 100
bases of a 100
circular 101
circumscribed 103
element of a 100
inscribed 103
lateral area of a . . . 105, 108
oblique 101
plane tangent to a 103
of revolution 101
right 101
right section of a 100
total area of a . . . 105, 108
volume of a 106
Cylinders, similar 107

Degree, spherical 183
Diameter of a sphere 151
Dihedral angles 55
acute 55
adjacent 55
complementary 55
edges of 55
equal 55
faces of 55
obtuse 55
plane angles of 55
of polyhedral angles . . . 67
right 55
supplementary 55
vertical 55

PAGE

Directrix . . . 81, 100, 119, 132
Distance
of a point from a plane . . 32
polar 155
spherical 153
Dodecahedron 205

Element 81, 100, 119, 132
Ellipse 133
Euler's Theorem 208
Excess, spherical 175

Face angles 67
Faces
of a dihedral angle 55
lateral 82, 119
of a polyhedral angle . . . 67
of a polyhedron 81
Foot of a line 25
Formulas
of plane geometry 253
of solid geometry 254
Frustum of a cone 132
altitude of a 132
bases of a 132
volume of a 139
Frustum of a pyramid . . . 123
altitude of a 123
bases of a 123
volume of a 131

Generatrix . . . 81, 100, 119, 132

Hexahedron 205
Historical notes 60, 96, 171,
189–191, 206, 209, 217
Hyperbola 133

Icosahedron 205

Limit 103, 104
cone as a 135
cylinder as a 104

PAGE

Line
  foot of a 25
  oblique to a plane 25
  parallel to a plane 37
  perpendicular to a plane . . 25
  projection of a 61
Lines
  concurrent 3
  coplanar 3
  skew 37
List of Exercises viii
Locus 32
  compound 72
Lune 183
  angle of a 183
  area of a 183

Methods of proof
  chapter summaries of 48–50,
      76, 112–114, 144–146,
          199–201, 220–221
  general summary of . . 229–237

Nappe 119, 132

Octahedron 205

Parabola 133
Parallelepiped 91
  oblique 91
  rectangular 91
  right 91
  volume of a 94
Plane 1
  determination of a 2
  fundamental properties of a 4
  line perpendicular to a . . . 25
  parallel to a line 37
  parallel to a plane 37
  perpendicular to a plane . . 55
  projection on a 61
  tangent to a cylinder . . . 103
  tangent to a sphere 156

PAGE

Plane geometry, references to
          3, 6–20, 245
Point
  projection of a 61
  of tangency 156
Points
  collinear 3
  coplanar 3
Poles of a circle 153
Polyhedral angles 67, 169
  congruent 67
  convex 67
  dihedral angles of 67
  edges of 67
  equal 67
  face angles of 67
  faces of 67
  symmetric 67
  vertices of 67
Polyhedrons 81
  classified 205
  convex 81
  diagonals of 81
  edges of 210
  faces of 81
  regular 205
  similar 210
  vertices of 81
Postulates
  of plane geometry 8, 9
  of solid geometry 4, 93, 104,
          135, 151, 165, 187
Prism 82
  altitude of a 82
  bases of a 82
  circumscribed 103
  inscribed 103
  lateral area of a 82, 89
  lateral edges of a 82
  lateral faces of a 82
  oblique section of a 82
  pentagonal 83
  quadrangular 83

PAGE

Prism

regular 82
right 82
right section of a 82
total area of a 82
triangular 83
truncated 84
volume of a 97, 98

Prismatoid 215
altitude of a 215
bases of a 215
midsection of a 215
volume of a 216

Prisms classified 83

Projection
of a line 61
of a point 61

Pyramid 119
altitude of a 119
base of a 119
circumscribed 135
frustum of a 123
inscribed 135
lateral area of a 119, 121
lateral edges of a 119
lateral faces of a 119
pentagonal 120
quadrangular 120
regular 120
slant height of a 120
spherical 186
triangular 120
vertex of a 119
volume of a 128, 130

Quadrant 153

Radius
of a cone 132
of a sphere 151

Reviews
chapter . . 46–48, 74–75,
111–112, 143–144, 198

Reviews
PAGE
of important words 50, 76,
114, 146, 201, 221

Section
of a cone 133
of a cylinder 100
of a prism 82
of a solid 81

Sector, spherical 187
Segment, spherical 187

Solids
congruent 85
equal (or equivalent) . . . 85
geometric 2
rectangular 91, 93
sections of 81
volume of 85

Sphere 151
area of a 166, 167
axis of a circle of a . . . 153
center of a 151
circles of a 152, 153
circumscribed 159
diameter of a 151
inscribed 157
line tangent to a 156
plane tangent to a 156
radius of a 151
volume of a 187–189

Spheres, tangent 156

Spherical polygon 168
angles of a 168
area of a 185
diagonal of a 168
sides of a 168
spherical excess of a . . . 175
vertices of a 168

Spherical triangles . . . 169, 175
area of 184, 185
congruent 175
spherical excess of 175
symmetric 176

Supplementary exercises . 223–228

PAGE

Surfaces
closed prismatic 81
conical 132
curved 2
cylindrical 100
elements of . . 81, 100, 119, 132
intersection of 2
plane 1
pyramidal 119

Tables
of formulas 253, 254
of logarithms 242, 250
of measures 253
of roots 238
of trigonometric ratios . . . 249
Tangency 103, 156
Tests
Applications 79, 117, 149, 204, 222
Completion, of proofs . . 53–54
of statements 52–53, 78–79,
115–116, 147–148, 203, 222
True-False . 50–51, 77–78,
114–115, 146–147, 202, 221
Tetrahedron 205
Trigonometry, applications of . 244

Vertex
of a cone 132
of a polyhedral angle . . . 67

PAGE

Vertex
of a polyhedron 81
of a pyramid 119
Volume
of a circular cone . . . 138, 139
of a circular cylinder . . . 106
of a frustum of a circular
cone 139
of a frustum of a pyramid . 131
of a parallelepiped 94
of a prism 97, 98
of a prismatoid 216
of a pyramid 128, 130
of a rectangular solid . . . 93
of a solid 85, 93
of a sphere 187–189
of a spherical pyramid . . . 194
of a spherical sector 194
of a spherical segment . . . 194
of a spherical wedge 194
of a truncated triangular
prism 218
unit of 93

Wedge, spherical 187

Zone . . . . : . 165
altitude of a 165
area of a 167
bases of a 165